MW00837461
160 lbs MASS
MAIN
TIME FOR DEFLECTION
Crack
MOMENT OF IMPACT

MYTHBUSTERS

MYTHBUSTING FROM A TO Z

MYTHOPEDIA

written and researched by
Nicholas Searle

Published by Wilkinson Publishing Pty Ltd
ACN 006 042 173
2 Collins St
Melbourne Vic 3000
Ph: (03) 9654 5446
www.wilkinsonpublishing.com.au

First published 2008

National Libraries of Australia Cataloguing-in-Publication data:

Author: Searle, Nicholas.

Title: Mythopedia : mythbusting from a to z / Nicholas Searle.

ISBN: 9781921332401 (hbk.)

Subjects: Mythbusters (Television program)
Science–Experiments
Parapsychology and science
Belief and doubt
Urban folklore

Dewey Number: 507.8

Page and cover design by Spike Creative Pty Ltd.
Prahran, Victoria. Ph: (03) 9525 0900.
www.spikecreative.com.au

Printed in China

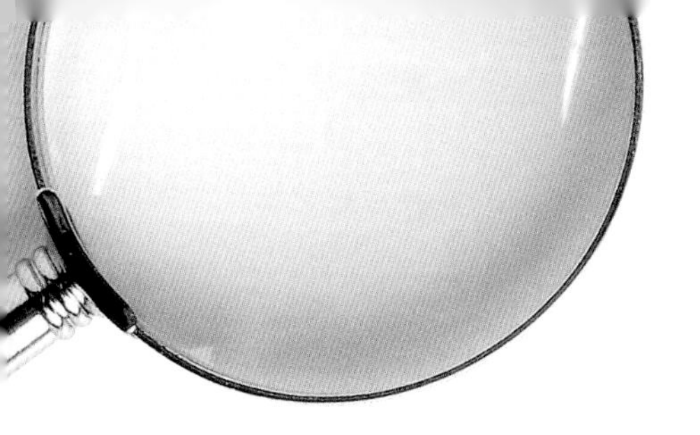

CONTENTS

One of these chapters is SUBSTANTIALLY longer than any of the others - which is it? And why?

About the Author

By offering insights into the career and life experience of the author, a publication aims to bring the readership closer to the text. Nicholas Searle was a writer FOR Mythbusters before becoming a writer ABOUT Mythbusters. Two previous books are *Mythbusters: Zaps, Rays and Waves* and *Rock the Body* and not a single warrant has been issued to date for crimes against science. Nicholas himself is a giant of a man, skilled in many arts ancient and arcane, has read Newton in the original Latin and was among the first to denounce the Piltdown Hoax. Now aged a spritely 238 years, he resides in Sydney among his collection of 17th and 18th century Swedish chemistry apparatus.

See also: introduction

INTRODUCTION

Also known as a prologue, prolusion or prolegomenon, an introduction offers the reader an opportunity to understand a little about the background and context of a manuscript. The introduction to Mythopedia presents the theory behind turning the world's most popular science television program into a thick book of facts, dotted with pictures and laced with classic Mythbusters-style humour. A world, nay, a universe of material beckoned, and the Mythopedia was developed along what soon became known among the team as 'the Jamie Hyneman model'. Based on Jamie's orderly storage system of labelled tubs, boxes and drawers, it was conceived that the Mythopedia would leave no rolling stone unturned in a quest for a thorough and complete list of everything Mythbusters. As the project developed and deadlines approached, the Hyneman model shifted somewhat – and understandably. There is a lot of material to cover, a lot of themes based on many subjects that lead to many concepts relying on much knowledge and many facts, places, people and things. In short, the world of the Mythbusters contains lots of stuff. The Mythopedia began to deform, hybridise, and coalesce into a new model. An eclectic model. An… Adam Savage Model. Thus you have before you now, at a low, low price, the Mythopedia – The Adam Savage Model. Enjoy before it blows up in your face, then demands a cookie.

***See also:* About the Author**

A word about alphabetical order

The Mythbusters fully endorse the English alphabet and the order in which the letters appear. However, the Mythopedia has had occasion to subtly disrupt that order for the sake of logic and good reading. We trust you enjoy the results.

A is for ... Adam

Aaron Rodriguez

The *Snow Special* saw a few firsts for the Mythbusters – not the least of which was Adam tossing sticks of live dynamite out of the window of a helicopter, in the hope that it would start a much-needed avalanche. Operations Director for the Dynamite Tossing Helicopter Unit of the Telluride Ski Patrol was Aaron Rodriguez.

***Myths:* Snow Special, Avalanche Adventure**

"AARON – I'm going to throw it out the window, okay, and I'm going to do that when the spotter, who is in the front seat, tells me to do it.

ADAM – That seems pretty straightforward.

AARON – Yeah, considering you're throwing dynamite out the window."

Absolute Zero

If you were to ask a fellow passenger on a bus 'what is the average temperature of the universe?' you will get a lot of weird looks and a seat to yourself. Yet those same passengers will be later wondering to themselves 'is there such a thing… and why?' The simple answer is that yes, the universe does have an average temperature. In fact it's about 2.7ºK (about -270.45ºC) so it is expected that when they arrive, aliens will be wearing good quality hats and overcoats. But why is the universe so cold? The point about temperature is that it is a measure of energy – and in the vastness of space, despite all the stars and black holes and supernova and pulsars, there just isn't that much of it. In fact, scientists theorise that there is a temperature at which the whatever-it-is has theoretically no energy, at least, no energy worth speaking of (unless you're Albert Einstein and thus enthusiastic to make up terms like 'zero-point energy'). That temperature is absolute zero – 0ºK or -273.15ºC. As soon as they rig out the M5 workshop with superconducting, superfluidity test equipment, you better believe Adam and Jamie will be testing Adam and Jamie just how close to absolute zero you can really go – if not beyond.

See also:* *Kelvin, temperature, Einstein

Acceleration

It's daft describing something as 'the rate of change of velocity' when the image in your head right now is stamping on that pedal until the engine squeals like a pig and your V8 explodes down the highway so much more powerfully than 400 horses ever could (no matter how cunningly they were harnessed). Yet, yet, yet…the bald truth is that acceleration is really a measurement of how much faster you're NOW going then you were BEFORE. Hence it is quite sensibly measured in metres per second *per second*, and even that is making it sound much simpler than really it is. If we were to throw the SI unit m/s^{-2} at you it might make you ponder that things are not quite as they seem, and as you get more involved with the gradient of tangents and vectors you slowly understand that although you can comprehend acceleration people have gone and made it much more complex than you could have expected. Stick with the gut instinct we say.

See also:* *SI, velocity

Accelerometer

You'll find them in your car's airbag deployment system, in modern video cameras, computer game hand controls and even the latest mobile phones – and inside Buster's head, where there is room for a hunk of metal about the size of a tennis ball. An accelerometer measures the velocity of an object (like Buster) along with the changes in that velocity. The Mythbusters have used different accelerometers for different myths; from top-of-the-line super-fancy computerised accelerometers that could read a mosquito's hiccup in the back of a pick-up truck, such as were used in *Bridge Drop* and *Killer Tissue Box* to record the extraordinary forces Buster experienced as he fell from the giant Whirley crane to the water below, all the way to light globes filled with fake blood sealed inside two aluminium

sugar scoops as used in *Plywood Builder*. Why the change in technology? Well, a head full of blood makes for a more dramatic reveal than tooling around with a laptop!

***See also:* acceleration, gravity, Whirley, g-force**
***Myths:* Bridge Drop, Plywood Builder, Killer Tissue Box**

Accordion

A delightful musical instrument with a sound all its own built around a wind-squeezing bellows (and hence sometimes called a squeeze box). Bellows? Air? No wonder then that, according to the FBI, it was a heavily modified accordion that gave Frank Morris and the Anglin Brothers' raincoat boat the breath of life for *Alcatraz Escape*. In their recreation, Jamie used a ping pong ball to create a one-way valve, and pretty soon their boat too was holding air.

***See also:* valves, ping pong ball**
***Myths:* Alcatraz Escape**

Acetone

You'll find it in thinners like nail polish remover, but as a solvent it can work on all kinds of plastics. It turned up as a miracle additive to petrol in the *Great Gas Conspiracy* where it was supposed to help burn the petrol more efficiently, but turned out to do the reverse.

Acoustician

Any scientist who meddles with sound is just asking to be called an acoustician. Roger Schwenkee is one such reprobate, and without him Adam and Jamie might still be trying to

catch a *Duck Quack Echo*, feel the *Brown Note* and catch a singer *Breaking Glass* on film. Myths are rife with sound, probably because there's so much of it wafting about the place generally, and in an ideal world an acoustician would be on hand at all times to tell you exactly why decibels are such weird things. Sadly, this is very rarely the case.
***See also:* Roger Schwenkee, sound, decibels**
***Myths:* Duck Quack Echo, Brown Note, Breaking Glass**

Acronyms

Itself a portmanteau of 'akros', Greek for 'tip', and the Greek suffix –onym which means 'name' (as in homonym), an acronym is a work made up of the first letters or syllables of other words. The top five Mythbusters acronyms (in order) are scuba, laser, radar, CIA, and FBI. RFID comes a close sixth.
***See also:* homonym, portmanteau, scuba, laser, radar, CIA, FBI, RFID**

Acrophobia

Not to be confused with the fear of spiders, acrophobia is a severe fear of heights that takes its name from the Greek for 'summit'. A poor choice really, surely it should have taken the Greek for 'hugging the ground in terror'. It should also not be confused with vertigo, which is something entirely different. Jamie wasn't confused about anything when he was stuck up on the giant Whirley crane testing the myth of the *Bridge Drop*:

***See also:* Mare Island, Whirley, vertigo**
***Myths:* Bridge Drop**

Actuator

Put simply 'actuate' is just a fancy way of saying – 'make it move'. Hence an actuator is something that makes something else move, perform an action, open or close something … and there are all kinds of actuators, or things you can turn into actuators. The Mythbusters like their actuators to be fast, reliable and reusable, and will haul out a pneumatic actuator at a moment's notice to swing a hammer in *Exploding Hammers* or take it laterally and fire water into a bed of red hot copper nails in *Steam Cannon*.

***See also:* pneumatic, copper**

Adam Savage

Adam 'John' Savage was born in 1967, the same year tornadoes struck St Louis (in winter!), health warnings appeared on television cigarette ads, and scientists discovered radio waves coming from a source in deep space. Although the official line is still that these radio waves come from highly magnetized neutron stars (or Pulsars) this and other intergalactic coincidences dogged the young Savage through his early days growing up in New York. He shielded himself from the looks and whispers of relations and classmates by creating a world of his own, literally building his own toys from

ADAM – I reject your reality and substitute my own!

scratch. With a father who was an animator and film director, Adam soon entered the world of bright lights and cameras, working as a voiceover artist and actor. But it was behind the scenes that Adam made a home for many years, working in film, theatre and commercials and learning the tricks of special effects wizardry until he was eventually called to that SFX nirvana - the workshop of George Lucas's Industrial Light and Magic. Adam's first meeting with Jamie was presaged by colleagues in-common telling the M5I boss he 'had to meet this crazy guy'. Adam and Jamie worked together on projects including the infamous 'Blendo' robot before an Australian television producer called Peter Rees came hunting for a couple of men to bust myths. Jamie called Adam, they cut a demo and the rest is history. Despite being more famous than John Lennon, Adam continues to collect skills to add to sculpting and rigging, vacu-forming and animatronics, woodworking and teaching, model-making and Jamie-impersonating, and many, many more. Although working as host, builder and scienticians for Mythbusters takes up much of his time, Adam is in truth a simple family man with an unhealthy obsession with toolboxes, and a substantial fear of spiders.

***See also:** everything*

***Myths:** all of them*

Adhesive

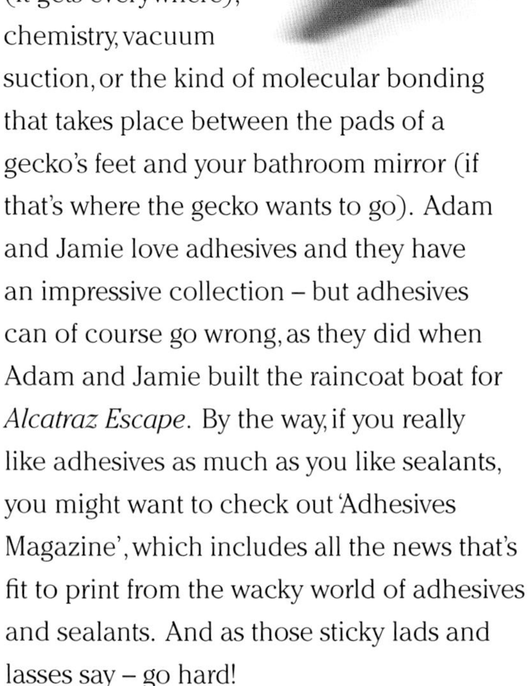

If it's stuck, there is adhesion. Now, it might be to do with electromagnetism (it gets everywhere), chemistry, vacuum suction, or the kind of molecular bonding that takes place between the pads of a gecko's feet and your bathroom mirror (if that's where the gecko wants to go). Adam and Jamie love adhesives and they have an impressive collection – but adhesives can of course go wrong, as they did when Adam and Jamie built the raincoat boat for *Alcatraz Escape*. By the way, if you really like adhesives as much as you like sealants, you might want to check out 'Adhesives Magazine', which includes all the news that's fit to print from the wacky world of adhesives and sealants. And as those sticky lads and lasses say – go hard!

***See also:** contact cement, superglue*

Adsorbtion

You would be right in thinking this is the opposite of absorbent, but did you know that the ability of something to create a molecular film on the surface of a material is key to the manufacture of dynamite?

***See also:** dynamite*

Aerate

'To add air' would be baldly accurate, but nonetheless a very short definition which doesn't go to the material to which you are adding air. If that material is soil, then the action of air (at least, the oxygen in the air) will have certain effects (making that oxygen stick for later release into plants and seeds). If it is water to which you are adding air, the effects will be to create bubbles, as was the case in *Sinking Titanic*. Here the Mythbusters tested several theories about why a sinking ship might pull you down, and one of these was that water above the sinking ship becomes so aerated (by air from cavities in the ship) that the water actually becomes less dense, and hence anything being buoyed up by that density might not be, and sink – giving the impression that it's being sucked down by the sinking ship. Medium scale tests of this theory conducted in a swimming pool at Encinal High worked a treat – it just didn't happen when they sank a real boat. Nice theory though, makes you want to stay off sinking ships.

***See also:* density, buoyancy, air**

***Myths:* Sinking Titanic**

Aerosol

Although aerosol usually refers to a can of something deadly to bugs, an aerosol is more generally a suspension of any kind of tiny drops of matter in a gaseous medium. The whole shooting spray of stuff is more about the propellant than the fact that an aerosol is involved – as was demonstrated when Adam and Jamie found themselves faced with the myth of *Toothbrush Surprise* – where the toilet was creating an aerosol by mixing tiny droplets of faecal matter air. And what was malfunctioning in this toilet that it was doing this disgusting thing? Disturbingly … it was working perfectly normally! The Mythbusters have taken on the classic propellent aerosol cans in a couple of ways – most obviously in *Exploding House* where dozens and dozens of 'bug bombs' were all set off in a single house to see if they could be made to explode (they certainly could). They also tested how hot your car would have to be before an aerosol can would blow up – the answer being 'very hot indeed'.

***See also:* propellent, bug bombs, toilet**

***Myths:* Toothbrush Surprise, Exploding House, Biscuit Bazooka**

Airbags

Do not be fooled by the common airbag: those nylon containers of air that inflate (and deflate) in milliseconds are a marvel of engineering. When your car is involved in an accident, an accelerometer senses that the impact is greater than someone kicking your car because you pinched their parking space and triggers canisters of compressed air to fire their contents. The airbag then cushions the blow that would otherwise result as your head strikes the steering wheel at 55 mph, or 24.5 metres per second (sounds a lot faster that way doesn't it? No wonder 1.2 million people die on the planet's roads annually). Thankfully when the Mythbusters grappled with the myth of *Air Bag Annihilation* they discovered that even car thieves were safe, and you won't get your thumbs ripped off when an air-bag deploys on them (broken, maybe).

***See also:* Thomas Hannan, accelerometer**

***Myths:* that one right there, next page…**

GRANT …'cause technically they are explosives, which is ironic because they're meant to save your life, but they go off right in your face.

Airbag Annihilation

From the Mythbusters fansite comes this tale of car pilfering and airbag justice; if you try to break into a car with a lock-pick and you trigger the side airbag, will that pick launch itself into your skull … with all the side-effects associated with pushing pieces of sharp metal into your brain? First things first – this lock picking thing – how does that work? Of course the most sensible thing to do is trot along to the training facility of the Livermore Pleasanton Fire Department and take a lesson or two. According to our legal team there's nothing we can share with you solid citizens about these lessons, except to say that larceny of this kind will get you 18 months (with good behaviour). Of course if you're a fireman it's all about saving lives madam, and soon the Build Team have a nice line in auto theft down pat. Noting that the fire team DON'T actually train on cars with side air bags (just in case) the Build Team return to HQ and create a robot to do the picking for them. The bag refuses to blow, so they modify the sword-swinging robot from *Ninja Special* and *Myth Evolution* to kick the car into releasing it's airbag of death, but finally shoot the pick out of an air cannon to create any kind of satisfactorily fatal result.

The team returned to airbags in *Myth Evolution* to discover whether you could be thumbed if driving when an airbag deployed. Fortunately it turned out that even if you had both thumbs right on the airbag when it exploded from your steering wheel, the worst you could get is a couple of broken thumbs – not pleasant, but not permanent.

***See also:* airbags, Josh Gaskin, Thomas Hannan**

Air Cylinder Rocket

Compressed air has a lot of potential energy, in fact, most of the energy it took to compress the air in the first pace, and anyone who caught the *Jaws Special* will attest to this. But, if you knocked a hole in a tank of the stuff, could it take off with enough force to blow right through a cinder block wall? There's plenty of opportunity for a catastrophe here – a hole in the wrong place of the tank and it could go anywhere. Jamie designs a rig to aim the tank at the wall, and a guillotine to neatly knock the valve off the tank. A little lard on the rails is a nice touch, but the first attempt sees the guillotine only crack the tank, and so the experiment is halted for some time while the tank slowly but (potentially) dangerously discharges its air. Jamie calls for more weight for the guillotine, and more lard on anything that's moving, and a successful launch ensues, with a nice hole in the cinder block wall along with an impressive dent in the wall behind it. Well – that was fun, what next? The impressive potential of air cylinders has given Jamie an idea … could they power a boat? A fan supplies the shell, the team kit it out with two chunky air cylinders fitted with a lever-activated ball-valve throttle, and the answer is a resounding YES … but only at about five knots. Time spent rejigging the rocket rig so the air is forced out underwater made it … about half as effective.

***See also:* Joe Hughes, George Raterman, compressed air, knots**

Airplane Graveyards

These are places where old planes go to rust out their retirement when they've flown their last mile, or just get parked for reasons of economy, or (bizarrely) just coz the hangars are full. Really, the air industry is weird like that. These graveyards can look very attractive from the air (ironically) but utterly bizarre from the ground, and Flightline 1434 in the Mojave Desert was no exception. The lads came here when tinkering with the myth of *Explosive Decompression*.

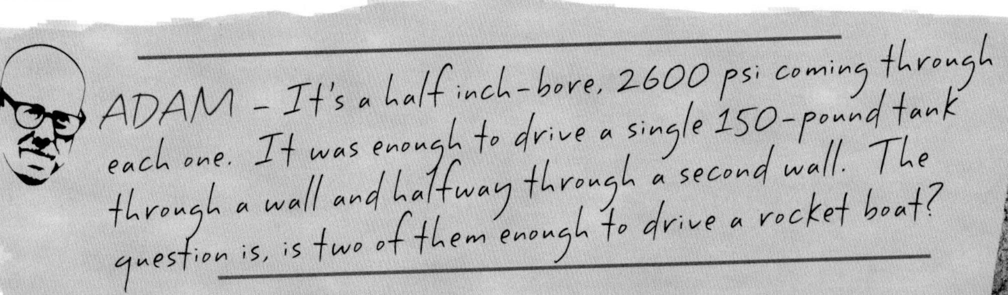

Aeschylus

The lauded ancient Greek playwright has not yet received a mention in Mythbusters, and appears in this volume simply because he died as a result of an eagle dropping a tortoise on his head. Bald men take note: do like Jamie does and wear a beret.

***See also:* beret**

Don't fall in...

African Emperor Scorpion

Scorpions at the best of times are evil, and so you would reasonably expect that anything called the Emperor would be particularly so. However, despite its fearsome appearance, its poison is relatively low on the 'toxic death agony' scale, and hence it has somehow become quite a popular pet (popular being a relative term). Adam and Jamie were confronted by this beastie during the Fear Test for the *Ultimate Mythbuster Special*. [most scary]

***See also:* Fear Test, Giant Tanzanian Millipede, Tarantula, Corn Snake, John Emberton**

***Myths:* Ultimate Mythbuster**

Air Fuel Mixture

Fuels ain't fuels without an ally – and generally that's oxygen, also known as 20 per cent of the air you breathe. It's when a fuel vaporises and mixes with oxygen (in air) in the presence of a spark (or some other form of ignition) that you get some combustion action. However, different mixtures of vaporised fuel and air will give different kinds of results, being more or less easy to ignite, as the guys found in several explosive myths, including *Cell Phone Gas Station* and *Exploding Toilet.*

***See also:* oxygen, air, ignition, air fuel ratio**

***Myths:* Cell Phone Gas Station, Exploding Toilet.**

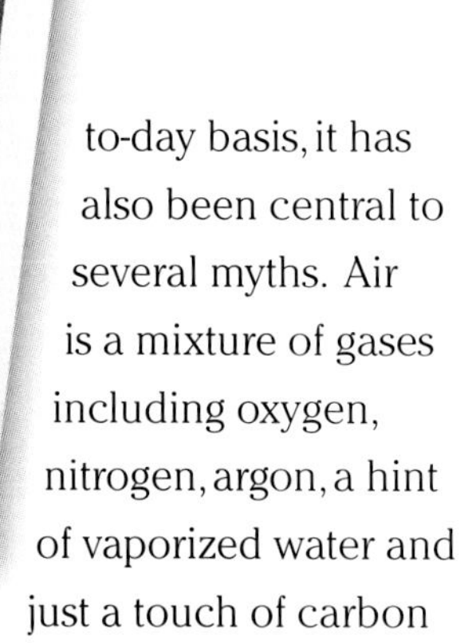

Air Fuel Ratio

This is the mixture of air and vaporised fuel used to create an explosion, or combustion. The calculation of this ratio has gone and got itself a fabulous name; Stoichiometry. For petrol the ideal stoichiometric mixture would see you with 14.7 times the mass of air as you have fuel. If your mixture is too lean on the fuel, you can end up with frustrating 'no blow' events, as Adam and Jamie found when testing the myth of *Cell Phone Gas Station*.

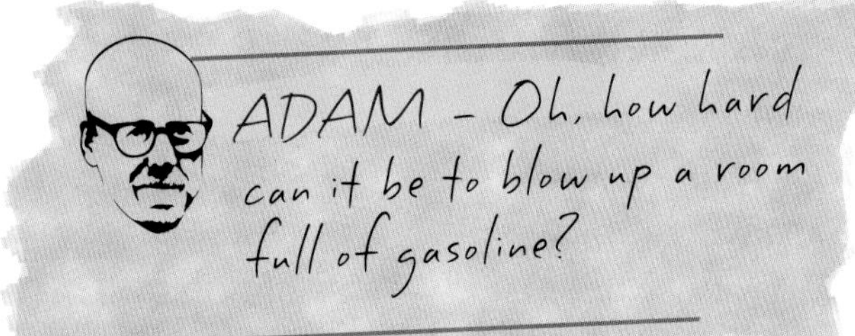

… and moments later Adam was missing an eyebrow.

See also: **combustion, explosion, petrol**
Myths: **Cell Phone Gas Station**

Air

Useful stuff, and apart from keeping the cast of Mythbusting characters alive on a day-to-day basis, it has also been central to several myths. Air is a mixture of gases including oxygen, nitrogen, argon, a hint of vaporized water and just a touch of carbon dioxide (you don't want too much of that, as Jamie found out in *Buried Alive*). Air gradually thins out as you travel higher and higher through the atmosphere into space, but you can also compress it to achieve spectacular devices like the *Chicken Cannon*.

See also: **compressed air**

Air-tight

A seal that is air-tight has been designed to keep air (and other things) out – or in. Another useful phrase to remember is 'hermetically sealed' – which does not mean sealed by a hermit. Tin cans are air-tight to keep out bacteria that would quickly use the air turn the food bad. Air-tight seals and the vacuums they contain can be remarkably strong. If you've eve had problems opening a jar of jam, then recall the tale of the pioneer of vacuums, Otto von Guericke. Otto's party trick for interested 17th Century aristocrats was to draw all the air from between two copper

hemispheres with a vacuum pump he'd invented, and then tie teams of horses to each hemisphere. The hemispheres could not be parted. Another thing to do that will remove air is to seal two dead pigs in a 1987 Corvette and then leave them for two months, just to see if you can clean up what was left well enough to sell the car. The bacteria eat up all the air and when they're done with that, start belching out all kinds of nasty gases and turn the place into something Adam could only describe in this way –

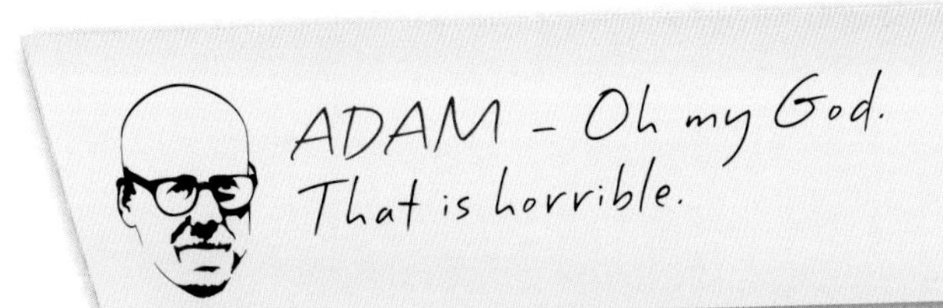

Remember that next time you consider an hermetically sealed coffin for a loved one …
***See also:* bacteria, coffins, copper, vacuum, pressure**
***Myths:* Stinky Car**

Alameda Airstrip (aka Alameda Runway)

Tucked way in the bustling port of Oakland, California, across the bay from San Francisco, is a triangle of reclaimed land, criss-crossed by long strips of flat concrete. Dotted only by a control tower, a couple of helipads and what remains of a fence, this is the Alameda Airstrip. It belongs to the US Navy, who have most graciously allowed the Mythbusters to use the facilities on many occasions to test myths that need, shall we say, a little extra distance between subject and object. It was also host to two miles of concrete highway overpass constructed for the film *Matrix Reloaded* which also came in handy for testing the myth of *Compact Compact*.
***Myths:* Steam Cannon, Tree Cannon, Steam Machine Gun, Shredded Aeroplane, Killer Tissue Box, Border Slingshot and many more**

Alameda County Bomb Disposal Range

If you wanted to blow up a big something, where would you take it? If you were the Mythbusters in this little mental puzzle then you'd use your network of contacts and fans to get you onto the Alameda County Bomb Disposal Range of course!
***Myths:* Painting With Explosives**

Alan Normandy

Sergeant Normandy is the chief firearms instructor with the South San Francisco

Police Department and a very, very knowledgeable, useful and patient sharp shooter. He's been the weaponry expert in several including *Blown Away, Firearms Folklore* and *Bulletproof Teeth* where he had some personal recollections to share.

ALAN – I've seen the aftermath of someone who's attempted that. The damage is fairly devastating.

***Myths:* Blown Away, Firearms Folklore, Bulletproof Teeth**

Alan West

Alan was a car thief originally, but not such a good one that he didn't end up on Alcatraz. He became the fourth member of the original *Alcatraz Escape* team and was, fortunately or not (depending on whether you think the others in the team escaped to sunny Mexico or drowned in the freezing waters of San Francisco Bay) left behind. He told the FBI plenty of details about the escape – but did he know the real location that Frank Morris and the Anglin Brothers were headed for?

***See also:* Frank Morris, Anglin Brothers, FBI**

***Myths:* Alcatraz Escape**

Alaskan Malamutes

Alaskan Malamutes are delightful sled pullers and great companions if you fancy life in the Arctic Circle – or anywhere that's a bit cool. They are in fact one of the oldest distinct dog breeds, but whether this rubs off contemporary 'mutes and make them just that little bit harder to train than other dogs is anyone's guess. Adam and Jamie took in an old pair called Bobo and Cece to see if they could teach them some new tricks for the *Dog Special*.

***See also:* Bobo & Cece**

***Myths:* Dog Special**

Mush

JAMIE – Bobo and Cece appear to be Alaskan Malamutes. This breed is notoriously difficult to train. They're headstrong. So you know, if we can train these old dogs, this being the worst case scenario, we should be able to trai[n] any old dogs.

Albert Einstein

The father of modern physics gave the world insights into the universe with which we are still grappling, but it was the physics of the humble drinking straw that saw him first published in a scientific journal.

Alcatraz

Although this island in San Francisco Bay is named for either the Spanish for lily or pelican (depending on your reference), its fate was to become neither a place neither delicate and fragrant, nor web-footed and long-billed (long-sentenced perhaps). Its formal use began as a lighthouse before it became a military fort then found infamy as a prison. No prisoner ever escaped from Alcatraz – except for those who escaped. In *Alcatraz Escape* Adam and Jamie demonstrated that, although remarkable and officially denied, the notorious three-man escape of 1962 was entirely plausible. The island itself is a cosy size, a smidge less than 150 metres wide and trifle more than 500 metres long, but otherwise is remarkable for its strong currents of uncomfortably cold water. The island is rather barren, rocky and more than two kilometres from the shore. Nevertheless, in 2006 a seven-year-old made the swim to the island, though in the warmth of the day and with plenty of support vessels around. Nevertheless, the mythology of Alcatraz is being gradually chipped away.

Escape-proof?

See also: **swimming**
Myths: ***Alcatraz Escape***

Alcatraz Escape

In June 1962 three men set in motion a plan that might – just might – have been the only successful escape from Alcatraz in that gaol's 29 year history (yep, that's all – we thought it would have been longer). The

fact that of the 34 prisoners who tried to escape, only these three were never heard from again has left a frisson to the tale, and Adam and Jamie were determined to test all the details of the plot as best they could discover them. 50 prison-issue raincoats were immediately purchased, and then 50 *rubber* ones rather than PVC that they bought first up. Eventually their replica pontoon raft was made, and when Adam, Jamie and Will Abbot (a stand in for the third escapee) were in their retro prison garb, paddling a 3 knot current on 60ºF (15ºC) water, they were very impressed and grateful that the thing didn't fall apart. In fact the team actually made it all the way to the Marin Headland, and although this does not constitute proof that the prisoners did – they certainly might have. It was an experiment that left the Mythbusters very, very impressed.

ADAM – You whisper and everybody can hear it. You can't drop a single bolt or nail, you can't kick a piece of wood without everybody on the cellblocks hearing you do it. Imagine that every night for months in pitch black.

Alcohol

A beverage made from the fermentation of sugars that has an intoxicatingly poisonous effect on human beings that some among the species find not intolerable.

Myths: ***Beat the Breath Test, Cell Phone vs Drink Driving, Vodka Myths***

Alloy

If you take two elements, one of them being a metal, then mix them up together (probably at a very high temperature rather than in your ma's cake bowl) you'll have yourself an alloy. With different atoms working together you may find your alloy improves upon the qualities of the original elements – as steel is stronger than iron.

Altitude

The measure of distance in the direction known as 'up'. The cunning thing about altitude is that it can be measured with a pressure gauge (a barometer) rather than a tape measure or ruler because atmospheric pressure drops away the higher you get up into the atmosphere (and because you'd need a lot of rulers). This drop in atmospheric pressure is not a problem for human

beings that are climbing a tree, but if they were to climb a tree that was several kilometres up a mountain, or one growing inside a hot air balloon (unlikely, but who knows what Richard Branson will do next?) you'd find that you were being affected by the lack of oxygen that results from the lower atmospheric pressure. See, atmospheric pressure at sea-level makes it easy to find the next lungful, but at high altitude the oxygen is free to float around a bit.

***See also:* Charles's Law, pressure gauge, atmospheric pressure, oxygen**

***Myths:* Silicone Breasts, Explosive Decompression**

Aluminium

A highly ductile metal whose usefulness has been reserved mostly for the 20th century owing to the great difficulty those previous century dwellers had in extracting it in a sufficiently pure form to turn it into anything other than a pin head. Back then aluminium was the equal of silver and gold; hoarded by Napoleon and a serious contender as a material for the Washington Monument. Aluminium is actually very common in the Earth's crust, approaching one-tenth of its weight (8 per cent for the geological purists). What the Mythbusters like about aluminium is that it is cheap and easily machined, and so it has become ubiquitous with busting myths; from the mould turning out wacky bullets in *Ice Bullet*, to Buster 2.0's joints, to the frame of the blast chamber itself. However, sometimes it just isn't up to the job, as in the test rig built from 200lbs (90kg) of aluminium that failed to pull up to the task in *Killer Tissue Box*.

***Myths:* Ice Bullet, Buster 2.0, Killer Tissue Box**

Amps

'Amperes' to their friends, they are the unit of electric current, named for André-Marie Ampere who earned the honour because of his work establishing the relationship between electricity and magnetism. Amps describe the flow of electricity through a conductor, and are best understood as being conceptually similar to the flow of water in a river. Now, you might canoe on the mighty Amazon without raising a sweat, but be swept away by a stormwater drain. And with electrocution it is the amps that kill you – a meagre few milliamps will have you pushing up the daisies, whereas a little static shock from the carpet might be 5000 volts or more…

***See also:* electricity, magnetism, current, voltage, resistance, power**

Anaerobic

Without air, nasty things happen to organic stuff. If you've got sewage, and say, it's got a very long trip to the local treatment facility, then after a few miles that sewage has turned septic. The bacteria in the poo are to blame – they suck down all the oxygen and turn out a bunch of nasty gas instead – hydrogen sulphide. They'll even make sulphuric acid after a while which will eat into everything. A similar thing happened when Adam and Jamie fronted up to the myth of the *Stinky Car*. This was the myth that a really stinky car, say, one in which someone died, could simply not be cleaned, and no matter how cool the car was, no-one would buy it. Well, Adam and Jamie got hold of a couple of recently deceased pigs, sat them up in a lovely 1987 Corvette and sealed them up tight with tape, then rolled the whole thing inside a shipping container. They came back two months later and the horror of the putrescent beasts could not be believed. Bacteria had filled the car with liquid waste from the orgy of liquefying putrefaction they'd enjoyed. The car was filled with ammonia and gore lurked in every crevice and cup holder. It was not at all a nice place to be – let alone have to CLEAN.

JAMIE – One thing that bothers me is that it is totally, it's ... RAINING in there. Like any place that I move around I'm gonna get covered ... I hope these things are waterproof. Are these waterproof?

He was referring to the full body environment suit he was wearing, and no, it was not. Yuck.

***See also:* putrefaction, bacteria, shipping container**
***Myths:* Stinky Car**

Ancient Death Ray

Never let it be said that the ancient Greeks didn't have a few half-decent thinkers floating about the place. Archimedes was one of them, and the Mythbusters have delighted in coming to grips with the old guy's crazy schemes on several occasions – *Steam Cannon* being another. But the original and many would argue, the best, was the tussle with the death ray. See, there's a lot of energy in sunlight – about one megawatt per square metre in fact. If you can harness and focus enough of that energy using even the simple reflecting technology available to the Greeks you MIGHT be able to throw it against an enemy ship and set it on fire. But … could this death ray be a realistic proposition? After turning out a rig with 300 adjustable mirrors to throw the light of Sol onto a replica ancient Roman trireme, the devastating conclusion is … no.

JAMIE – Our death ray doesn't seem to be working. I'm standing right in it and I'm not dead yet.

But that was not the end of the matter – not by a LOOOONG shot. So many fans wrote into the show that a second attempt was filed as the *Mailbag Special*.

See also: **parabolic mirror, Archimedes**
Myths: **Steam Cannon**

Ancient Electricity

This myth postulates that thousands of years ago, bunches of archaeo-boffins discovered a way in which they could make jolly nice zaps out of popping an acidic liquid into terracotta pots fitted with a copper pipe, an iron rod, and an asphalt cork. Now this was a little strange for those historians of electricity who might otherwise have stuck to Alexandra Volta (yes, the humble volt was named for him) made the first battery some thousands of years later. The fact that the Build Team turned out a zap of 4.3 volts was impressive. However, to make it more impressive yet they wired up something with a little more kick …

ADAM – Ohh %&$#♥-!!!!

SCOTTIE – Did you get the kick in the chest?

ADAM – Ah, yeah, and the head, and the entire body. That was 10,000 volts through my heart!!!

Ancient Prototypes

Also known as 'Gunpowder Engine' for the very good reason that the myth tests whether gunpowder can be used to … make an engine. This is one for the Build Team to get excited about, because not only will there be plenty of explosions for everyone, the designs for these ancient engines already exist! Initially their test of the energetic potential of gunpowder versus petrol leaves the test kit reeling, and a big tick in the 'gunpowder is more energetic' box. They move on to test the crazy designs of such 18th and 19th century engineering worthies as Christiaan Huygens, Sir George Cayley and Thomas Paine. Deciding that the proof of concept for these engines rests in their ability to perform two strokes of a piston, they set about the Huygens engine with enthusiasm and good humour – only to discover some significant flaws in the design. Take two with the Cayley engine, which was designed to create powered flight … but despite getting one stroke out of the design, the engine fails to reload its powder for a second blast. Finally the Paine Engine is given its moment of revived glory, and although it seemed to work under the power of compressed air, the final results were less than breathtaking. Meanwhile, a regular lawnmower engine is drawn into service to see if it will work under the explosive influence of gunpowder. However, like its ancient forebears, the gunpowder lawnmower engine can only achieve a single stroke. Half a proof of concept anyone?

KARI – We did get one push. We got one charge. We got one 'poof'.

See also: piston, stroke

Andy Granatelli

Motor sport promoter, entrepreneur and driver, Andy Granatelli set over 400 world records behind the wheel, including 241 mph (387 km/h) in a street legal, petrol-powered car (and the guy was 62 at the time). Andy assisted Adam and Jamie in their very first myth, the *Jet Car*. He'd had some previous experience with JATO rockets – adding 8 to an Indy car that reached 180 mph (289 km/h) and some suspect he may even have been the origin of the myth!

ANDY – The explosion was horrendous. And the thrust was such that you couldn't believe it. We looked at each other as if we were going to the moon.

Anechoic Chamber

Now that is a fantastic word. Say it with us – 'anechoic'. Hmmm … it would sound even better in an anechoic chamber, which is a room that sucks down every scrap of echo into weirdly shaped baffles on the walls, ceiling and floor, and hence looks a little bit sci-fi meets psycho ward. The chamber the Mythbusters used in *Duck Quack Echo* was a perfect example, and demonstrated its qualities in helping isolate a pristine quack.

***See also:* sound, echo**

***Myths:* Duck Quack Echo**

Duck Quack Echo

Angel Island

A charming retreat from the bustle of San Francisco, this island in the middle of the Bay is a great place to rent a Segway and enjoy the wonders of nature. It was however, NOT the place that Frank Morris and the Anglin Brothers set out for in their *Alcatraz Escape*, as Adam and Jamie amply demonstrated at the San Francisco Bay Model. These escapees were on their way to the Marin Headlands.

***See also:* segway, Marin Headlands, Anglin Brothers, San Francisco Bay Model**

Anglin Brothers

Clarence & John were bankrobbers from Georgia who teamed up with Frank Morris and Alan West to mount an escape from their prison home, the delightful Alcatraz Penitentiary. The brothers were never seen or heard from again, and are presumed dead. A plastic bag of photos and contact addresses was found after the escape, along with bits of the raft and a paddle.

***See also:* Frank Morris, IQ, Alan West**

***Myths:* Alcatraz Escape**

Animatronics

The 18th Century world of automata ushered in a much more precise, lifelike and manoeuvrable world of animatronics. For want of a better term, animatronics are robot animals, but tend to function along programmed lines of movement and audio rather than responding via sensors to the world as they find it. Popular in commercials and useful toys for surprising old people, Adam, Jamie and Grant all have had a hand in designing, building and operating animatronic devices – which have made brief appearances in *Dog Myths*.

***See also:* portmanteau**

Anthropomorphism

Yes, it's a long word, but if you've ever put sunglasses on your dog, talked to your car or hugged your television then it could be applied to you. Human beings such as you constantly imagine human characteristics and motivations within animals, objects and natural phenomena. And why not? There's no law against it! (except in some of the more God-fearing states of the Union). What's more, you're sure that your dog LOVES his little taupe cardigan with leather elbow patches. Sadly, we can never really know the inner workings of a dog, car, thunderstorm or lottery ticket, and if we ever could they'd probably tell you to mind your own business – and quite rightly.

***See also:* pick-up truck**

Anti-gravity

Alright, now, there's a chunk of the readership thinking right now that this is just an easy score on the 'busted' side of the equation. However, Grant would ask you to consider that …

GRANT … there's a lot of credible research going on all around the world. There's a Russian scientist doing a lot of cool stuff with super-conductors. … NASA, the European Space Agency are all interested.

Hairstyles of the rich & famous

Really? NASA? Anti-gravity? On Mythbusters? *Breaking glass* was a world-first, but … switching gravity off? With several patents issued for supposed anti-gravity devices (look them up – crazy but true) the Build Team get hold of a couple of gravity-altering contenders; for entrée, a spinning top that appears to defy gravity turns out to be manipulating magnetic fields with centrifugal force. More substantial perhaps is a triangular device which melds electromagnetism with something called the Biefeld-Brown Effect to create … astonishingly … lift! With not a propeller or booster in sight! Is this anti-gravity? At first it's cheers all round, mainly because they've bought something from the internet something that does ANYTHING other than sit on the ground buzzing), but then Grant catches wind of something – the 30,000 volts of DC current zapping around the thing is actually moving a substantial amount of air. Could this be generating the lift? It's easily tested – pop the thing in a vacuum. Sure enough, their antigravity triangle is grounded.

Appliances in the Bath

JAMIE – What's with the bathrobe?

ADAM – Well Jamie, this time we are attacking one of the classic Hollywood movie myths, which is simply, if you threw an electrical appliance into my bath, I'd get electrocuted.

Simple as that really – find some appliances, rig up a bath with a plug hole attached to a ground wire (as per building code), make a ballistics gel dummy

rigged to a flash-pot that will go off once a deadly current is reached, and turn on the water! OK, well there's a few problems in fact: regular water needs a little something extra to function as a top notch conductor (bath salts or urine are great); appliances with pesky life-saving ground fault interruptors need to be avoided; exactly where in the bath you drop the appliance has a huge impact on the deadliness of the current; their dummy has an electrical resistance much greater than a human body would; Jamie was reading volts rather than amps on his multi-meter; and everyone involved miscalculated the current needed to cause electrocution. Whoops. But the Mythbusters are certainly not above admitting to mistakes and asking for help, and soon enough all the problems are sorted out and they've got a functional bathtub electrical circuit that can do some killing with appliances. First a hairdryer (8.5 milliamps), then a toaster (12 milliamps) and an iron (32 milliamps) are all above the 6 milliamps required across the heart to stop it working. A curling iron (4 milliamps) would be enough to make you very sorry you tried to curl your hair in the bath. Adding bath salts makes the whole experience all the deadlier.

See also: ***ground fault interruptors, multi-meter, electricity***

Arc

Electricity can zap its way through just about anything, and when it ionises its way through the air it's called an arc. If you've ever enjoyed a static zap from a mix of carpet and shoes, then you'll know all about it. Arcs can be small like these ones, or large like a bolt of lightning. Large or small they can be dangerous, if for example the arc starts a fire from your *Christmas Lights* or *Lightning Strikes Tongue Stud*. Short circuits are also an arc danger leading to electrocution. None of these things are as fun as a little static zap to be sure.

See also: ***lightning, static, electrocution***
Myths: ***Christmas Lights, Lightning Strikes Tongue Stud***

ARCHIMEDES

Otherwise known as the Mythbuster of Syracuse, Archimedes got stuck into levers, block-and-tackle lifting systems, screws, the centre of gravity, volumes, geometry (including work on everyone's favourite, parabolas), and of course, lots and lots of crazy weapons … But how much is known about the man himself? Not much sadly, but he did get SO excited about discovering a method of calculating the density of an object he ran naked down the road shouting 'Eureka!' which is Greek for 'I've found it!' If that's not a Mythbuster at work, we don't know what is. Archimedes lived during a period of history when the Romans were the local troublemakers, and the island of Sicily was in their sights. Archimedes was called upon to defend his city, and came up with a range of startling weapons that included a terrifying crane-like device simple called The Claw that could literally pick up an enemy ship and drop it, giant catapults, a massive ship 'The Syracusia', and the all-time Archimedean favourites … the *Steam Cannon* and the *Death Ray*.

***See also:* parabolic mirror, density, Syracuse**

***Myths:* Ancient Death Ray, Steam Cannon**

ARROWBOT

Fashioned from bits of square steel tubing, a winch and line and a quick release, the arrowbot was capable of firing arrows from a real bow with astonishing accuracy. Devised by Grant Imahara for the myth *Splitting an Arrow* the bot did its job, but was unable to split the arrow from nock to tip. So confident were the team with their 'busted' result that the arrowbot was dismantled, and subsequently had to be rebuilt when a massive wave of vitriol surfaced from the archery-loving segment of the Mythbusters fanbase, and you don't mess with those guys. The second arrowbot was capable of firing a traditional longbow, but with no more success than his predecessor.

***See also:* Grant Imahara**

***Myth:* Splitting an Arrow (and revisit)**

Arrows

What were once hewn from fair yew are today extruded from aluminium, fibre glass or carbon fibre. And who wouldn't extrude rather then hew? You'd have to be a church short a few pews to hew yew just for a new arrow or two. But the ye olde names for various parts of the arrow are still with us – from the arrowhead, through the shaft to the fletching and the nock at the end. The Mythbusters took on the myth of *Splitting an Arrow* but found it a hard shaft to crack, and even after a revisit the only full-length split was achieved by a bamboo arrow. Is this because arrows don't fly straight, but rather flex in the air as they fly? Check out the high speed for proof.

***See also:* nock, fletching, broadhead**

***Myth:* Splitting an Arrow**

Artillery

If it's bigger than a rifle but smaller than a submarine then chances are you've got yourself a piece of artillery. You can go ahead and call it a 'gun' – for that's what a 'gun' is (as opposed to a rifle or revolver or anything really piddling like that).

Asphyxiation

More properly we should speak of asphyxia, which (aside from being a very powerful word on the Scrabble board) describes the deprivation of oxygen from the parts of the body that would like some – such as the brain. Asphyxia is bad, and if practised for long enough will result in a mild to heavy case of death. Interestingly, the need to take the next breath does not come from being deprived of oxygen so much as wanting to get rid of carbon dioxide. If air has been displaced by an inert gas, like the balloon-filling classic, helium, then this carbon dioxide trigger is averted and you can fall unconscious simply because you 'forgot to breathe'. Don't try it at home. Asphyxia was a significant risk in a couple of classic Mythbusters episodes, namely *Buried Alive* and *Goldfinger*.

***See also:* carbon dioxide, air, lungs, brain**

***Myths:* Buried Alive, Goldfinger**

Atmospheric Pressure

You probably don't stop to consider this too frequently when wandering through a park, but right above you is a column of air stretching up many kilometres. Although there are heavier things in the world, this column of air has weight, and it's pressing down on you all the time. Atmospheric pressure is the measure of the weight of air above the point of measurement. As you go higher and higher into the column of air, there is less air above it to weigh it down. Thus, the pressure drops, and in fact the air wafts around a bit more and is harder to catch in a lungful of air. This is why mountaineers need to carry their own up onto very high peaks, and why they don't let you open the windows on aeroplanes.

See also: ***compressed air, altitude***

Myths: ***Silicone Breasts, Explosive Decompression***

Atoms

Atoms are so very, very small that to see one you'd have to be so truncated that a million million of you could rock out on the head of a pin. If this was not impossible then you'd be looking at a kind of furry, fuzzy thing of no colour in particular because light isn't really doing much here. But moving on, the reason that the atom is fuzzy is that it has a couple of electrons spinning at a speed approaching the speed of light. These electrons aren't really ever in one place at a time, so reaching out and grabbing one is tricky, but if you stuck your head inside the atom you might catch a glimpse of its nucleus. Again, the

problem here is one of scale, for if the fuzzy outside of the atom was a metre across then the nucleus would be just a tiny grain of couscous inside. Not that the universe is made of couscous, that nucleus is itself made up of protons and neutrons...the number of the former gives the atom its identity: be that hydrogen, helium, gold, copper or whatever. Adam and Jamie don't bring Mythbusting down to this level because a couple of miles of superconductor and associated supermagnets and other bits of kit would cut into their petrol budget, and be hard to squeeze into M5 anyway.

***See also:* electricity, elements**

Avalanche Adventure

Avalanches look kind of fun from a distance, yet they are a tragedy wrapped in a disaster for anyone in their path. The myth of *Avalanche Adventure* was one of three snow-related myths appearing in the aptly named *Snow Special*. Adam and Jamie were keen to discover if yodelling could start an avalanche, and if not, could a bullwhip or firearms? Despite the fact that their scale model made of flour seemed to suggest yodelling was in with a chance, when it came to the field test not even yodelling champion Liz Masterson behind a megaphone turned up to 11 could start the Colorado snow a-movin'. No shame on Liz, even an MP5 submachine gun didn't shake the mountain. One hundred pounds of high explosives on the other hand ...

"ADAM – Well you know, all of our field tests said the same thing, as far as I'm concerned, that no yodeller in the world is truly in danger from an avalanche, merely by yodelling.

JAMIE – You know, I agree with you, but I have to put in a caveat. I mean, the variety of snowfields that are out there that would precipitate an avalanche is infinite, almost, and I can't help but think that some of them are going to be more sensitive than the ones that we saw."

***See also:* Liz Masterson, MP5 submachine gun, explosives**

Backhoe Loader

You've seen them on the sides of roads forever, but you may never get the chance to drive this very cool piece of equipment. Part tractor, part digger, part ... pusher? These things can dig with a force exceeding several thousand kilograms, and to a depth of several metres. The 'backhoe' part is named not because it's hydraulic arm is on the back of the tractor, but because it digs backwards, as opposed to the front hoe which pushes, digs and lifts forwards. You dig? When the lads had their first opportunity to get their hands on a backhoe to dig in the big pipe for *Racoon Rocket* they were very excited – but there was a small problem to do with how it worked.

Myths: Racoon Rocket, Chinese Invasion Alarm

JAMIE – So did you get any instructions on it?

ADAM – I did not.

Bacteria

Bacteria lurk at the very small, very old, very weird, but very, very fundamental end of life itself. Adam and Jamie have come face to face with these tiny life-forms (which, we should point out – for the sake of accuracy, don't actually have faces ... or heads, eyes, brains or the latest 4G phone come to that) in several myths, including *Toothbrush Surprise*, *Five Second Rule* and *Stinky Car*. Bacteria are as small as life gets (if we discount viruses, which we will, for the very good reason that all clever people do). Each bacterium is but a single cell, yet despite (or perhaps because of) their minimal footprint, bacteria are some of the toughest forms of life around.

Baghdad Battery

See Ancient Electricity.

Baking Soda

Sodium Bicarbonate or $NaHCO_3$ to the pocket protector set, this stuff is a real, live chemical compound in your very own pantry waiting to make an appearance in cakes or breads. In the days before Alka Seltzer and sensible eating habits, people would take it raw by the spoonful, and in the myth *Pop Rocks and Soda* Adam and Jamie give their hapless pig's stomach not one, not two but THREE big spoonfuls then add carbonated lolly water. They eventually get a pressure reading of 3 PSI, enough to literally bust your gut.

***Myths:* Pop Rocks and Soda, Killer Washing Machine**

JAMIE – That's an awful lot of sodium bicarb.

ADAM – Well I've taken two with heartburn.

Ballista

While the rest of the team were busying themselves with giant rigs of polished bronze mirrors to retest the *Ancient Death Ray* in the *Mailbag Special,* Grant had a special sideline – 'Project X'. This was to build a ballista, a giant catapult known colloquially a 'scorpion' with a supposed range of 600 feet (183 metres) that was powered by torsion springs. The fun part was that the only kinds of torsion (or 'twisting') springs available to the Greeks came from a bull …

***Myths:* Ancient Death Ray, Mailbag Special**

GRANT – What is it?

KARI – Penis.

GRANT – This is the bull penis?

TORY – Come again?

GRANT – This is …

TORY – Are you serious?

GRANT – No!

KARI – Yeah. Yeah, its penis.

Ballistics Gel

How many times have you seen the Mythbusters reach for the trusty tin of ballistics gel and you've thought to yourself 'what the hell is that stuff?' Ballistics gel is a water-soluble powder that mirrors the qualities of human flesh. It's greatest proponents are weapons testers who use it in trials of what they discreetly call 'terminal ballistics' (or in other words,'will this gun kill you or what?'). Ballistics gel mirrors flesh because it's made principally (if not exclusively) from gelatine, which is typically made from the collagen in animal flesh. Some classic uses of ballistics gel have been to make legs to test whether urinating on a railway track would electrocute you in *The Third Rail,* a full body cast to test *Appliances in the Bath* and a few expendable hands to test *Finger in the Barrel.* Ballistics gel is so central to the Mythbusting process that Adam and Jamie once had to call up a local forensics lab and beg for more; fortunately the technicians were fans and rushed some straight over.

***See also:* Collagen, Permagel**

***Myths:* so many, so SOOO many...**

ADAM – It's a little bit flexible. A little bit hard. It's a little bit country, a little bit rock n roll.

Adam chats to Buster

Balls of Death

These were the impact-meters (or accelerometers) developed by Mythbusters to gauge the impact Buster took when dropped from a six-storey building in pursuit of the truth behind the myth of the *Plywood Builder.* Made from aluminium shells and filled with light globes with fake blood inside, they worked well and were rather more dramatic than reading graphs from a laptop screen (as the team had done previously with the computerized accelerometers in *Hammer Bridge Drop*).

***See also:* gauge, sensors, accelerometer**

***Myths:* Plywood Builder**

Barrel

The traditional barrel is a cylindrical container no larger than could comfortably be rolled by a single person, and made of strips of wood that bulge generously around the middle, all bound by metal hoops. This kind of barrel was encountered in the myth *Barrel of Bricks* and was found to be much, much stronger than the destructive desires of the myth at hand. A barrel can also be found on the end of a firearm, rifle or cannon, and became the focus of Mythbusting attention in *Finger in the Barrel*, where the lads aimed to discover if sticking your finger in the barrel of a gun could make it backfire.

***See also:* gun, firearm**

***Myths:* Barrel of Bricks, Finger in the Barrel**

Barrel of Bricks

This myth supposedly started life as a gag in a book of jokes printed circa 1918 – but could it really have happened? Is it possible that a barrel of bricks on a pulley could drop whilst a hapless worker hangs on to the rope, and gets walloped by the bricks on their way down? But there's more – as the bricks hit the ground the barrel breaks, releasing the weighty bricks, meaning the worker falls back to Earth, getting another whack from the empty barrel. When he hits the ground he lets go of the rope, whereupon the barrel drops once again, right onto the worker. Impossible? Not if you're really, really determined or hugely unlucky, suggest Adam and Jamie, who broke Buster in making the myth plausible.

ADAM – In five, four, three, two ... ha, ha, ha, ha, ha – hey! It worked perfectly!

JAMIE – That was fun. That was really cool. I mean it went up it went down, it went up it went down ... That was hysterical.

Battle of Fredericksburg

In December 1862 one of the bloodier battles of the US Civil War took place in Fredericksburg, Virginia, where Union soldiers took on well-established Confederate lines and were massacred. This one-sided affair did see one extraordinary moment – a one in a goodness-knows-how-many shot, where

two bullets mashed into one another in mid air, and dropped, fused into one, on the ground. This was the basis for one of the myths in *Firearms Folkore* that Adam and Jamie were … eventually … able to reproduce with very significant reliance on very 21st century technology.

***See also:* laser, Minié Ball, US Civil War**
***Myths:* Firearms Folklore**

Bayshore Metals

When Adam and Jamie want to feel cold, hard steel (or aluminium) their first stop is the big warehouse on Napoleon Street, San Francisco. Bayshore have plate, pipes, square tubes, gratings, I beams, T bars YOU NAME IT they'll pull out 10 or 20 feet of it, mark it up and give you a quote. The management don't mind a bit of camera crew action, so you'll have seen some of the staff and interiors of the place in myths such as *Killer Tissue Box* and *Steam Cannon*.

Beat the Breath Test

Can you beat the breath test? Adam and Jamie front up bright and early to the San Francisco Police Department Crime Lab for what was always going to be a very strange day at work. Surrounded by police, they were forced to drink large quantities of alcohol so they could test what mythical remedies might affect their breath test. Could peppermint help? Or chewing into an onion? What about a couple of pennies under your tongue? Or a battery? Denture cream? What about mouth wash? Something more physiological … maybe hyperventilating? No, no, no, no, no, no, no and no. Nothing the Mythbusters did would have got them anything more than an 'Excuse me sir, please take out the keys and step out of the vehicle' from the cops. The breath test 'beats' were busted. Oh and useful info if you meet Adam or Jamie at the bar – Adam is a Scotch man, Jamie likes vodka with cranberry juice.

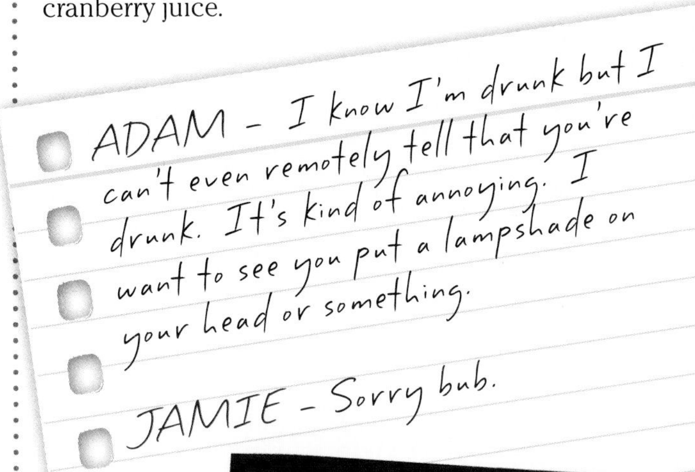

Becky O'Connor

Working for the American Red Cross, Becky was in a perfect position to confirm or deny whether her organization inserted *Mind Control Chips* in blood donors. She denied it, but thought that it was not such a bad idea to keep up supplies of life-giving blood:

Myths: Mind Control Chips

BECKY – I would think that if we were actually somehow controlling people, we probably wouldn't have a shortage, because the first thing we might do is to encourage them to come in more often.

Beaver

These famous dam-building rodents have made only a minor contribution to the Mythbusters stage, that being the use of beaver felt hats in *Hat Shooting*. However, the species has suffered at least one indignity.

ADAM – Do I look like a beaver to you?

JAMIE – Sometimes

See also: ricin

Myths: Hat Shooting, Cardboard Breakfast

Belt Sander

Whether it's the full and glorious electric bench top model, or the basic hand tool, a belt sander consists of a 'continuous' loop of sandpaper or abrasive material driven around two rollers (like a conveyor belt) by an electric motor. A belt sander is a serious piece of kit, and the Mythbusters use them as frequently as possible, often in unusual ways in myths such as *Pants on Fire*, where a belt sander was used to mimic the action of the ground underneath the jeans of a cowboy being dragged by a runaway horse.

See also: tools

Bench Grinder

Just one of Jamie's many favourite tools, most especially because the bench grinder sharpens up many of the other tools in the workshop. Essentially the bench grinder spins a big abrasive disc (or sometimes a wire brush) against which the tool, piece or job is held in such a manner that it is sharpened rather than the hands of the holder. Protective gear a must, sparks guaranteed.

***See also:* tools**

Ben Rillie

Ben had an old Cadillac sitting around taking up space. One day we were flipping channels ...

JAMIE ... you saw us on TV and you figured, 'I'll take it to them, they'll blow it up!'

BEN – I was hoping, yeah.

TORY – What have you got there, a little doll?

GRANT – No, it's called an action figure and it's Ben Franklin.

Benjamin Franklin

Aside from inventing a maddeningly improved glass harmonica and a little thing called the United States of America, Ben also toyed with electricity in unconventional ways. However, as the convention at the time was to rub bits of glass on wool and give each other zaps, pretty much anything was unconventional. But when Ben wrote about flying a kite in a thunderstorm with a key attached to demonstrate the electrical potential of atmospheric conditions, he was fated to be misunderstood almost immediately. Only months after the experiment was written up a Russian scientician was killed by a lightning strike... so, don't trust everything you read.

***See also:* conductance**

***Myths:* Franklin's Kite**

Beret

If you've never worn a beret then you should really try one. There is a reason that military, para-miliary and police units around the world have taken them on as their headwear of choice – they're extra snug and really cute! Seriously, Jamie knows utility when he sees it, and he does so every time he picks up his beret. So go on, get yourself down to your local peasant market and get yourself a traditional woollen beret – ask for the traditional Basque styling for extra points.

Best Music Company

This Oakland outfit are such professionals in the sale and rental of brass band instruments that they barely shed a tear over the brace of trombones they sold into certain destruction to the Mythbusters for the myth of *Trombone Explosion*.

Bet

The idea of turning a lucky guess, discretionary information or athletic prowess into ready cash or other valuables is a concept as old as civilization. Any day now we expect chimpanzees to be found staking bananas on who can be the first to the top of the big umbrella tree. So too do Adam and Jamie indulge in a little bet from time to time. These wagers are always suggested by Adam, but rarely does Jamie not take him up on the offer.

ADAM – The barrel didn't fail. All right I owe you a dollar. There you go. Oh – that's a five.

JAMIE – I'll take that.

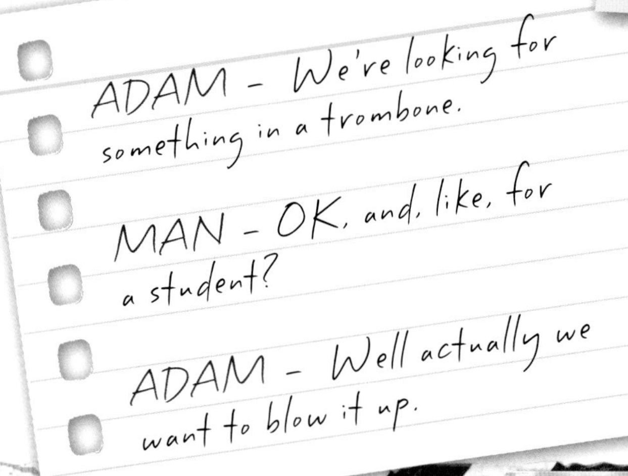

Beverly Ulbrich

When Beverly started to train dogs at the age of nine it was all about fun, and even though she's now one of the most respected dog trainers on the West Coast of the USA, it still is today. When Adam needed to train up an Alaskan Malamute called Cece for the *Dog Special* Beverly was there to lend her experience.

BEVERLEY – OK, sit. Good baby.

Oh, yes – it was Cece she was talking to.

***See also:* Bobo & Cece, Alaskan Malamutes**

***Myths:* Dog Special**

Beyond Productions

Formed in 1985 to make a science television series called 'Beyond 2000' the company has managed to live up to that title themselves, in terms of longevity and hours of factual television produced. Oh, and they're responsible for a show called Mythbusters. You might have seen it.

***See also:* Mythbusters, Peter Rees, Dan Tapster, John Luscombe**

Big Bang

Adam and Jamie are both enthusiastic about explosions – usually the bigger the better, but we'll have to keep you posted on the 'myth' of the Big Bang. If the lads can get themselves a few days with the CERN super-collider then you might get lucky.

Biefeld-Brown Effect

The fact is that if you whack a sufficiently large DC voltage across wires with a couple of sufficiently sharp points in them (say, a nice triangle) then the air around those points actually ionises and pushes away from other neutral air molecules to create enough thrust to make people gawp and reach for the telephone or video camera. However, popping such a device in a vacuum soon dulls the curious and leaves NASA to continue their research in private…

***See also:* ions**

***Myths:* Anti-Gravity**

Bill Knudsen

He's been voted 'Best Living Hatmaker' and so was the natural choice when Adam and Jamie lifted the brim of *Hat Shooting* – a decent target was obviously a matter of top priority.

BILL – And this is typical of what John Wayne wore, and we've stained it, and we've got the cowboy cord on there just like his … and you notice it's a very tall crown.

***See also:* Golden Gate Western Wear**
***Myths:* Hat Shooting**

Biodiesel

Welcome to the strange new world of alternative fuels. Biodiesel is a highly refined and temperamental product that is produced by researchers at NASA … AHA! Got you good that time. Biodiesel is IN FACT a fancy name for used cooking oil. 'What kind of cooking oil?' we hear you ask. ANY OLD KIND – you just filter the stuff (don't ask us how exactly) and then pop it into the nearest diesel-engine car. Prepare for your exhaust to smell kind of … tasty. The Mythbusters did this in *Great Gas Conspiracy* and were astounded – especially because you can often pick this oil up for free from a local fast food eatery!

***See also:* cooking oil**

ADAM – Number one, I'm surprised and impressed that the car runs on just straight filtered used kitchen oil. But number two, the fuel efficiency, it's only 10 per cent less than, you know, regular diesel fuel.

JAMIE – Yep, that's cool.

ADAM – The other thing is, we didn't make any modifications to this car. That means anybody who had a diesel car could just pour this stuff straight into the gas tank and it would run fine. Whoa yeah, baby!

Biometrics

In the paranoid world of security, no means is too maniacal to the end of absolutely security. The technologies of biometrics allow the identification of an individual to take place automatically via intimate measurements of your fingerprints, face, iris, voice, veins, hands, handwriting, heartbeat, DNA, knee print, nose swab or vein scan (three of these may be apocryphal – can you tell which?). The term 'biometrics' was actually pinched from softly-spoken biologists some decades ago, perhaps because what is popularly known as biometrics today actually has a longer history than it likes to let on. Back in the increasingly misnamed 'good old days' the fashion among law enforcement units was to take measurements of the human body; from the nose to the ear, the nape of the neck across the head to the point of the chin, all sorts of crazy things. Wasn't as useful as it was thought to be, and the associated sideline 'science' of phrenology even less so. Security advisors will happily take your money with assurances that the $5.4 million you've just parted with was well spent, but as Adam and Jamie showed in *Crimes and MythDemeanours 2*, there ain't a system invented by humans that can't be beaten by humans.

See also: ***fingerprint scanner, friction ridges, phrenology***

Myths: ***Crimes and MythDemeanours 2***

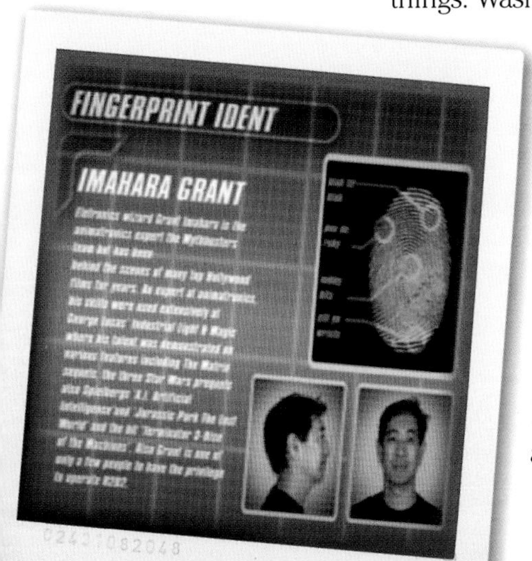

The Imahara file

Bi-metal

All sorts of lifestyle choices spring to mind, but in fact the most exciting thing you can say about a piece of bi-metal is that it is two pieces of metal slapped together, often for the purpose of operating a thermostat between certain temperatures. As the temperature rises, one side of the metal expands faster than does the other side, which makes the metal bend in one direction – enough to flick a switch, turning off the system that is making the temperature rise. As the temperature drops, the metal bends back to its original shape until it flicks another switch which turns the juice on again. Adam and Jamie love bi-metal, especially when its removal (in the shape of the thermostat it controls) will render an appliance dangerous.

See also: ***thermostat***

Myths: ***Water Heater Rocket***

Birds in a Truck

Do you think Isaac Newton was out there with birdseed and a pneumatic net trying to catch pigeons to demonstrate whether or not his third law of motion was just another apple-induced daydream? No, neither can we – but that's why Isaac was a 17th century scientist not a 21st century pop-science superstar! With the pigeons firmly disinclined to treat science as anything more than something to poo on, the 21st century fortunately offers Adam and Jamie recourse to a remote control helicopter. Why, why and why? It's all to do with a silly story about a truckie taking a load of birds across some bridges; a driver behind him wants to know why he stops before every bridge and bangs the side of the truck. 'I'm over the weight limit if the birds don't fly' is his (paraphrased) response. Well, Adam, Jamie and Isaac Newton all agree – that story is bubkus (or the weight limits have a little give in them). When a bird or R/C chopper takes to the air, they push down with the same force that accounts for their weight…thus, the third law is saved and at least one R/C helicopter is toast.

See also:* *Isaac Newton, laws of motion, Ilkka Koskelo

Bird Strike

Although this has nothing to do with mass action of the aerial proletariat, it has a lot to do with the action of a mass. That mass is specifically a bird that has the bad luck to strike a plane and turn itself into snarge. Bird strike is a dangerous thing for an aeroplane (to say nothing of the bird) and has led to the creation of the *Chicken Gun*, therewith to test various elements of the plane that are likely to be so struck.

***See also:* snarge**

***Myths:* Chicken Gun**

Bischoff's Taxidermists

Unless it dies right in front of you, dead animals can be hard to get your hands on. Ask a butcher to sell you a whole pig (say, to test a myth called *Stinky Car*) and they'll happily do so – sans the guts and other organs they crazily assume you don't want. This is where Bischoff's come in. Taxidermists to the stars, their

contacts can get hold of whatever animal you need and stuff it to your requirements … and there's nothing suspicious about it at all.

JAMIE – So these things by and large are dying of natural causes then.

GARY – Yes, yeah. These animals are all of natural causes. We don't go out and get animals and kill them for the movies at all.

See also: ***taxidermy***
Myths: ***Stinky Car***

Biscuit Bazooka

We're all partial to cookies, and the modern convenience of canned cookie dough just makes those homemade treats all the sweeter. But should you leave that can in the car, then leave that car in the sun and just about anything can happen. OK, it's not going to ACTUALLY take your head off – but it might just feel like it. Sure enough after Adam and Jamie rigged up a car with heat lamps at around 137ºF (58.3ºC) which is a credible temperature inside a car on a very hot day – the sounds of tins a'poppin' is suddenly everywhere.

ADAM – We should do this in Vegas then we could say I went to Vegas and I blew some dough … I definitely can understand how you can mistake this for brains. Here.

JAMIE – I'm not going to do anything with it.

ADAM – Well, no feel it. Feel it.

JAMIE – Yeah it's definitely brains…

But that wasn't enough – the fans were baying for more in-car explosions of household products (we're only human after all – if that). A revisit was called for where cans of soda and aerosol cans were testes,

but it took much higher temperatures to get the desired effect. But the wait did give Jamie a chance for some 'me time':

ADAM – ... You wanna take off your hood and participate in this conversation?

JAMIE – I kind of like it in here – it's private.

And even THAT wasn't all! Viewers then wanted to know if a white or a black car would heat up faster and get hotter. The black car did both, hands down.

See also: **Fred Caporaso**

Black Powder

Brought into the world by the Chinese who have a liking of crazy mixtures you'd only think of after 5000 years (the Chinese have had that long) black powder is the name given to a cheeky little mixture of stuff that just loves to go BANG. Three ingredients are all it takes: filled with the kind of pits and divots that make it burn baby burn, powdered carbon is the fuel. Then there's saltpetre which adds the extra oxygen you need to make all that carbon burn up nice and fast. Finally and just to make everything move a little faster is everyone's favourite yellow element, sulphur. To say that the Mythbusters like black powder is rather like saying Imelda Marcos didn't mind the occasional stroll around the mall to pick up a new pair of heels. Black powder (aka gunpowder – did we mention that?) is the one essential ingredient to help a myth go off with a bang. Some of the highlights (we can't take you into every black powder adventure) of black powder have included *Trail of Powder* where the lads worked out you can in fact outrun a trail of black powder and stamp on it before it blows the inevitable keg at the end, the archaic *Tree Cannon* which met its end after five pounds (oh yes five POUNDS – aka 2.2 kgs) of black powder was poured down its barrel, and

finally, it was a dose of the black stuff that finally made the *Exploding Toilet* live up to it's name. 'But, hang on, that's not enough!' we hear you shout, 'How do we make our own black powder? What are the proportions?' That's one for the legal department I'm afraid, and as with the entry on the CIA, if you find the entry ends suddenly, then …

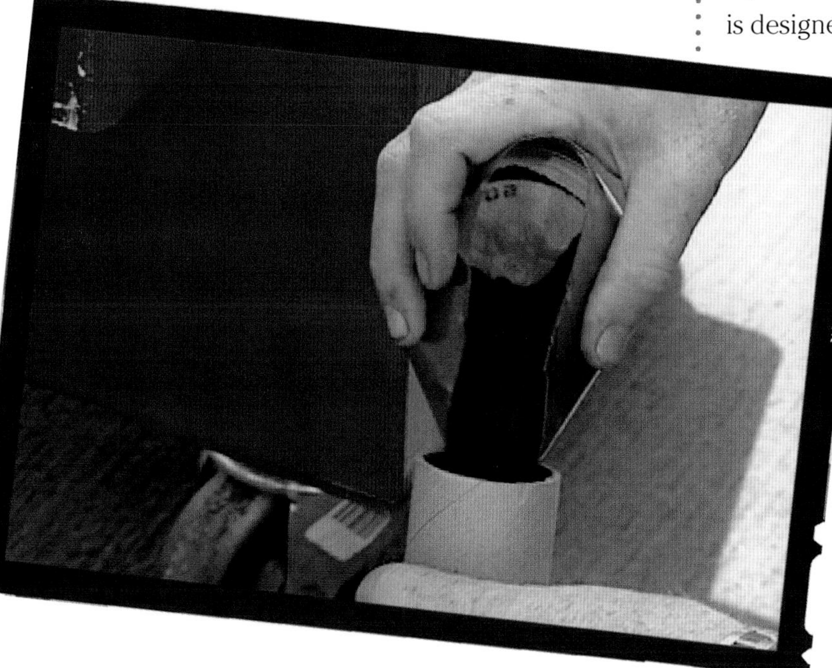

***See also:* paper, saltpetre, sulfur, carbon, explosives**
***Myths:* Trail of Powder, Exploding Toilet, Tree Cannon, Racoon Rocket, Trombone Explosion and many, many more**

Blast Chamber and Screens

This non-human Mythbusters character joined the cast in the very first broadcast episode of Mythbusters and is still a firm favourite of the crew and cast – because it keeps them alive and healthy. Made of the impact and bullet-resistant material Lexan™ beloved of race drivers, jet pilots and Jamie Hyneman, the Mythbusters' blast chamber is designed to contain the impact of small explosions, such as those in *Exploding Toilet* and *Cell Phone Gas Station*. The blast chamber was built in two parts with four walls each, framed with aluminium and pushed together to make an enclosed space. Jamie and Adam have also built blast screens of the same material, but which are slightly more transportable and not quite so heavy. Nevertheless, their weight is a significant problem for both chamber and screens, which are 1.25 inches or 3.17 centimetres thick (one of the more serious accidents borne by the crew was the result of an accident transporting a blast screen - ouch!). The blast chamber was originally described as 'bulletproof', however, this is a term is

contested by many, including the lads themselves in the myth *What is Bulletproof?* Some very large and potentially catastrophic explosions have called for the use of a shipping container as a blast chamber.

JAMIE – So we've designed this, you know, it's covered with polycarbonate that won't shatter or go anywhere. It's securely bolted as well. It's made in two separate halves so that if there is any kind of general explosion in there, it'll just open like a flower.

FIRE MARSHALL – So there's nothing holding it together in other words.

JAMIE – No …

See also: ***Buster, Lexan™, bulletproof, aluminium, shipping container,***
Myths: ***Cell Phone Gas Station, Exploding Toilet, What is Bulletproof, etc.***

Blendo

Possibly the most terrifying robot ever to glide across a combat robot arena, Blendo was in fact two woks, a lawnmower engine and some bits from a photocopier. Oh, and two razor sharp steel blades. Blendo would scatter bits of its opponents high into the air and into the baying crowd, and was eventually forced into retirement by the insurance concerns. The robot is of interest to us here as it was one of the first projects to bring Adam and Jamie together.

Block and Tackle

One of the all time great pieces of equipment and one that has many people nodding sagely without the faintest idea what it actually is. Wonder no more friends, for a block and tackle is nothing more than a bunch of pulleys and a generous coil of rope (or other flexible pulling material – chain for example). By distributing pulleys in such a way that some are anchored above the weight, and some are attached to the item being hefted, the fact is that a mechanical advantage can be realised. 'Aha!' you say – hoping that the next explanation will be exactly what is a mechanical advantage. Not a chance – alphabetical order is established!

See also: ***pulley, rope, mechanical advantage***
Myths: ***Barrel of Bricks***

Blood Alcohol Content

It is startling to think that the alcohol from any alcoholic beverage you drink zooms about in your blood until your liver has the time to get rid of it. That means there is alcohol in your toes, your eyes, your brain and your ear lobes. OK, it won't do much harm in your lobes, but when you hear the phrase 'blood alcohol content' next time, consider what that actually means. A measurement of blood alcohol content as made with a professional device tells you how much of your blood is in fact not blood at all, but alcohol. Given no one knows exactly how alcohol works in your body, many would think you a little foolish for putting ANY IN YOUR BLOOD in the first place, but when you're then told that a couple of 'standard' drinks would result in half a gram of alcohol sneaking into each litre of your blood (a reading of 0.05%), you would probably agree that this should result in your arrest in nine out of 10 countries if you pop behind the wheel of a car (which indeed it does).

See also: ***alcohol***

Myths: ***Beat the Breath Test, Cell Phone vs Drink Driving***

Blood

You really could go on all day about the five litres (10.5 pints) of blood that keep you on your toes, but we don't have that kind of time so we will confine ourselves to the following: blood is a suspension, like milk. Rather than fats floating in water, its different kinds of cells (red and white) that do the floating, and something called plasma that does the suspending. If you leave a vial of your blood just sitting around, all the red blood cells are suspended at the bottom, which looks distinctly odd. Next, the rest of the blood that is still zooming around your body at up to 0.3 m/s (nearly a foot a second) has a raft of vital functions including carrying oxygen around your body, taking away wastes, passing on messages with hormones, keeping

your body temperature nice and stable – it almost goes without saying that blood is life, and you should get yourself down to the local blood bank as soon as possible. Adam and Jamie did just that when they busted the myth of *Mind Control Chips*, a myth which supposed that hospitals and blood banks were responsible for popping these chips in your bloodstream whilst you were in their care which then made you do weird things (like, invent myths about mind control chips). Naturally the hospitals and blood banks deny this – which they would even if they WERE doing such thing, which clearly they're not. Finally, the colour of human blood is given by the oxygen-carrying protein called haemoglobin, which subtly changes colour depending on the amount of oxygen (or other things) that it's carrying. The blood you give at the blood bank always looks darker than the blood you squeeze out through your knees when you come off your bike.

KARI – This myth is actually kind of beautiful to me. For some reason I just think blood's really pretty, so this isn't grossing me out at all. It's just kind of a neat little blood fountain.

Bloodhound

They're goofy looking but deadly accurate trackers – in the *Dog Special* it was uncanny how Morgan the professional bloodhound with the San Mateo Sheriff Unit was able to find Adam in minutes, despite the wily one pulling every trick in the book. It was Adam's skin cells that gave him away – the bloodhound's extraordinary nasal sensitivity means they can spot a freckle's worth of skin cell scent in a whole field. Even water isn't an object. It's perhaps not so surprising – Adam and Jamie discovered that bloodhounds have been at it a while …

***See also:* Morgan, Matt Broad**

***Myths:* Dog Special**

ADAM – Well we have citations referring to sleuth hands hunting men as early as the 13th century.

JAMIE – Yeah, but back then, noblemen mainly used them for hunting deer and boar.

ADAM – And it is commonly believed that the breed was refined and originated at the Saint Hubert Monastery in Belgium in the 11th century.

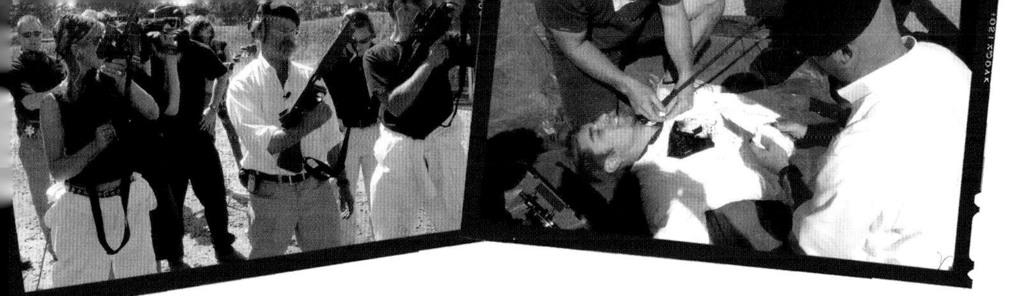

Blown Away – and revisit

It's another chance to open the Mythbusters gun cabinet as Adam and Jamie stakeout a Hollywood shoot 'em up myth – the classic question of whether being shot in the chest will actually knock you off your feet (as well as kill you). After learning that 70 per cent of fatal shootings happening within a distance of 22 feet (6.7 metres) that seems the ideal point to set up their dead pig target rig. Weapon after weapon leaves the porker unmoved, until a solid deer slug from a shot gun eventually topples porky from his hook. A swan dive it ain't. Even with a bulletproof vest on there's nothing getting 'blown away' but the myth itself. And why the hell not? It's all about Isaac Newton – the old Limey strikes again. The fact is that if 'every action has an equal and opposite reaction' then the amount of force to knock a couple of hundred ponds of someone a few metres backwards would also be enough to also knock the shooter on their tushie. We expect it to happen because filmmakers accomplish the trick with hidden vests, ropes and the precision timing of special effects experts. HOWEVER some fans were simply not satisfied and so the lads revisited the myth with a different rig and more powerful weapon. The new rig supported Buster around his centre of gravity, and the new gun was … the 50 cal Browning. AND they added a steel plate vest to make sure every foot ounce of force was sent right into him. The result? He just drooped off the rig like towel off a rail.

KARI – We had 100 per cent of the kinetic energy on Buster and he still did not fly back. I would say that this is busted, busted, rebusted and busted.

See also: ***Brian Feige, Firearms, Matt Heron***

Blueprint

Every myth is introduced with a drawing done in white on blue paper. The actual paper the lads use is called Pacon Spectra Fadeless Art Paper, but it should be pointed out that these are not blueprints in the strict sense of the term. Blueprints were in fact the earliest method of mechanically reproducing an engineering drawing with a process called cyanotype. To do one of these

you coat paper with light-sensitive chemicals, then trace your original onto tracing paper, slap it into a frame with your light-sensitive paper behind it and leave it out in the sun for a few minutes. The light-sensitive paper would turn a bold blue, EXCEPT for where the lines of the drawing had blocked the sunlight. The resulting blueprint was then washed to remove the chemical from those lines and you ended up with a gorgeous blue reproduction of your ship, car, *Steam Cannon* or whatever.

Blunt Trauma

Blunt trauma is just another way of saying 'hit hard with something that didn't end up lodged inside the body'. Otherwise it would be called penetrating trauma. But as nasty as a penetrating trauma can be, your body doesn't like blunt trauma either. Not one little bit. Sure a bruise or two is all part of life, but the kind of blunt trauma that would cause your internal organs to be ripped from their mooring is to be avoided at all costs. It's this kind of trauma that the Mythbusters are measuring every time they drop Buster from a decent height, or put him in a car destined for an accident.

See also: ***Killer Tissue Box, Bridge Drop***

Bob Brozman

If you've ever listened to the title music for Mythbusters and wondered … "who is DOING that killer slide work?" then wonder no longer. His name is at the top of this entry. Nice work Bob.

See also: ***Neil Sutherland***

Boat Trailer

Called 'Trailer Troubles' by some, this myth asks the question – are modern boaties so dumb that they actually send their pride and joys into the water attached to their trailer, and then drive it like that out to their favourite fishing spot? Well, perhaps just a few. The fact that it can be done is a little odd, but then if expert boaties like Jay Meiswinkel freely admit to having done it themselves, then … who are we to call them fools?

See also: ***Jay Meiswinkel***

Bob Renkes

Consulted for the myth of *Cell Phone Gas Station*, the executive vice-president for the Petroluem Equipment Institute knows his petrol tools, and Bob was able to point Adam and Jamie in the direction of research that showed who was in the most danger from a petrol station explosion, and why the explosion might happen in the first place. The facts showed that mobile phones are in the clear: but that it is people who get back into their car, then climb out with a fresh zap of static on them from the seat, and when they reach out for the bowser … BOOM.

BOB – We've had 152 cases now that we've confirmed. Seventy-eight per cent are women, 22 per cent are men.

***See also:* static**
***Myths:* Cell Phone Gas Station**

Bob Stein

Sergeant Stein of the Arizona Department of Public Safety heard about the myth of the *Jet Car* in 1994. Back then he was the departmental spokesperson when a reporter called with a story circulating on the internet which suggested that an Arizona citizen had received a Darwin Award for fitting his car with a rocket and smashing it into a mountain.

BOB – I thought it was a very real possibility that it could have happened because Arizona is home to several air bases thus military personnel could have gotten hold of a Jato unit to use in this fashion.

However, as Bob tells it, no crash site for this supposed rocket car wreck was ever found in Arizona.

***See also:* Jato, Darwin Awards**
***Myths:* Jet Car**

Bobo & Cece

Imagine being taken from a dog home and plunged into a whirlwind of training and television stardom! A tough call, but seven-year-old Alaskan Malamutes Bobo and Cece learned their lessons so damn near perfectly

that they busted the *Dog Special* myth that you can't teach an old dog new tricks.

JAMIE – Nine-and-a-half out of 10 ain't bad at all. So it seems to me you can in fact teach an old dog new tricks.

ADAM – I agree. This one's totally busted and one of the more cuddly myths we've ever done.

***Myths:* Dog Special**

Bob & Roy

These two ducks walked free from Jim Reichardt's duck ranch when their quacks lead to the busting of that great mystery, does a *Duck Quack Echo?*

***See also:* Jim Reichardt**

***Myths:* Duck Quack Echo**

Bodkin

Arrows have different kinds of arrowheads, and one of these is the bodkin, a four-sided metal spike that narrows to a sharp and deadly point. Bodkins may have been made for armour piercing or for long flight, but when Tory knocked up a few for the revisit of the myth *Splitting an Arrow* they were unable to do the arrow splitting business.

***Myth:* Splitting an Arrow**

Body Temperature

You may think it's all about 36.8°C (98.2°F) but in reality body temperature moves around all over the place – or at least within a certain range – depending on how much exercise you've just put yourself

through, whether you're eating, how pregnant you are, whether you're awake or asleep … Of course, it's a fraction of a degree either way we're talking about, and body temperature that gets out of control in either direction can have very serious consequences up to and including death. That's why whenever the Mythbusters are putting themselves on the line by taking on a human body myth, as they did in *Goldfinger*, body temperature is something they keep a very close eye on. Just how they do that is a matter for discussion:

***Myths:* Goldfinger**

ADAM – You know there's only two ways to monitor your core body temperature. Through your ear and a rectal thermometer … Do you have a preference?

JAMIE – Yes I would prefer to be eared. Especially if I'm running on a treadmill.

Booster

In the world of explosives (ahhh – explosives) sometimes a very big explosive might not be sensitive to an ordinary detonator, and needs something more like an explosion to get it going. Such explosives are called 'boosters' so named because they boost the larger and more explosive explosive into action. Adam and Jamie used a five pound (2.27kg) booster with a high detonation velocity to set off 100 pounds (45.3 kg) of explosives in the *Snow Special* to see if they could make an avalanche. Ironically, the lads had Craig from the Telluride Snow Safety Team help them do all this.

***See also:* detonation velocity, explosives, irony**

***Myths:* Snow Special**

Border Slingshot

How big can a slingshot get? This myth suggests that the US of A is being invaded by migrants from Canada (?!) who are entering God's Own Country via a giant slingshot that fires them 200 yards (182 metres) right onto a well-placed mattress. This is not just individuals mind, family packages were available as well. Mock you may, but this episode gave Adam and Jamie the excuse to build the world's

two biggest slingshots. The first is made using football goal posts. The second? Radio towers – no, we're not kidding. But first it's ordinary slingshots to test for a base speed, then a slingshot built onto the scissor lift to test materials. Then they trip out to Encinal High to turn their football goal posts into a 1:10 scale slingshot. Only then do they bring in the radio towers to create an engineering marvel fraught with problems that nevertheless manages to fire the 200-pound (90kg) Rescue Randy 211 feet (64 metres), breaking the world human cannonball mark into the bargain. Although both Adam and Jamie agreed that the engineering was not impossible to fling someone the full 200 yards, in the end there was no way such a rig could be made portable or it's fall survivable; myth busted.

See also: **Encinal High**

JAMIE – Just like throw a blanket over the razor wire or whatever and go for it, you know? This is going to kill you, mattress or not.

Boron

Sitting at number five on the atomic hit parade, boron is a key nutrient for plants and – coincidentally – burns with a green flame (you'll have seen it used in pyrotechnics). It's also the key ingredient in Pyrex® glass.

Borosilicate Glass

With an extraordinary low thermal expansion thanks to the boron added during its high-temperature manufacture, borosilicate glass (every heard of Pyrex®?) is great for lab equipment and kitchenware because it's resistant to breaking when introduced to different extremes of temperature.

See also: **Pyrex®, boron**

Boyd Lacosse

There's not another Boyd alive like this Boyd. This Boyd blows things up for a living. He has a very bold opinion of what his work can achieve.

Myths: **Explosive Decompression**

BOYD – Hell yeah. I think I can solve all your problems.

Break Step Bridge

The frustrating thing about Break Step Bridge and its almost endless revisits was the dreadful feeling that the Mythbusters might only be half a hertz away from … something… The myth is that you can't let an army march across a bridge 'in step' just in case that march is 'in tune with the resonant frequency of the bridge itself. The concept, as with the myth of Breaking Glass is that if you can create a frequency that matches the resonant frequency of an object then you can make that object oscillate (or shake) until it breaks. However, the thing with a crystal wine glass is that you can find out the resonant frequency of the glass by giving it the merest tap and listening for the tone. Ever tried to tap a bridge? Even a bridge like the one Adam built for this myth? Didn't think so – the point is you take pot luck, and the cute little army of marching pneumatic robots didn't find that frequency (sure they knocked the bridge down, but … there might have been some engineering problems…). Then Jamie built a big arm-swinging robot, and although you got the sense they were getting close (see sentence one of this entry) they never quite destroyed the bridge with vibrations. Adam did by jumping on it. In a revisit that's knocking around the Discovery website they did tests on smaller scale bridges and came up with a plausible, but improbable conclusion. They got better results with Earthquake Machine some time later… and even better creating fractious little harmonic oscillations between one another…

ADAM – I have to say that actually at the very start of this Jamie and I had a big argument about whether to do this electrically or pneumatically with air. And I strongly suggested that we not use air. I explained it to him in great detail and he decided to ignore a good portion of it.

JAMIE – I'm pleased the actuators are definitely doing what we needed, they're the right choice for the job. And they'll certainly go as fast or slow as we need to get them to go. I think the biggest problem is not my little soldiers, it's the bridge.

Breakfast Cereal

See *Cardboard Breakfast*

Breaking Glass

One of the great myths ever busted on the show, for it ticks all the boxes. Is the idea that a singer could break a wine glass with his voice alone a well-known urban myth? Most definitely. Is there any filmed evidence whatsoever that such a feat has even been achieved by an unamplified human being? None whatsoever? Did the Mythbusters manage to confirm the myth? Yes, they most certainly did! After Adam and Jamie took some help from Roger Schwenkee to bust wine glasses with amplification it was all down to heavy metal singer Jaime Vendera who took several tried but eventually did the business. The question is … how? Well, a decent wine glass has a resonant frequency which you can hear when you tap it or run your finger around the lip. It is at this frequency that the glass is at it's most vulnerable to vibration – but you have to hit it loud and strong (and right in front of your lips … don't try it at home!).

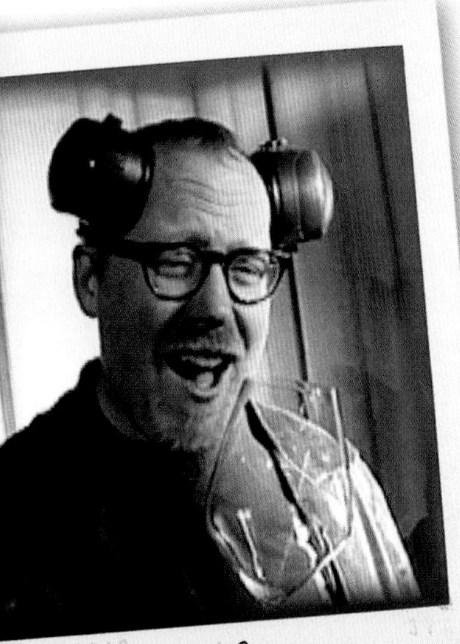

The face alone would do it…

ADAM – Well that's it. We proved that there is a tone that you can use to match the resonant frequency of glass in order to shatter it. And most importantly of all, we proved for the first time that an unassisted human voice can actually generate that tone and shatter a glass. I'm amazed by that…

***See also:* resonance, frequency**

Breast Implants

Over the centuries (yes, centuries) so many attempts have been made to augment the humble breast that you think we'd be running out of interest in it by now

– we've tried glass, rubber, air, ivory and other things you'd never imagine people would let anywhere near their breasts. The Mythbusters were able to demonstrate that modern silicone breast implants could survive a range of pressure environments, but even so … do we need them?

Breath Test

See Beat the Breath Test

Breath Testing Machine (AKA Breathalyser)

In the 1950s a state trooper in Indiana had a bit of a brainwave – a drunk's breath is smelly with booze, why don't we test that boozy breath as a shorthand for the more complicated blood test? Well, they did, and it turned out that the alcohol expressed in the breath of a drunk was proportional to the amount flowing through his veins. OK, so this Indiana trooper wasn't your average trooper (he later became a professor at Bloomington University) but even so, it was not surprising that this device was invented, because the alcohol that ends up in the lungs arrives via your blood in the first place. In the myth *Beat the Breath Test* Adam and Jamie agreed to a morning of heavy drinking (13 drinks in three hours) and were then tested on a breathalyser. Adam tested 0.11 and Jamie 0.09 – both were over the legal driving limit in California (0.08). These figures are the Blood Alcohol Content – in Adam's case the device found there to be the equivalent of 0.11 grams of alcohol in 100 grams of his blood (as measured via his breath).

***See also:* blood, lungs, blood alcohol content**

***Myths:* Beat the Breath Test, Cell Phone vs Drink Driving**

Brian Feige

Brian owns the Browning 50 cal sniper's rifle that was used in the *Blown Away* revisit and the myth of *Bullet's Underwater.* Weirdly, he'd not actually fired the thing until the revisit ep… why not Bri?

BRIAN – Well it's too powerful for most of the local ranges, and the property I have to shoot it at is a swamp for six months out of the year.

BRIAN – Are you excited?

BRIAN – Oh yeah.

Brian Sullivan

Propeller specialist Brian worked with his mechanic pal Earl Hibler to right the wrongs done to the ex-aviation school engine that Jamie bought to test the myth of *Shredded Aeroplane.* It was never going to be good enough to take to the air again, but …

BRIAN – It will run good enough to do what they want to do.

***See also:* Earl Hibler**
***Myths:* Shredded Aeroplane**

Bricks

The humble brick is approaching its 10,000th anniversary, but for those who've never encountered one, a brick is a cuboid-shaped object of some hardened material, usually baked in some way, light enough to be laid by hand by a muscular gentleman in shorts who uses a gummy, self-hardening substance to stick them all together into a wall, house or path (among other things). The Mythbusters have turned to bricks irregularly as a building or model-making material, but they took pride of place in *Barrel of Bricks*, and to some extent in *Salsa Escape*.

***Myths:* Barrel of Bricks, Salsa Escape**

Bridge Drop

Also called Hammer Drop by some fans and Bridge Jump by others (who weren't paying attention – who would jump?), this is one that you'd want to believe if you worked on a bridge. Say you're swinging from your harness, smacking a few rivets into place when all of a sudden, you feel a certain … lightness. Whoops – you're falling towards the harbour or river at an alarming rate, and that water is looking awful hard. Do you try the swan dive? Or do you reach back into the memory of a coffee break long months ago when a colleague told you that your only hope if you fell from the bridge would be to throw down a hammer to break the surface tension of the water before you hit it? Naturally you'd swing that hammer towards the water without a milliseconds thought (and be quick about it). BUT WOULD IT SAVE YOU? Falling from The Whirley on Mare Island (and it took Jamie some doing to get up there – he's not one for heights) Buster was, hitting the water at 60 mph (96km/h) and decelerating at 287Gs! He lost limb after limb, so… the eventual answer

Adam and Jamie hit on was 'absolutely not'. Let us do our part now to reinforce that a fall onto water from any height above about 200 feet (60 metres) will kill you as surely as falling onto a truckload of refrigerators. The Mythbusters busted Buster from 150 feet (45 meters) in this myth. Surface tension – you can't beat it, can you? By the way, if you were thinking of a cheeky little leap from 59 metres remember that people have died falling into water from *the edge of a pool*.

***See also:* surface tension, hammer, The Whirley, Mare Island**

JAMIE – You know the thought that jumping off something and hitting water is gonna like literally rip your limbs off your body, it's surprising. I never would have thought that.

Broadhead

A type of arrowhead that's broader than a narrow head. You think we're kidding? We probably are. How are you ever going to know?

***Myth:* Splitting Arrow**

Brother Guire Cleary

Priest and historian at Mission Dolores, Brother Cleary is also a dab hand at myth research. This was what he'd dug up on *Buried Alive*:

GUIRE – Well I've heard stories that some people would insist on perhaps having bells – ropes going to bells from the coffin so if they woke up underground they could ring it. Or perhaps they would have their veins drained of blood to make sure they were genuinely dead.

***See also:* Mission Dolores**

***Myths:* Buried Alive**

Browning 50 Calibre

John Browning had 21 siblings and three mothers. It will be no surprise then that he grew up in Utah, but the fact that he could name every part of a gun before he could read was unusual. Today the company that

Just hold still...

bears his name produces an enticing range of death makers of different kinds, including the terrifying 50 cal used in *Bulletproof Water*. It fires a round nearly 14 cms (5.5 inches) long.
***See also:* calibre, round**
***Myths:* Bulletproof Water**

Brown Note

Fans of SouthPark and CIA conspiracy theories will have been itching for Adam and Jamie to take on this myth – is there a certain subsonic frequency that when played with sufficient amplification at the human body, will make a person involuntarily defecate? With adult nappies on hand, this was another chance for the Roger Schwenkee and his lads from Meyer Sound to dip into their box of tricks – specifically, $60,000 worth of tricked up 25,000 watt speakers specially modified to boom out frequencies far below the range of human hearing – but perhaps not defecation. Confusion is the other possible side effect, and Adam was tested both mentally and physically as he took on the brunt of 108dB of sub sonic slam. Then 114dB, then 128dB, then they start pulling the foam out of the speakers and reach 154dB …, and all the time the worst effect on Adam is that his eyeballs and voice get a bit wobbly. But downstairs?
***See also:* decibels**

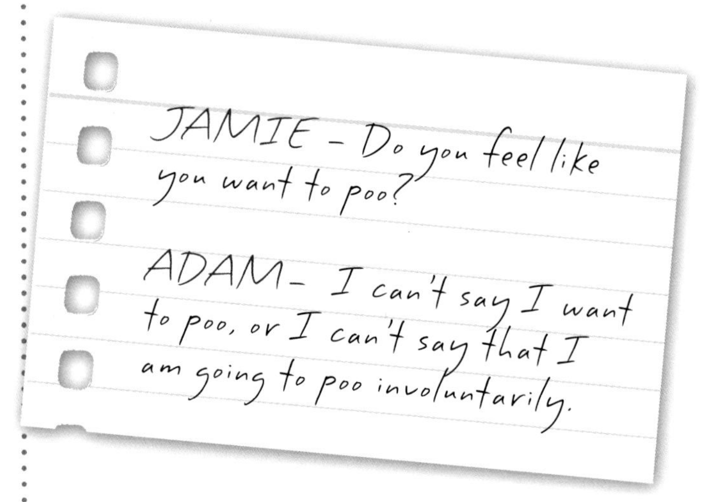

Bruce Bradford

If you didn't know that the activity of throwing a pumpkin with a mechanical device to achieve the greatest distance is called Pinkin' Chunkin', then now you do. Bruce knows – his gigantic gun 'Second

Amendment' chunk'd a punkin' 4434 ft (1351 metres) in 2003. He was brought in by the Mythbusters to pass judgement on the soundness of their *Chicken Gun*.

BRUCE - I think it's a great looking gun. It's got all the basics. It's got a tank, it's got a valve and it's got a barrel. Excellent job of welding by Adam that's for sure. And it's going to shoot a chicken at high velocity.

Bruce DeMara

As a reporter with the *Toronto Star*, Bruce has had the skinny on many a crazy tale – but none more freakish than that of the *Falling Lawyer.*

***Myth:* Falling Lawyer**

BRUCE - This is absolutely a true story. It happened at this location, at this office tower behind us. The coroner who investigated the incident decided not to hold an inquest because it was such a freak accident and it would be extremely rare to imagine someone else doing the same thing purposefully.

Bruce Gendron

Despite its serious name, the San Francisco Police Department Crime Lab is a happy-go-lucky sort of place, and Officer Gendron is one of its most charming lights. No wonder it was the 'drinking and testing' location of choice when Adam and Jamie tried to *Beat the Breath Test*. Bruce is the kind of guy who tells it like it is, professional to a fault, and with a nose that knows.

***Myths:* Beat the Breath Test**

BRUCE - You are pretty smelly.

Bryan Niswonger

If you were going to attempt to blow up a car packed with 500 disposable lighters, you would probably check with the local fire department first. But don't expect them to be as accommodating as was the San Francisco Fire Department's marshal Bryan Niswonger.

***Myths:* Exploding Lighter**

BRYAN – As long as you don't blow up the city we're fine with it...

Bug Bombs

They often go by less dramatic names, but the principle is simple enough – an aerosol of bug poison is rigged with a nozzle and a catch such that when you press the nozzle, the spray keeps spraying until it's entire flammable contents have been pushed out by the propellant. Although M5 is light on bugs (Jamie won't allow them) that didn't stop the Mythbusters taking on the *Exploding House* myth, with appropriate results.

***See also:* aerosol**

***Myths:* Exploding House**

Building Code

Over the many generations human beings have been building houses, gradually we've decided that certain things should become standard to prevent them falling down, burning up, getting fried in a lighting strike or exploding in a fireball of natural gas and who-knows-what. Building codes vary in different parts of the world, and in some places don't exist at all, but where they do they can save your life. Little things like ground wires for example can stop you from getting an earful of lightning when you go to answer your *Phone in a Thunderstorm*. So let's hear three cheers for building codes and the inspectors that enforce them … who's with us? Anyone? Come on – Adam LOVES the code!

***Myths:* Phone in a Thunderstorm, Painting With Explosives**

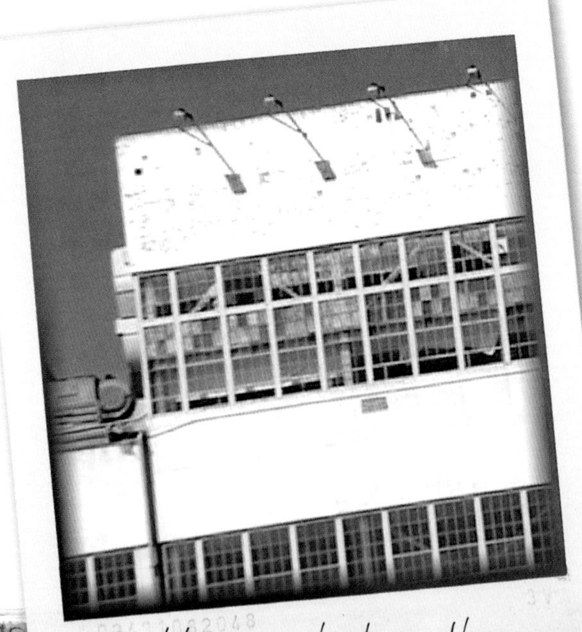

Buildings – who knew they spoke in code?

ADAM – Our little shotgun shack is all ready to go. We've got the computer set up, we've got two kinds of phones, we've got a television, we've got wall switches, plugs, junction boxes, everything to code. Plus, a shower that will be fully grounded and we're ready to shoot lightning bolts at this thing. I mean, I've been ready to shoot lightning bolts through it from the beginning, but now we're officially ready.

Bull in a China Shop

Who would have thought? Seriously, who watched this myth expecting something other than fast and furious destruction of ceramics and porcelain? The Build Team went to town buying cheap china and building mock shelving so they could set up Mythbusters Best China in a cattleyard and let a bull loose … for it to knock one, ONLY ONE, shelf down and then miraculously pick its way around the others like some giant four-legged Nureyev. Then two bulls dance around the breakables as if choreographing a new ballet. This was Bull Lake if we ever saw it – yet it was all true! That's a myth busted …

GRANT – … I have to say, I am really surprised at how nimble they are. They're almost daintily avoiding the shelves that we've set up.

TORY – They just don't want to break the china!

GRANT – You know what? I don't think even I could run that fast in a china shop.

Bull

Not just a male cow (or elephant, elk, seal or walrus), this is a male with ALL his genitals intact. What difference does it make? Well, enough for a genital-free male cow to be called a steer. Why? Because you have some measure of control over the damn beast. A bull is full of the joy of life, love and hormones.

***Myths:* Red Rag to a Bull, Bull in a China Shop**

Bullet Catching Rig

This cunning deployment of unpatented Imahara technology has the unusual distinction of being used for two different purposes in two myths in the same episode – in *Bulletproof Teeth* it just about managed to snag enough lead to be labelled a success, and in *Helium Football* it kicked balls filled alternately with air and helium to prove that Sir Isaac Newton wasn't joking when he set down the first law of motion. Check it out yourself – nice work Grant.

***See also:* Sir Isaac Newton, law of motion**

Bulletproof

This is a tricky concept but an important one. 'Bullet-resistant' is the preferred term used by the makers of vests, windows and shields, because of the extra wiggle room it contains. Their point (and ours) is that there are all sorts of bullets with all sorts of masses and coatings and that move at all sorts of speeds fired by all manner of firearms. The key questions are 'what do you expect to be shot by' and 'how frequently in pretty much the same place?' When Adam and Jamie pulled apart the bulletproof myths associated with decks of playing cards, Zippo lighters, Bibles and certain brand-name polycarbonates they demonstrated that while some will stop some bullets, if you keep raising the calibre of the weapon, you'll get through eventually. So check the rating on your vest before you pick your next fight, or better yet, don't pick the fight in the first place, at least not until the new breed of bullet-resistant t-shirts made of single-walled carbon nanotubes is available.

***See also:* Lexan™, bullets, calibre, carbon**

ADAM – Yeah well last season Jamie we protected ourselves with a blast chamber of quarter inch polycarbonate which you told us all was actually bulletproof and it's not.

JAMIE – I never said that quarter inch was bulletproof.

ADAM – Well I believe that the very next cut from this segment is you saying bulletproof from last season.

JAMIE (FROM LAST SEASON) – It'll stop a bullet, it'll stop all sorts of shrapnel and I just love the stuff.

Bulletproof Teeth

Don't ever EVER try it – this is one myth that is straight out of carnival fakery land. The idea that you can actually catch a bullet in your teeth is as ludicrous as the idea you could put your underpants on over your head. For all that, the Mythbusters gave it the full treatment – measuring the time it took for someone (Kari) to clamp down on a signal, testing what kinds of impact force teeth could actually withstand, shooting Kari with a paintball gun, even building a high-tech limited-edition Grant Imahara bullet-catching rig … and although EVENTUALLY this rig caught just enough lead to make the Build Team happy, the idea that any human could catch a bullet was rubbish on not one but a number of levels.

KARI – There's absolutely no way the human response time could remotely catch a bullet. It's … I mean, we've got timers. This is the closest thing to a sure thing that we could possibly have.

Bullets

Whether made of lead, ice, meat or depleted uranium, a bullet is the projectile – as opposed to the 'round' or cartridge – fired from a firearm. A bullet does not carry any explosive material itself (which would make it a 'shell') but that is not to say that you should stand in front of one. The energy imparted by a bullet into its target ('ouch force' to you and I) is a factor of its mass and its speed (which thanks to all kinds of hot gases from the barrel, actually can increase after being fired). That's all fine, but the element that makes a bullet, shall we say, functional is its accuracy. It was archers who first recognised that making their arrow spin with a bit of a twist in its tail feathers would vastly improve its accuracy. The thing is, a little zippy centrifugal force counteract all sorts of wobbly, distracting

forces a projectile might come across in its journey towards your head. Bring on the bullet, where the mirror principle of making long, twisted grooves inside the barrel has been incorporated into various firearms for probably 500 years or so. This 'rifling' gives the rifle its name, and bullets such as the infamous Minié Balls of the American Civil War were designed to expand into those grooves when fired. Centuries of research later the world of lethal weapons has brought Spitzers, boat-tails, copper jackets, hollow points ... an apparent infinite variety of innovations that all mean we can shoot you faster, more often and from even further away. Bullets have been the focus of much focused and determined innovation over the centuries, and we should all be very grateful to the tireless pioneers who spent long hours inventing fresh ways to penetrate flesh with metal. Quite seriously, the race to produce the best bullet is literally the pointy end of the arms race, and it continues to this day. Hopefully there's no-one reading this who still confuses a bullet with a cartridge, or round (quick catch-up, the bullet is the bit that moves, the cartridge/round is the bit that moves it). A fast revision – a bullet sits in a case which is loaded with gunpowder. When the trigger is pulled a primer ignites the gunpowder and the explosion drives the bullet out of the case and down the barrel. Interestingly a bullet does not stop accelerating once it leaves the gun. It actually gets propelled by heated gases exploding from the barrel.

See also; firearm, Minié Balls, artillery
Myths: Ice Bullet, Frog Giggin, Bulletproof Water

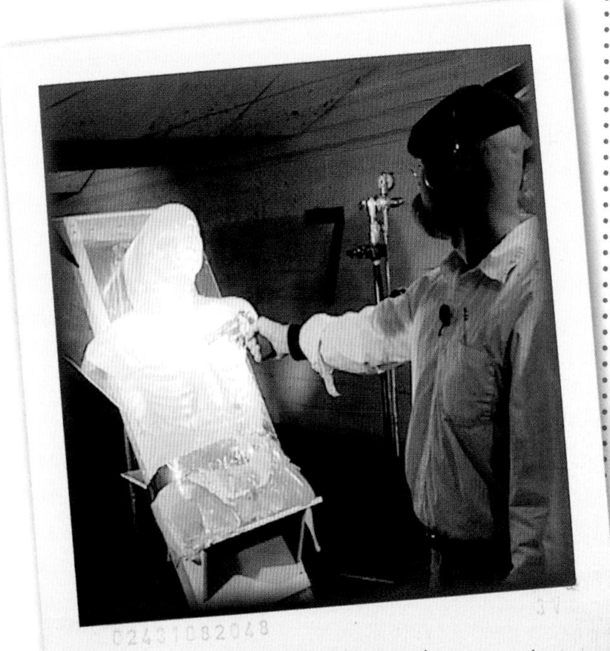
This won't hurt a bit

Bulletproof Water

Can you escape the wrath of armed pursuers by simply slipping beneath the surface of the nearest body of water? It's scary to think that subsequent to the broadcast of this episode, there must have been gun designers all over the US thinking 'Now there's an

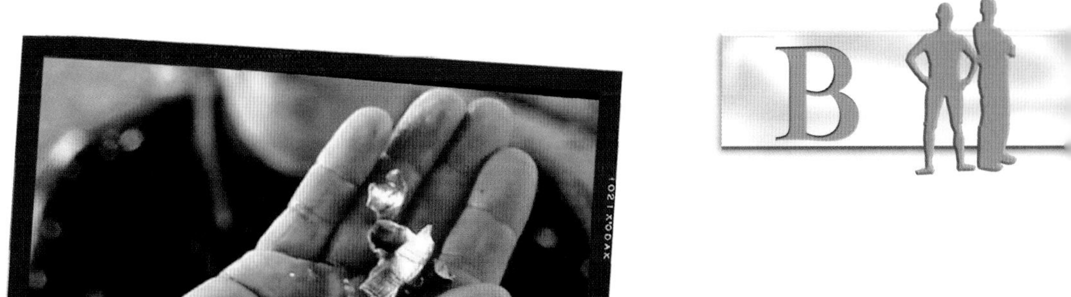

opportunity for a new firearm!' Why? Because it turns out that there is barely a weapon that can penetrate more than a few feet (less than a metre) into water. They simply disintegrate! But a little more detail if you please: the lads begin to test this myth by building a giant tank out of inch-thick (2.5cm) acrylic borrowed from Jamie's trophy room. With a chunk of movable ballistics gel inside and a few leaks patched (and a few others ignored) the lads set about their testing – which goes fine up until the shotgun which destroys the tank. However the lads manage somehow to convince a local public pool to shut down for the day so they could fire a range of deadly weapons into it at close range (amazing what fans will do). A terrifying range of weapons are brought to the pool by firearms expert Jenna Rolsky are then tested one after another to discover that … the faster the bullet is fired, the faster it completely disintegrates into a tiny handful of fragments on contact with the water. And they fire some terrifyingly large bullets – the Browning .50 Calibre sniper's rifle for example?

***See also:* Jenna Rolsky**

JAMIE – So can I see one of the bullets?

JENNA – Yeah.

JAMIE – Yeah. All right. Well …

ADAM – THAT's what this fires?

JAMIE – It's smaller than my head. It's alright.

Bungee Cords

Cords of military and 'commercial' strength were just two of five different kinds of rubber tested in *Border Slingshot* when the lads were developing their prototype giant slingshot. 'What', we hear you ask in that slightly whiney taxpayer tone, 'are the military doing with bungee cords?' Good question – the answer is classified. The word 'bungee' is apparently of British schoolboy origin, although some claim that it is also the

sound of a bunch of the eponymous cords stretching all at once. The first recorded bungee jump (as opposed to the ancient 'naghol' ritual performed on Pentecost Island) was made by four top-hatted students from the Oxford University Dangerous Sports Club, on April Fools Day 1979. Bungee cord is made often from a mix of natural and synthetic rubber materials, inside a cotton (or braided rubber) sheath, up to 0.6 inches (or 1.6cms) thick.

***See also:* eponymous, rubber, naghol, Pentecost Island**

***Myths:* Border Slingshot, Helium Football**

Buoyancy

The idea that certain things float in other things is as simple and orderly as it is wrong. What looks like something floating is really something being pushed upwards by something else. This all has to do with density, and being dense is not such a stupid thing. A dense something like a body of water, despite its drippy, wet appearance, has all the authority (or rather, density) it needs to keep a mighty beast like a 100,000-ton Nimitz-class aircraft supercarrier, or even a fully loaded 600,000 ton supertanker, afloat, despite the fact that both vessels are made of steel (denser than water) and the latter is pumped full of oil (also denser than water). 'Full' is probably overstating it, as the ship would certainly sink (lose buoyancy) if it was exactly full of oil. The point is to keep the ship afloat by having its average density less than that of water. Ships do this by having a shape that allows for air to lower this average.

***See also:* ton, displacement**

Burble

Although it looks like a word that could mean just about anything 'burble' does in fact have a very specific meaning in world of sky diving. When you jump from a plane towards the planet where you were born (and might now die from falling into), then the air turbulence that exists specifically above your back as you plunge forward at terminal velocity is a burble. Burbles make life very difficult for groups of skydivers when they're all clinging together trying to break a record by assembling themselves into Mount Rushmore, because the dynamics of fluids such as air (oh yes, air is scientifically a 'fluid' – don't get *that* wrong at a dinner party) are very complicated things to predict accurately. They exist disguised by other names – behind a boat it might be called a wake, and behind a pick-up truck, a vortex.

***See also:* vortex, terminal velocity**

***Myths:* Penny Drop**

ADAM – I opened one hand and then the other and the pennies just like shot out towards the sky. Out of one hand they hovered for a second in like the burble above my hand.

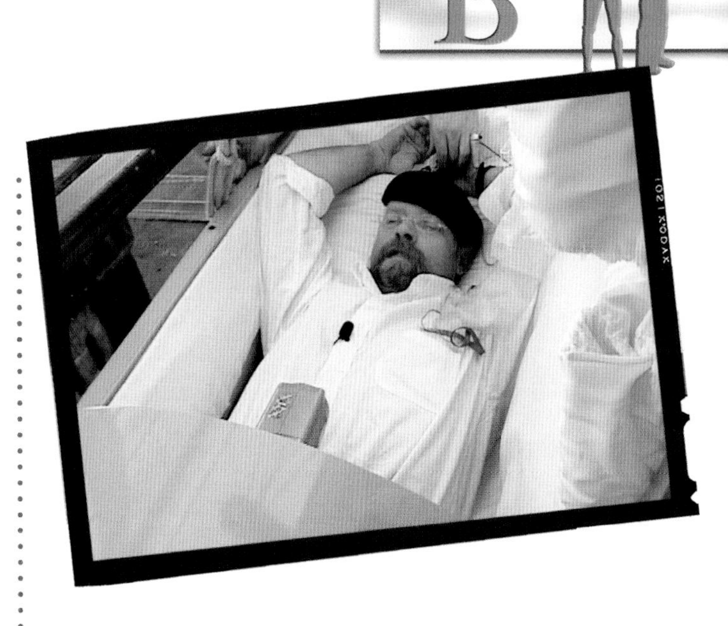

Buried Alive

The taphophobics among you won't need to be told this, but there's not an upside to the idea of being buried alive. The views are bad, the service is terrible, and after about three hours when you die of asphyxiation you're so damn bored that you probably welcome it. Or you die in the kind of screaming agony the rest of us can barely imagine. Anyway, there is not a culture on Earth who's not turned up at least one tall tale on the subject, so, dutifully, Adam and Jamie got themselves a nice strong coffin, kitted it with enough meters and sensors to measure the life signs of an army (a small one) plus a night vision camera, then stuck Jamie inside and dumped a grave's worth of dirt on him. Jamie thought he would make it for two hours. In the end, when the coffin started to crumple under the dirt Jamie's pulse began

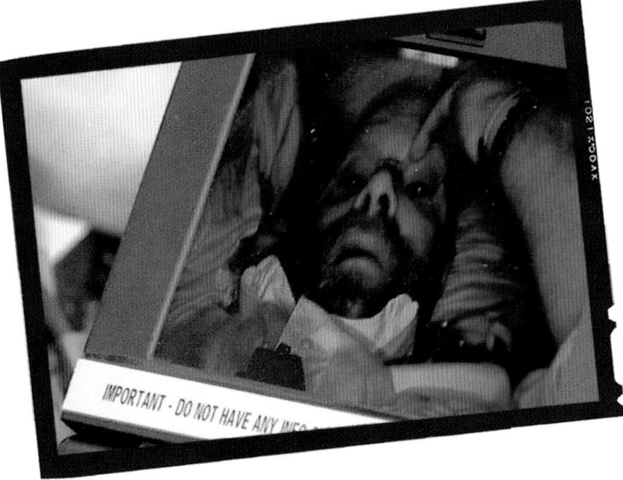

to race just a little bit more, so he sucked down a little more oxygen and … well, the threat of losing a host in the first half of the first season was enough to have the Mythbusters pull the plug. But could it happen? Could you be buried alive? Not according to the best medical advice – it simply wouldn't happen.

ADAM – I don't think it's possible for someone to survive a couple of hours in the panicked state of being buried with the coffin crushing and all of that stuff let alone until a couple of days until they're exhumed and found to be alive. That's just patently ridiculous to me.

Buster

Introduced in the very first episode of Mythbusters, Buster (and his replacements of the same name) is a key character on Mythbusters. A crash test dummy (series two) the original was brought out of 'crash test dummy' retirement to work on the show as a stand-in for any experiment too dangerous to put a human being into.

ADAM – Whoa. He's completely, completely trashed. The cast aluminium of his thighbone right here absolutely just shattered.

He was first used when Jamie was too much of a WOOS to sit on the *Exploding Toilet*, claiming the impact-resistant foam was going to burn like napalm. Buster weighs just over 81 kilograms (180 pounds) and stands 178 centimetres (5 feet, 10 inches) high. He was so vigorously tested in season one of the show that he was substantially rebuilt into Buster 2.0.

Buster Rebuild

Also known as Buster 2.0, this 'myth' is actually a chance to focus completely on the new Buster – Buster 2.0. Whereas the Buster Special hinted at the newer, shinier, better Buster that was built, in Buster Rebuild you got to see the nuts and bolts as the lads rebuild their old mate from the ground up. Then they pop Buster 2.0, fresh as a new pin, inside Earl the Caddy, and drop him 60 feet off a building.

Buster Special, The

A celebration, funeral and christening all in one, the Buster Special is set against the backdrop of the complete rebuilding of Buster into Buster 2.0, reviewing the many knocks, burns and falls that Buster took for the Mythbusters team in the first 30 episodes (see table below). As the flashbacks roll, Adam and Jamie build a rig to assess the shear strength of a human femur – 600+ pounds! (272+ kg) and also discover that the most accurate replacement for human bone (in experimental, repeatable, mimicking terms) is spars of wood from a poplar tree. They put this and other knowledge to good use as they build a newer, better Buster..

ADAM – I think Buster is toast. But then that's his job.

See Also:* *Buster 2.0, poplar, bone, femur, dragon skin, balls of death

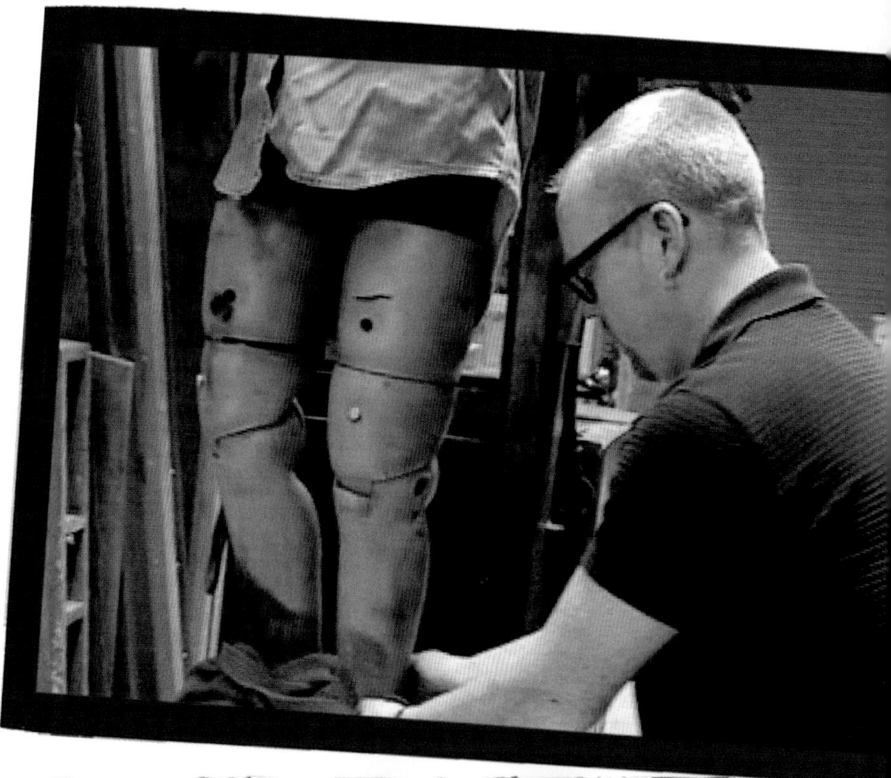

The Buster Table

Original Buster Myths	Significant modifications 'mods' if any	Resulting damage
Exploding Toilet	finger release for cigarette drop	scorched bum
Barrel of Bricks	buster had a quick release hand to let go of the rope	broken ribs and legs
Bridge Hammer Drop	accelerometer added	cracked his head just in testing the accelerometer, then busted two legs in 'control' test – sans hammer
Raccoon Rocket	–	scorched
Killer Washing Machine	–	unscathed
Trombone Explosion	–	scorched
Forest Fire Scuba Diver	–	got wet
Elevator of Death	added a 'pogo' jumping release	decapitated, dearmulated, cracked bones
Boom Lift Catapult	–	lost two legs, a hand
Plywood Builder	added 'balls of death' impact meter	'bleeding' from back of his head
Ming Dynasty Astronaut	(dragon skin)	burnt to a crisp, twice

Buster 2.0 (character)

Still representative of 95 per cent of American men, Buster was rebuilt to Mythbusters specifications, with more flexile (and easily replacable) aluminium joints and bones of poplar wood that mimic the resilience of human bones. Still weighing in at a spry 81 kilograms (180 pounds) the new Buster 2.0 had realistic (although vey pink) flesh made of Dragon Skin™ that gave him a more realistic distribution of body mass, and each fleshy body part was made in two halves for easy replacement. It took the lads four and a half days to get Buster assembled in his various parts – from frame to flesh.

***See also:* dragon skin, poplar**

JAMIE – The key things that make this Buster better are that he's constructed almost entirely out of blocks of aluminium that are really quite massive and so they're going to be very strong ... They'll take a good impact without breaking or jamming. All of the components are loose fitting, again, so that on impact or anything like that, they won't jam. And then lastly, it's all made so that anything that does get broken or messed up we can get to it really quickly and easily. Make another part without, any, you know, fussing..

Butane

One of many varieties of hydrocarbon (most closely related to propane and pentane), butane is a gas at room temperature, and is a component of LPG or liquid petroleum gas. Plain old butane is found most frequently in aerosol-style cans for fuelling everything from your camp light or cooker to your exploding toilet. It burns up ok, but as Adam and Jamie discovered ...

JAMIE – not enough to blast somebody off the seat.

ADAM – You don't think so?

JAMIE – No.

***See also:* hydrocarbons**
***Myths:* Exploding Toilet, Exploding Lighter**

Buttered Toast

Does toast have a tendency to fall butter side down? Does the world conspire to ruin our breakfast? Or are we just a bunch of unlucky pessimists? The first problem the Mythbusters

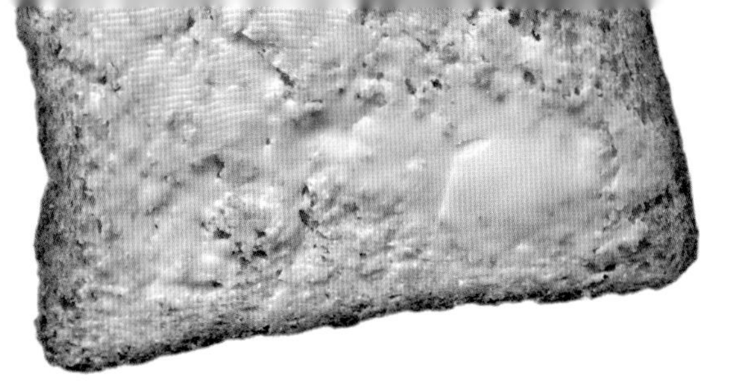

must overcome is to build a rig to drop dry toast in a sufficiently randomized way to act as a control. The final conveyor belt rig was so perfect that it sent Jamie spiralling into a fit of the giggles, busted the myth, and had Scottie eating toast off the sidewalk.

Butterfly Valve

There are all kinds of valves and butterfly valves are some of the prettiest. Hmmm, not necessarily – not if it's the chunky industrial-strength butterfly valves that went into the *Chicken Gun*. Although beautifully machined, these butterfly valves were designed with business not pleasure in mind.

Butter Zone

When you're experimenting with a rig that deals in variables like pressure or heat, voltage or wind speed, there is a point where that variable hits its mark and makes the rig work just perfectly (and lots and lots of points on the way there when the variable works not at all). This is the 'butter zone', so called because it's just the right point to do what you want to do, and if you've ever worked with butter (ever made a fruit cake?), you'll know what we're talking about. Butter can be hard as a rock or as runny as a milkshake – but if it's just right it can spread, slice, cream or carve as easy as you like. The phrase seems to come from the 1995 film *Hackers* and also turned up in one of the *Matrix* films, so … it's the world of IT that we have to thank (rather than the world of cake making) for the phrase 'butter zone'.

See also:* *fruit cake

Butyl

This chemistry word is used in engineering and film making circles to refer to rubber butyl tape, which is used as an adhesive and sealant in all kinds of situations. In *Crimes and MythDemeanours 2* Adam and Jamie pulled out the butyl to seal up the giant safe so it would hold enough water to blow the door off with TNT.

See also:* *sealant, adhesive
Myths:* *Crimes and MythDemeanours 2

Byram Abbot

When the Build Team went searching for tunes to play to a bunch of pea pods, where else to go but the oldest independent record store in San Francisco? And behind the counter of Aquarius Records that day was one Byram Abbot.

See also:* *Death Metal
Myth:* *Talking to Plants

Cabal

A group of sneaky types attempting some dastardly and/or cunning plan.

Cable

Cables are made by pulling metal through a hole to make wire, then twisting those wires to make strands, then twisting those strands around a core (often of another material) to make cable. Cables of different materials could be made for communications or power distribution, and the Mythbusters use plenty of those (particularly behind the scenes), but it's cable that is used as rope that gets all the glory. These kinds of cables (or wire rope) are made to suit particular jobs – depending on whether they need to be resistant to rotation, abrasion, metal loss (or 'peening'), deformation, crushing or just fatigue. The best day for cables came in *Killer Cable Snaps* when the lads designed rigs to see if it was possible for the whip end of a snapped cable to cut you in half.

But many other myths have relied on cables to deliver results, such as *Killer Tissue Box* and *Compact Compact*.

***Myths:* Killer Cable Snaps, Killer Tissue Box, Compact Compact**

One-man tug-of-war

Caffeine

There won't be too many other entries in this volume devoted to psychoactive stimulants, but this one most certainly is, so buckle in. Caffeine exists in at least 60 different kinds of plants where it gives feasting insects the last rush they'll every get. For most of us (9 out of 10 by last count) it is the first rush we get – every day. Caffeine gives you that snap in your step by acting on your central nervous system to increase alertness and make you work just that little bit faster, harder and longer. Adam and Jamie are not averse to an occasional caffeinated beverage, and have occasionally brought caffeine to the Mythbusting table in *Cola Myths* and *Pop Rocks and Soda.*

ADAM – This is a couple of tablespoons of caffeine in solution. Pure powdered caffeine. This is probably enough to kill you. It's scary stuff when you start to increase the concentration.

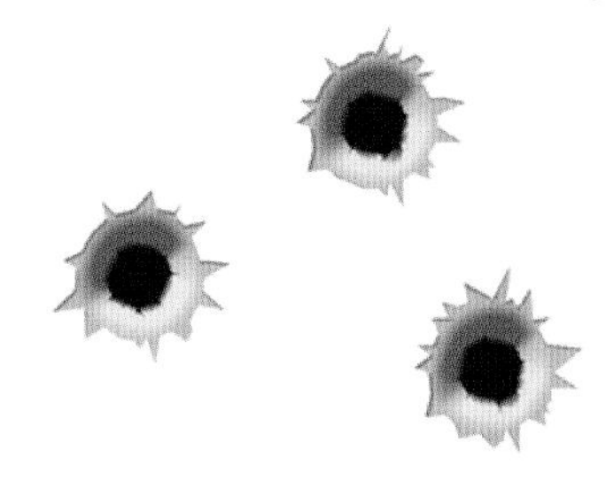

Calibre

For the barrel of a firearm, the calibre is the internal diameter. It's the opposite for a rope or cable, and fair enough because (not being hollow) these don't have an internal diameter. That's just about where the simplicity stops and arcana begins, because about half the firearms in the world are described in terms of a calibre measurement which is in fact made in inches. A 22 calibre rifle is a rifle with a barrel that is 0.22 inches across. Same for a 357 or 44 magnum, and the giant 50 cal Browning. The other half of the firearms are also measured in terms of their calibre, but because they're all in metric millimetres somehow they missed out on using 'calibre' and got stuck just with millimetres, as in the 7mm Remington or the 105mm field gun.

See also: **gauge**

Calorimeter

If you like knowing just how much energy there is inside something, then a calorimeter is dead cert for you this Christmas.

See also: **Cardboard Cereal**

Calories

Looking at the basic definition of a calorie – that being the amount of heat needed to raise the temperature of one litre of water by 1°C – you notice that a calorie is not a unit of food so much as it is a unit of energy. Stick with us now because this is actually interesting as well as important, and more important still if we were talking about the real unit of energy, the kilojoule (in fact, why don't we? See you in kilojoules in five seconds) … eh?

***See also:* kilojoules**

***Myths:* Cardboard Cereal**

Canada

A large landmass to the north of the USA known for their linguistic peculiarities, their cold winters and their large mammals. It was discovered in the myth of *Border Slingshot* that Canadians were attempting to sling themselves over the border to avoid moose, buy guns and enlist for active service. Not only that, several freak accidents in the Canadian Air Force led to the myth of *Hair Cream Explosion*, and the extraordinary tidal vortex called Old Sow offered at least some credence at least to the myth of the *Killer Whirlpool*.

***Myths:* Killer Whirlpool, Border Slingshot**

KARI – Well, I've got to establish that this is Canada, so I'm going to throw a Canadian flag up here.

Capacitor

A capacitor is a device that can store an electric charge between two pieces of metal – an electricity sandwich if you will (though you will seldom hear it called this in electrical engineering circles). The entry-level model was invented in 1745 in Holland and called a Leyden Jar, but since then electronics has called for many versions from chunky numbers you'd really know about if you dropped one on your foot, all the way to teeny tiny 'where did I drop that wee 1000 μF jobbie' fellow. But much, much larger capacitors appear to exist in nature - the kind of capacitors that express themselves in terms of rain, thunder and sizzling bolts of 100 million volt lightning. Yes, thunderstorms appear to be made up of clouds acting as capacitors, storing up charge then zapping it off all at once – right into your tongue stud for example.

***See also:* Leyden Jar, lightning, electricity**

***Myths:* Mind Control Chips, Lightning Strikes Tongue Piercing, Static Cannon**

Carburettor

Another of those elements of a great many car engines that you should probably have an ounce-worth's (28.3 grams) of an idea about before you start a conversation with your mechanic. The carburettor mixes air and fuel in your car's engine – air and fuel being the key components of the explosions that make your car's pistons turn and its wheels roll. There are many ways in which carburettors have been developed since they were introduced into the very first automobiles in the 1890s, yet we're not going to say anything more about them other than to say that adjusting them until they're just right can be the work of a lifetime.

***See also:* air/fuel mixture**
***Myths:* Great Gas Conspiracy**

Carbon

The element carbon is formed when there is a wacky triple collision of particles inside the nucleus of an atom of helium. This only happens inside the core of a star at least ten times as big as the sun. You wouldn't think there was so much carbon around, except that the evidence of carbon dioxide, gun powder, hydrocarbons and carbon based life forms suggests that it's everywhere.

Carbon Dioxide

As you exhale you (yes, you) produce about 900 grams (31.7 ounces) of carbon dioxide (CO_2) every day, which in terms of volume at sea-level would fill a decent-sized spa bath. But so dangerous is CO_2 that if you were to hop into that bath the CO_2 would kill you stone dead in a few breaths unless you had the good sense to get out. But before we condemn CO_2, you need a bit of it floating into your lungs to stimulate your breathing reflex. This is the risk you face when you suck down a little helium or sulphur hexafluoride for the comic (but opposite) effect each has on your voice box – each gas displaces the CO_2 and makes your lungs forget to stimulate you to take the next breath. Moving on, the fact that certain bodies of water can have a good amount of CO_2 lurking around inside them under pressure (which is the way CO_2 exists in a can of soda) which can suddenly erupt to the surface (like it can in a can of soda) and kill every air-breathing thing within a couple of miles is reason to treat CO_2 with a great deal of respect. Again, inside plants CO_2 is a key ingredient in photosynthesis, inside life jackets CO_2 performs life saving inflation for the purposes of buoyancy, bread would be a great deal flatter without CO_2's presence via yeast, then there's fire extinguishers

that extinguish fires, carbonated beverages that extinguish thirst, endless industrial purposes that extinguish economic needs and the amusing theatrics of dry ice (which is the solid state of carbon dioxide and wafts straight to gas – sublimates – at sea level pressures). For all this, the important thing the Mythbusters want not to do is die because of it…

***See also:* helium, sulphur hexafluoride, sensors, sublimation**

> JAMIE – You know the CO_2 level is going to build up really quickly in the volume and size of the casket.
>
> ADAM – How long do you think the average person might last?
>
> JAMIE – I'm guessing around maybe three hours tops.
>
> ADAM – How long do you think you're gonna last?
>
> JAMIE – Well three hours is like on the verge of death …

Carbon Dioxide Meter

If you're so foolish as to think that this sensor is designed to measure the amount of carbon dioxide in a given sample of air then you should be aware that you are COMPLETELY CORRECT. You should always go with your gut on these things. But perhaps it's not luck – who knows? You may work for a company specialising in just that sort of equipment, in which case we hardly need tell you that there are two methods employed to measure CO_2 – one being to flash some light through your sample and measure how the wavelengths are affected. The other is to measure the actual chemistry of the air. The Mythbusters reached for the CO_2 meter when they slapped Jamie into a steel box and dumped a few tonnes of quality dirt on him to test the myth of *Buried Alive*.

***See also:* sensors**

Cardboard

Paper is a pretty amazing thing, without which we would be lacking things like paper planes, phone bills, envelopes, wallpaper, and things even more important than those. Cardboard is a heavy-duty version of paper that will be thicker, stiffer and perhaps even made up of a variety of different corrugated

layers. Although Adam and Jamie are in and out of cardboard boxes all day every day without a second thought, they did take the time and trouble to actually test whether you can eat cardboard and whether it would do you any good.

See also: ***paper***

Myths: ***Cardboard Breakfast***

Cardboard Breakfast

When strolling through the supermarket did you mother ever look you (and your cereal preference) up and down and mutter the fateful words 'You'd be better off eating the box!'. It's certainly not the first household myth to be uttered by a mother (we're keen to see the lads tackle 'If you don't wash behind your ears then a plant will grow there!') but this time Adam and Jamie think they have breakfast cereal licked. At first the plan is to gear the whole thing towards a week-long eat-off, with Adam in the sugar frosted coco snaps corner, and Jamie on the box. But after a moment of clarity and some initial tests with a calorimeter, the lads dispensed with the human trials in favour of science. And what do you know? Science says Mum was wrong.

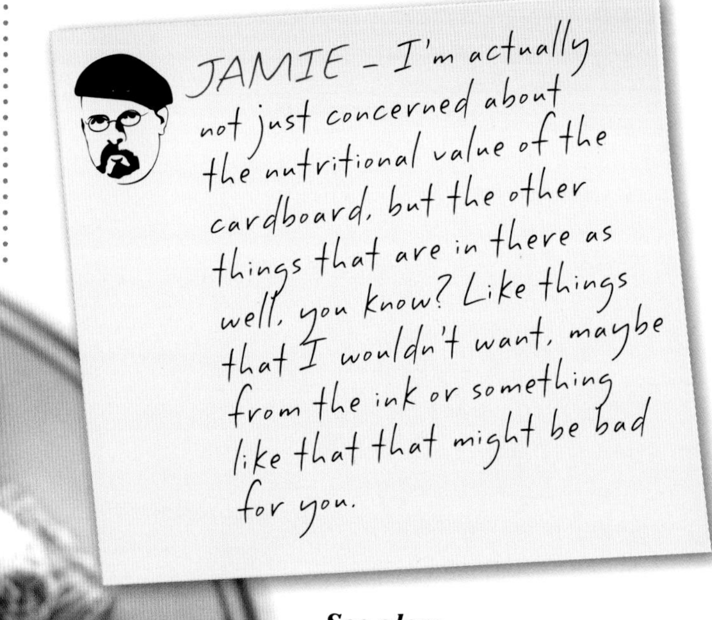

See also: ***calories, calorimeter***

Carlos Hathcock II

This extraordinary talented marksman was a US Marine in the Vietnam War, and apparently took out an enemy sniper by shooting him through his scope. The Mythbusters replicated the same shot (eventually, after a revisit) in *Firearms Folklore.*

Carried Away

If you were EVER worried about giving your precious little bundle of joy a couple of balloons at a fair or carnival, this myth will set your mind at rest. IN a fantastic and colourful way the scale of this experiment gets completely out of control. Initially calculating that 1900 balloons should be enough to lift a four year-old into the heavens, in the end Maddy, the soundman's daughter, is kicking her heels until 3500 balloons are inflated. That's probably just a few more than you'd buy for a medium to large-sized Olympic opening ceremony. So Maddy, how would you judge this myth?

MADDY – Busted busted busted.

The fact that some of the balloons were found later 300 miles (482 kilometres) away in Sequoia National Park was some consolation.

***See also:* Mr Bean**

Case Hardening

It's great to come across a term that means pretty much exactly what it says. The whole point about case hardening is that when you heat up a metal like steel, and then dunk it in something which has lots of carbon to spare (say, a barrel of used motor oil, also known as a 'hydrocarbon') you end up creating a hard shell (or case) of high-carbon steel alloy around your steel object. The carbon has actually melted into the steel and this just happens to be a great way to make steel extra hard. In the myth of the *Explosive Hammer* The Build Team followed Jamie's advice and followed this case-hardening process, and although they did start a small fire in their pan of motor oil, it resulted in a case hardened hammer. Best not to try it at home…

***See also:* hydrocarbon**

***Myths:* Explosive Hammers**

Cathe Ray

It was a no-brainer really – Adam and Jamie were looking for a place to sell the different kinds of needles for *Needle in a Haystack* and so they went to see Cathe, who's background in software engineering led her (naturally) to set up a shop called Needle in a Haystack which sells different kinds of needles (and just about everything else you could need in

a sewing vein). The point is – what kind of needles did the Mythbusters need?

CATHE ...because needles for many, many generations were made out of bone which would make them definitely much harder to find with modern technology.

Caveat

From the Latin for 'let him beware' all warnings including this word from the Mythbusters should be heeded (regardless of gender).

JAMIE – You know, I agree with you, but I have to put in a caveat.

CCs

Nothing to do with snacks whatsoever, cc stands for cubic centimetres – a measure of volume equivalent to 1cm x 1cm x 1cm. Hence it turns up in the measurement of smallish things, but not really small things. The sorts of things measured in cc include the capacity of small(ish) engines for motorcycles, lawnmowers etc.

Cedar

Trees grow at altitude and very straight to boot. Hence they are used for the shafts of arrows.

Myth: ***Splitting Arrow***

Cell Phone

It says something about the ubiquity of the mobile or 'cell' phone that in less than 20 years (remember the clunky bricks of the late eighties?) the little blighters have already squirmed their way into our urban mythology. If you tally up the number of Mythbusters episodes revolving around cell phones, then you truly are a geek and good on you. From whether they can blow up a gas station, to whether driving with them is as bad as driving drunk, the Mythbusters have done their very best to bring the cell truth out of the shadows. But what is cellular about a cell phone? Cell phones were so called in the USA because they are based on the idea that the transmitters that would send the call wirelessly to the phone would cover a 'cell' of a certain area. The call would

then be jumped between transmitters as the phone was taken from one cell to another.
See also: ***mobile phone***
Myths: ***Cell Phone Gas Station, Cell Phone Drink Driving***

Cell Phone Gas Station

When Adam and Jamie turned up in Fred Stoke's Gas and Memorabilia town (aka Stoke Ranch), in Santa Rosa, California, they had one thing on their minds and one thing only – could a giant gas station fireball be the responsibility of a tiny cell phone? The warning signs are ubiquitous on bowsers around the world – but Adam and Jamie found that there was absolutely no way that your phone could turn a fill-up into a fireball. However, there is a very real risk that a static spark could start a fire at the pump if you're in the habit of jumping in and out of your car seat while still pumping. A retest ages later revealed that even stripping a cell phone down to its underpants revealed nothing new about its potential for gas station busting behaviour.
See also: ***static, Fred Stoke***

Cell Phone v Drunk Driving

OK, we're not talking about the 'dialling' aspect here, where you attention is 100 per cent on the phone, we're just comparing talking on the phone with driving under the influence of those few alcoholic beverages you are legally allowed to suck down. That means a private test track rather than a public road and an independent tester in the form of Mark Wolocatiuk. In the control test both Adam and Kari pass with reasonable marks. The cell phone test is spiced up by Jamie's three-stage brain distracting test, and the results (failure to adequately complete the course by both test subjects) speak for themselves.

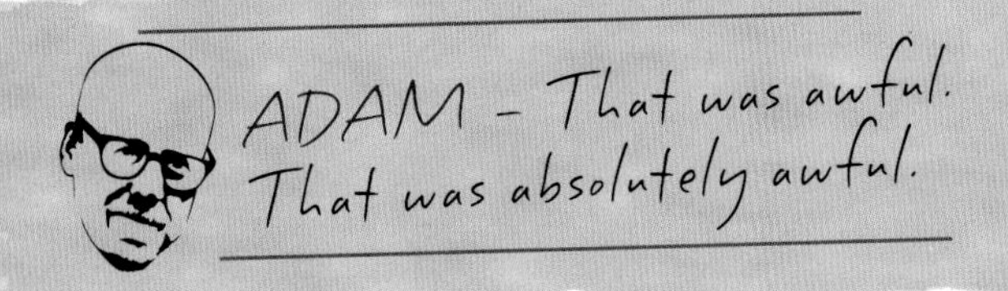

Next to that, the drink driving test was … almost as bad. A failure for both testees, but not by quite as much. The result? Confirmed – talking on a cell phone is as bad as driving when drunk.

***See also:* Mark Wolocatiuk, alcohol**

ADAM – all that being said, you can always put down the cell phone … I can't exactly just stop being drunk.

Been drinking on the job Miss?

Cenote

In the Mexican state of Yucatan lie a system of water-filled caves which rise to the surface as cenotes (seh-NOH-tays). Because many of these miles and miles of (often unexplored) caves have seawater and freshwater inside them, and because the caves are undisturbed by tides and waves, a curious phenomenon occurs where the freshwater rises to the top of the cave and the seawater sinks to the bottom. The very obvious division between the two gives a diver swimming through the caves the false impression that the cave is only half full of water… which can be dangerous.

***See also:* seawater, freshwater, density**

Centre of Gravity

More properly described as the centre of mass, this is a conceptual spot where the mass of an object behaves as if it were concentrated, and thus where gravity acts most gratuitously. A car with a high centre of gravity will be more likely to tip over than one with a low centre of gravity – which was the aim in setting up the *Snow Plow* experiment. Once again we have Archimedes to thank for introducing the idea when he was mucking around with levers, and floating stuff in the water.

***See also:* Archimedes**

***Myths:* Snow Plow**

Centrifugal

There seems to be a little misunderstanding about centrifugal force, so let's do our bit to clear that up right here and now. There is no such thing as a centrifugal force. Does that help? Not much? Then let's take a step to the side if you will. Say you're travelling in a car that's taking a tight bend. You feel as though you're moving towards the side of the car. When you say something like 'Gosh, that centrifugal force is really something!' the smart chick sitting next to you tells you that the only centrifugal force you can really experience is that which occurs if you were to actually lean against the side of the car as you're going round the bend. That reactive centrifugal force is real, but everything else is just the whacked-out experience of a guy travelling with a foxy science geek chick. You have to watch that…

***Myths:* 360º Swing**

Centripetal

Now this stuff is 100 per cent real. Centripetal force is the force required by that lasso you're swinging to stay swinging, rather than fly off into the trees. It is a force directed inward, towards the centre of rotation. That's something we can all appreciate and understand, yes?

***See also:* centrifugal**

CD

A compact disc is a circle (or perhaps given the hole in the centre, an annulus or toroid) of polycarbonate plastic with a very, very thin coating of aluminium in the middle, upon which a laser can etch information in the form

of multitudes of dents, in a spiral starting from the centre and working it s way to the outside. Other than the width of a CD being 1.2MM and its weight about 16grams, all the other measurements regarding a CD are microscopic – the width and depth of the dents, the distance between them, between the lines of dents and so on. All on a disturbingly small scale. CDs came to the fore in *Shattering CD ROM* when Adam and Jamie tried to destroy them with a combination of a souped up 52xCD ROM drive and various electromagnetic and corrosive inhibitors.

See also;* *electromagnetism, corrosive, 52xCD ROM, laser, aluminium

Myths:* *Shattering CD ROM

Chalk Outline

Although no longer standard practice, the idea of outlining a dead body with chalk certainly caught on with the guys and gals who write our murder mystery television shows (bless them all for bringing homicidal violence into lounge rooms around the world!). Of course, best avoided if you're a real law enforcement official who might actually need to take evidence uncontaminated by chalk to a court room. Adam and Jamie messed around with chalk

Self-portrait?

outlines only once (officer) in *Cola Myths* because they were testing if cola could clean up a blood spattered murder scene, which it did … a bit.

See also:* *cola

Myths:* *Cola Myths

Charles Joughin

The chief baker of the Titanic told a remarkable story of survival that entirely contradicted the myth of *Sinking Titanic*. Charles was a bit of a party guy, and had a few drinks on board the night that the big ship hit the bigger iceberg. He found himself at the stern as the Titanic was going down, as he recalled, 'like an escalator', but rather than being sucked into the deep blue sea, he simply stepped off into the water without getting his hair wet. Nice one Charles.

Myths:* *Sinking Titanic

Charles's Law

We are not the first to point out that Charles's Law could easily be an early 80s spinoff sitcom starring Scott Baio, rather than a basic law of physical properties. Charles's Law of Gases states that a given mass of a gas at a constant pressure will increase or decrease in volume by the same factor as its temperature (in Kelvin). If you're not grasping that, imagine that rather than reading an encyclopedia in bed (no comment), you are instead a bold contemporary adventurer filming a documentary series for the Discovery Channel in a wicker basket that is attached to a bag of hot air a few times higher than Everest. If you had the unlikely misfortune to have brought with you from sea level a small bubble of gas in the temperature-insulated comfort of your intestine, and you made the ascent sufficiently quickly that you could not rid yourself of said bubble on the way up, then the vastly decreased atmospheric pressure of the extreme high altitude of your wicker basket will turn your experience of that small bubble of gas from the insignificant to the gut-busting. Adam and Jamie have run into the effects of Charles's Law themselves in the myth *Exploding Implants* and *Explosive Decompression.*

***See also:* farts, atmospheric pressure, Kelvin**

***Myths:* Exploding Implants, Explosive Decompression**

Chevy Corvette

The first American sports car has been cutting up corners since 1953, yet the zoomer almost never made it out of the first corner had it not been for the introduction of a V8 and a Russian engineer. That's right – the Corvette you're (probably not) driving today is as much an example of US-Russian collaboration as any missile treaty. When the fourth generation 1987 Corvette was introduced, it leapt into a new world of aerodynamic design and LCD displays. Of course … none of this mattered to Adam and Jamie picked one of them up to fill with dead pigs and put in a shipping container for two months. How did the previous owner feel about it?

TOM – Well, not real happy to tell you the truth. I mean, because it's a really nice car.

***See also:* shipping container**

***Myths:* Stinky Car**

Chevy Impala

Chevrolet has been building and selling Impalas since 1958. Back then it was the most luxurious model they made, and massively popular as well. More than a million were sold in 1965, and so you'd think shopping for a '67 in California should be a breeze. Not so, as Adam and Jamie discovered when they hit the dealerships for a hint of a '67 Impala that wouldn't mind having some rocket engines strapped to its roof. Just as they were about to give up, a black '66 Impala was discovered with a working engine AND hydraulic suspension! Money changes hands and the Mythbusters were lowriding in style – for 8.5 miles (13.6 kilometres) when the engine died courtesy of a blocked fuel pump.

***See also:* fuel pump**

***Myth:* Jet Car**

Harder to catch than a real impala

Chicken Gun

Curiously enough, whether or not a Chicken Gun exists was not the myth at all – it seems that no decent-sized Air Force or aeroplane manufacturer is without one. The myth is all to do with the state of the chicken expressed by the gun. Frozen, or thawed? Seems that the British were testing a high-speed train, and borrowed a chicken gun rig from the States – international diplomacy is not dead yet! However it was strained by what happened next; chickens were quite literally flying through hardened windshields and into the seats well inside the train. The British (so politely) called their Stateside contacts and suggested that something was going ever so slightly wrong. The Yankees suggested the Brits might 'thaw your chickens'.

So then, does a frozen chicken pose a more destructive influence than a room temperature bird? Adam and Jamie could not wait to find out – even though their enthusiasm led directly to the purchase of non-bird strike rated windshields for their

test. A blunder to be sure, so let us focus on the results when finally they came in – which showed there was no difference. NO DIFFERENCE between the frozen chicken and it's thawed rival; each impart their energy into a windscreen in the same way.

JAMIE – You know that's about one of the more destructive things I've ever done. That was cool.

ADAM – Yeah, that was exceedingly cool. Let's do a thawed.

See also: ***bird strike, pressure, compressed air, frozen chicken***

Chicken Gun

This refers to the Chicken Gun itself, rather than the myth (for that, refer to the entry called 'Chicken Gun' which should be just up there). The Chicken Gun had to be built to test the myth of the *Chicken Gun* (which had to do with the difference between frozen and room temperature chickens … just read about it up there will you?) and it was a deliciously perfect piece of kit. A large pressure tank had a neat hole cut in it with a plasma cutter, then a barrel welded on. In line next was a high-pressure industrial strength butterfly valve, then plenty more barrel. Attached to the butterfly valve was a hand-operated release lever. Chickens (thawed or otherwise) were encase in a sabot and loaded from the front – olde worlde style. How well did this rig work?

ADAM – Feels like a Mack truck just drove by me! I just wonder what a chicken breaking the speed of sound sounds like.

See also: ***butterfly valve, plasma cutter***
Myths: ***Chicken Gun***

Chinese Invasion Alarm

Digging around in ancient Chinese history is quite productive for Mythbusting, because the idea that you could tell whether an advancing underground army was about to pull the rug from under your feet by sending a big drum down a shaft and posting some sharp-eared lieutenants around it is remarkable, and all the more so because it turned out to be true. The build team

combined with Adam and Jamie to set up a very realistic rig in the backblocks of San Francisco near to an old mine. With their own homemade 200-litre goatskin drum down a hole and Jamie and Tory smacking picks down an even deeper hole, both Kari and Grant's electronic ears were able to hear them, thanks to the resonance picked up and amplified by the drum.

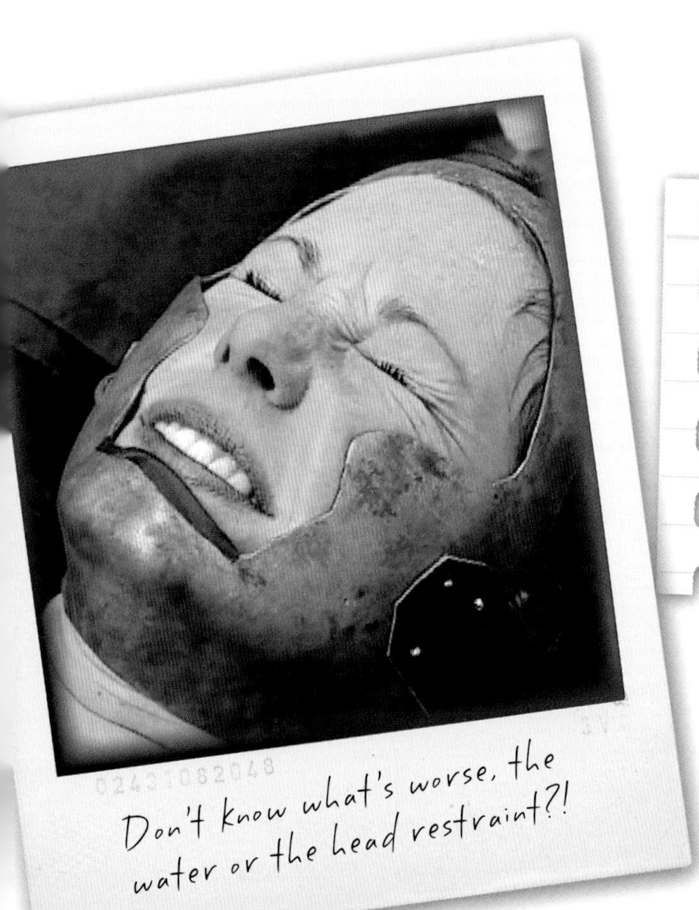

Don't know what's worse, the water or the head restraint?!

Chinese Water Torture

There are all manner of water tortures, each as inhumane as the last, but the one that the Mythbusters have really engaged with is what we know popularly as Chinese Water Torture (despite the fact that not a shred of evidence exists that the Chinese had anything to do with it). Nevertheless, the build team set about the task of setting up M5 Torture Inc with just a LITTLE too much glee, and before long, they're ready to begin grilling each other. By a long standing Mythbusters Build Team tradition, it's Kari first.

KARI – I can't even imagine this being for real. I'm around people that I'm secure with that I totally trust and that I know are gonna get me out of this. I have an ambulance standing by with paramedics. If this was for real, I would be screaming and struggling, I'd probably have bloody wrists and ankles by now.

Yet … the fun and the trust don't last long … about an hour and a half (and fully restrained). Adam lasts longer, but neither found Chinese water torture to be pleasant. In fact, it would feature in each of their 'not to do again' lists.

***See also:* Gerald Gray**

Chip Log

If you were a sailor in the mid 19th century (which, let's be serious, you patently are not) your chip log would have been your best friend. This simple quadrant of wood, weighted with lead and attached to the ship via a long rope on a reel and be-knotted at regular intervals could be tossed overboard to count the number of knots that went overboard over a certain period. When the time was up, you knew how fast (in knots) the boat was travelling, and hence where you were on the map.

***See also:* nautical miles, knots**

Chris Niemer

If you wanted to learn how to become a blacksmith, with all the sparks-flying, anvil-bashing, hammer-wielding implications of that trade, then you could do a great deal worse then present yourself to Chris Niemer and say in a loud, clear voice 'Smith me, Mr Niemer!'. Adam and Jamie did much the same in the myth *Tree Cannon* where they asked Chris to wrap red-hot iron bands around their proto-cannon to keep its blast from becoming a boom (at least, not too soon).

CHRIS – When we start wrapping this, I think I'm only going to have one of you two with a hammer, just kind of tapping behind me.

***Myths:* Tree Cannon**

Christiaan Huygens

Born Dutch in the first half of the 17th century, Huygens had the great fortune to live in a period of time when you could have a crack at just about anything scientific without stepping on too many toes. He investigated mathematics, observed the stars, considered life on other planets, invented chronometers and pondered the nature of light – in fact almost the only thing to let him down was his gunpowder engine.

GRANT – I am not sure if we're going to get a good enough vacuum, and that's the whole principle that this Huygens engine works on.

***Myths:* Ancient Prototypes**

Christine Chamberlain

Hailing from Virginia and DC, via Saudi Arabia Christine became the Mythtern on the series when picked by the Discovery Channel from a host of applicants for the role. Her first duties were to cover Adam with gold paint to revisit the myth of *Goldfinger*.

ADAM – Christine, when you sent in your tape to Mythbusters those many weeks ago.

CHRISTINE – This is totally what I had in mind. It's amazing.

Suffering the wrath of Jamie in 'training mode' or the wrath of hot candy in 'melted mode' Christine managed to hang in there for a season or more.

Christmas Lights

It's the festive season, you've spent all afternoon arranging your Christmas tree with the obligatory strings of electric lights. Doesn't it look lovely? You head to bed full of cheer and … other things … only to be woken by the fire alarm and the unmistakable smoky smell of an insurance nightmare. Could it have been … the lights? With several dozen boxes of America's favourite lights in hand, Adam and Jamie set up test after test incorporating extension cords, multi adaptors and WAY more lights than any manufacturer would condone. Eventually they get what they're after – a nice short circuit. Repeating the test at the local fire station with a nicely kiln-dried tree and 2500 lights soon sees smoke aplenty, and when Jamie ups the anti with a neon transformer, the firefighters are pretty quickly doing what they do best. But the myth? Can you start a fire just by leaving the lights on?

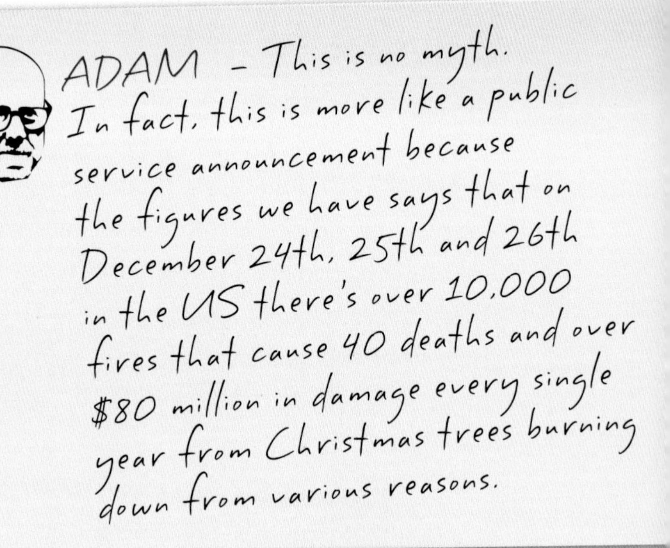

See also: **Fantastico, Kurtis Dickey**

Chuck Heger

Chuck designs and makes stud finders (not chucks, which are the bit of a drill where you put the bit). He works for Zircon tools and he was drafted in to advise Adam and Jamie on the madness that was the myth of *Mind Control Chips*. Chuck wasn't entirely sure that the idea of putting chips inside people to control their thoughts was entirely of this world:

> CHUCK ... sounds like something that might be right out of a science fiction novel.

***See also:* stud finder**
***Myths:* Mind Control Chips**

CIA

This definition has been covertly removed.

Cinder Block

You've probably seen them around – oversized grey-white bricks that get used as a cheap and cheerful building material. They're not particularly attractive, but are strong, utilitarian and many of them are made with cinders (a featherweight rock that springs from volcanoes). But ... what the Mythbusters wanted to know for *Air Cylinder Rocket* was this: can a cylinder of compressed air that's suddenly lost it's valve hit a wall of cinder blocks with such force that it busts right through?

Circuit

When electricity is flowing it likes to have somewhere to go, and if that somewhere has a few resistors, capacitors and switches in line, then all the better. A circuit is a path for electrical current, and if you grab hold of a high tension wire, you can be part of a circuit too. As their verticality suggests, Adam and Jamie have significant respect for electrical circuits.

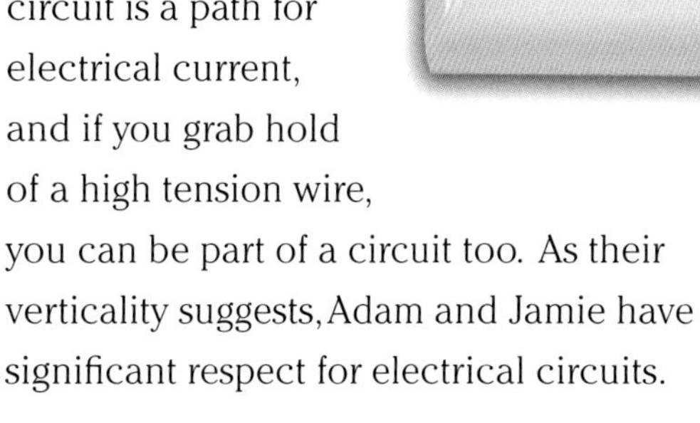

Clean Up or Die

A sign in a prominent place at the M5I workshop, placed there by Jamie Hyneman. While the word 'die' does not in this case refer to tools used to shape or punch holes out of other materials, you're getting close.

Clockwork

Springs are terrific – wind a little energy into them and they'll let you take that energy back out again and do something useful but dull, like tell the time. The mechanism that allows you to do this is called a clockwork, and although they seem very olde worlde, clockwork devices are really very, very cool and can be just as complicated as you have the patience, visual acuity and tiny tools to achieve. And when they work, they just work – like clockwork.

ADAM – Zis, this may look like a simple clockwork, but I think of it as a map of the most complex clockwork, like the planets. It is not a planetary gear, but I think of it as a planetary gear 'cause each thing, like a planet moves in its place and goes where it should. It is not only a map of the planets, it is also a map of the atom. In this way, the microcosm is the macroscosm and philogyny recapitulates autology. I call it my horary.

***Myth:* Steam Machine Gun**

Clutch

Where would a motor be without the humble clutch? We'll tell you - it would be as good as useless. The clutch gives the operator of a motor the ability to engage or disengage that engine's power at a whim, whether in a car, drill or washing machine. A clutch is basically just a flat plate that moves on and off another flat plate connected to the motor. When they're pushed together, friction between the two surfaces engages the power of the motor. That's why it is called a 'clutch'! And that's why there's trouble when you bust one, or even take one out deliberately to remove the last vestiges of safety from a washing machine as Adam did in *Killer Washing Machine*...

ADAM – Well, we have done what we can to modify this machine, to get rid of the clutch and get rid of actually every safety feature it possesses. Now we'll find out if it is in fact strong enough to do any damage ...

***Myths:* Killer Washing Machine**

COFFIN

This would be your final resting place if you're 70 per cent of the population of the USA (or 0.25 per cent of the population of Japan) – a big box, spruiked up with 'you name it' trimmings, and buried deep in the earth. Remember this when choosing a coffin for a loved one: the more air-tight the coffin, the more likely your dead body is to suffer the indignity of putrified liquifaction. The lads discovered this fact in the myth of *Stinky Car*, and they won't forget it in a hurry. Jamie came closer than most to the experience of 'life in a coffin' when the Mythbusters took on *Buried Alive*, but because the coffin was unable to stand up to the punishment of a few hundred pounds of dirt, Jamie pulled out rather than be crushed.

JAMIE ... Being in a box is one thing, but you've got all this stuff that's supposed to make it real nice and pleasant, and it's actually really kind of creepy I think. 'poof'.

COJONES

The good think about the Spanish slang for testicles is that you can always claim to the teacher that what you actually said was 'cajones' (ka-HO-nays) which means 'a chest of drawers'. Cojones means bravery, or guts. However if you were caught out in class saying something like:

JAMIE – Are you insinuating that I might not have the cojones to follow through?

You could always claim you said 'cajones' and meant 'storage'. If you had the cojones of course you'd just take the rap.

Cola

Invented as a cure-all patent remedy back in the days when cocaine was just another ingredient, the world's favourite tooth rot is the most obvious example of something entirely unnecessary becoming completely indispensable. These days the drink that is flavoured by the cola bean and the coca leaf has a world of myths swirling and bubbling around it that must be busted, and Adam and Jamie did that most effectively in *Cola Myths*. Enough said – this isn't an advertisement.

***See also:* caffeine**

***Myths:* Cola Myths**

The real thing....

Cola Myths

We know that it's 'it', but can IT do THAT? Can it clean up blood? Or chrome? Or a penny? Or the contacts of your car battery? Can it help shift a rusted bolt? Can it clean your laundry? Your car? Will it melt a steak? Will it melt your teeth? Will it melt your semen (or someone else's)? Let's make it quick – the drink that once contained 9mg of cocaine per glass (pre 1903) WILL clean up blood (a bit), can chrome really well (with aluminium foil), and a penny, but not your battery contacts, or shift that rusty bolt, or get your whites whiter than white (in fact they turn them a yukky brown), or do much for your car's engine. On the other hand, it won't ruin your car's paint job, or dissolve your sperm, or your steak ... but it CERTAINLY will mangle your teeth. So, a glass of water with your meal, please.

Colette the Researcher

Mythbusters researcher Colette Sandstedt stepped away from the computer and phones to stack several needles inside a pair of haystacks and kicked off the myth *Needle on a Haystack*.

COLETTE – All right you guys. Ready. The clock is ticking. Go.

Collagen

Collagen is a protein, and it's really amazingly strong. Your body is using it right now in a bunch of ways – inside bone, ligaments, tendons, cartilage, skin...you'd be a wobbly mess without it. It is also famously the component of the gelatine in ballistics gel that gives the stuff its fleshy qualities.

See also:* *ballistics gel

Combustion

Also known as burning, this is the process of releasing heat via a series of surprisingly complex chemical reactions. You can impress people with the term 'exothermic' if you like, but it's all about the vaporisation of a fuel, a mixing with oxygen (from regular strength air, if that's all you've got) and an ignition of some kind. Sounds simple, but if you just strike a match and watch it burn, there are dozens of chemical reactions going on so fast you'd have no chance of counting them. There are all kinds of combustion, including the metabolic kind that is happening right now in your body as glucose is combusted and turned into thermal heat as well as stored as chemical bonds to be used later when you need to switch off the light or go to the bathroom. At the other end of the spectrum is the speedy kind of combustion where fuel is burnt so quick it expands into what you can go ahead and call an explosion. As you can tell, at the heart of Mythbusting is a deep and abiding love for combustion.

See also:* *explosion, ignition, glucose, vaporise

Compound

If you've ever been bamboozled by a string of letters and numbers that look something like $C_6H_2(NO_2)_3CH_3$ then you've been overwhelmed by a chemical compound. Letters and tiny numbers aside, compounds are simply two elements or more that have

grown to like one another so much they've stuck together in a very intrinsic and molecular kind of way, much more stuck together than say a mixture like an alloy is. Mythbusting sometimes requires getting to grips with the intrinsic compounds in a material to see which one is responsible for the cool stuff, like an *Exploding Tattoo*.

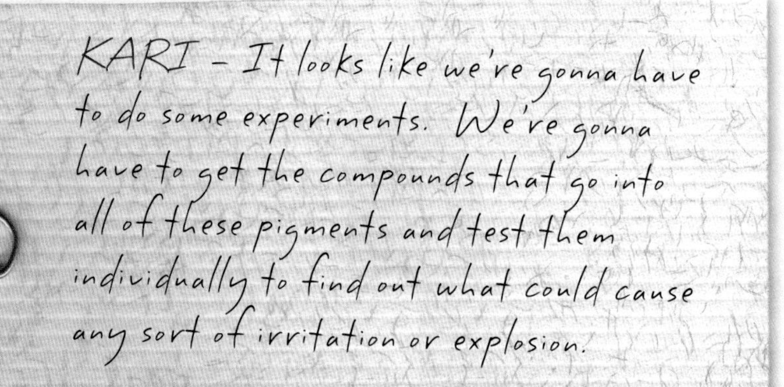

***See also:* mixture, alloy, element**

Compound Bow

These modern bows are made from aluminum or fibreglass or even funkier materials. They rely on a system of pulleys system to ease the burden of pulling the string from the archer, and letting them concentrate on where the arrow should go.

***See also:* pulley**

***Myth:* Splitting Arrow**

Compressed Air

Air is made up of molecules of different gases, but in between them there is a lot of space. Just how much space there is between the molecules depends how much pressure that batch of air is under. The regular air we breathe at sea-level is sucked in at a pressure imparted by the rather tall column of air that sits right above it. However, air can be put under a great deal more pressure than you'll find at sea level. A scuba tank, for example, compresses air more than 200 times its sea-level pressure and fits it into a cylinder at 3000 PSI. Adam and Jamie like putting air under pressure and seeing what they can do with it as it returns to normal atmospheric pressure in a few milliseconds – shoot chickens at dismembered aeroplanes with a 150 PSI compressed air-powered *Chicken Gun* for example. The lads are also not above just shooting a 3000 PSI scuba tank … just to see what happens. Or knocking the valve off to see if it can smash through a wall. Or retro fit a pair of them into boat.

ADAM – Remember Jamie, experiments like this are 90 per cent mental. I want you to be the boat. I want you to exist as one with the water. Think about the boat planing, the physics involved. Feel them in your body. Are you ready?

JAMIE – What?

ADAM – Ah, I said just go for it.

See also: ***the bends, nitrogen, decompression chamber***
Myths: ***Chicken Gun, Air Cylinder Rocket***

Computer

If you don't know by NOW, well, reading this definition isn't going to help you much. As far as this volume is concerned, a computer is an electronic machine for manipulating information to its own – and every so often, its user's – ends. The Mythbusters are hands-on types who rarely deal in the intricacies of towers and keyboards, however they have had recourse to use them to peel open myths like *Rough Road Driving*, and even taken on the occasional computer myth, that being *Shattering CD ROM*.
Myths: ***Rough Road Driving, Shattering CD ROM***

Conductor

On a bus, the conductor sells you a ticket. In an orchestra, the conductor leads the musicians. The Mythbusters are yet to bust a bus myth (anthough they did blow one away with a jet engine when they *Supersized* the myth of *Jet Taxi*) but they have taken on a conductor in the myth of the *Exploding Trombone*.
Myths: ***Exploding Trombone, Jet Taxi***

Watch out Jamie, that trombone is loaded!

Conductivity

Some things really enjoy letting a fizz of electricity zip through it – these things can be described as conductive. The reason that a length of copper wire is more conductive than a plank of wood is because the copper wire has all sorts of free electrons that are ready and willing to help out other electrons who have a place to go. Conductivity can change of course, as Jamie and Adam discovered in the myth of *Octopus Pregnancy*…

ADAM – Here we go.

JAMIE – What Adam is doing is measuring the electrical conductivity of his saliva. Now, we are going to try and replicate that conductivity in the water by adding salt to it.

***See also:* saline, resistance, electricity**
***Myths:* Octopus Pregnancy**

Adam proves to be highly conductive

Confederate Rocket

Secret weapons make for great myths, we're thinking the *Brown Note* here. Retro secret weapons make for even better myths, and here we can't go past *Ancient Death Ray* but *Steam Cannon* and *Steam Machine Gun* come close. But … sometimes these weapons get a little too scary – and the idea of a Civil War era multi-stage rocket capable of bombarding a city hundreds of miles away, well – there's steam punk and there's terrifying Civil War steam punk, if you know what we mean. The idea that such a weapon might actually have existed springs out of the fact that the lads start by building a couple (!) of rockets that the history buffs KNOW were used in the Civil War. Some seriously explosive chemistry and straight-shooting aerodynamics turns up in

this episode, with a few mis-fires, destroyed cameras and a flamed out hovercraft into the bargain. However, in two days and using only elements that could have been made by or available to Civil War racketeers, the team build a nitrous oxide and paraffin-fuelled rocket that flies 500 yards (457 metres)!

Five hundred yards is an extraordinary effort, but it was hardly the hundreds of miles claimed in the myth. Busted. A sideways revisit to this myth saw the lads use a salami as a fuel, along with various other elements to get it going. It worked, but only if you'd be happy with your pride and joy going about 20 feet (six metres) up.

***See also:* Steve Harrington, rockets, oxygen, nitrous oxide, Gates Brothers Rocketry**

Constance Smith-Golda

It's one thing to be watching a Civil War battle and get hit in the tummy by a bullet – but what if that bullet had already passed through the nether regions of a soldier? Constance had not experienced this herself, but her expertise in the medical practices of the US Civil War led her to surmise the following for the myth *Son of a Gun*.

CONSTANCE – If I'm not going to be naked in front of my husband when I am bearing his child or conceiving his child, I am not going to get naked in front of a strange doctor in the middle of a battlefield hospital and have him look at me.

She probably would have bled to death out of embarrassment more than anything else.

***Myths:* Son of a Gun**

Contact Cement

Some adhesives must be applied on both surfaces to be attached; that, and a little time to cure, and you can slap those two surfaces together without long periods of time clamping them together. This is worth

remembering if ever you're building a raft out of raincoats so that you can escape the most notorious prison in the world.
***See also:* adhesives, curing**
***Myths:* Alcatraz escape**

Controlled Conditions

Say you want to test a myth that includes a lot of different options – or variables – that must remain exactly the same for each test so that the results are meaningful. It is in circumstances like these that you need to control the conditions of your experiment, because these conditions would change in the 'real world'. In almost every experiment Adam and Jamie do they have to control something or other – whether it's the light source, an exact distance, or a series of things such as in the myth of *Who Gets Wetter?* when they had to measure out an exact, repeatable course indoors, set up rain-making equipment that would deliver an exact dosage of rain, wear identical coveralls which they keep free from their own perspiration by wearing body-hugging neck-entry latex bondage suits. Adam and Jamie will go to any lengths to create controlled conditions.
***See also:* scientific method**
***Myths:* Who Gets Wetter?, Seasickness; Kill or Cure? and many more**

JAMIE – We're gonna have to be really careful about this. It seems like a simple thing.

ADAM – It seems pretty straightforward really.

JAMIE – Yeah, but there are actually a lot of factors to consider.

Cooking Oil

If you're after the exciting world of biodiesel ala *Great Gas Conspiracy* then move on, hippy. If you're after the Mythbusters slant on regular cooking oil, then read on fellow patriot. The deep-frying of foods is as American as clogged arteries and heart disease, based on the fact that cooking oil can achieve startlingly high temperatures upwards of 280ºC (500ºF) which brings speed and flavour to just about anything you drop into it, from a chicken to a chocolate bar. Cooking oil is really just fat extracted from plants or animals (eww) and rendered down into a pure(ish) form. The good news Adam and Jamie brought from the first *Christmas Special* is that no matter how frozen your turkey, or how hot your oil, a turkey won't explode if you turf it straight from the deep freeze to the deep fryer.

Cooper Cranes

BK Cooper's started his company small; his first office was his crane – more than 30 years later he's the man to go to in San Francisco when you want advice on anything to do with rigging (or, uniquely, wetland restoration). Cooper was the man the lands tapped when they went to bust the *Bridge Drop* myth. He offered them the services of The Whirly, and by gum, that was exactly what was going on in Jamie's stomach all day.

See also: **Stephen Cassidy, Whirly**
Myths: **Bridge Drop**

Copper

Copper is a metal, an element and one hell of a conductor, of electricity as well as heat. Heard of copper wires? They're in just about anything of an electrical nature because the free electrons in copper just love helping other electrons zap around from one place to another. For pretty much the same reasons copper is an excellent thermal conductor, and in the myth of *Steam Cannon* the lads chose coper nails to fill their steel pipe 'gun barrel' in the hope that the nails would retain so much heat over such a vast surface area that when they blasted water into them, it would flash to steam instantly. Now, it didn't work, but the theory was entirely sound.

See also: ***conductivity, resistance, steam***

Snow drop

Cornice

When snow drifts over the top of a mountain or ridge, it can stick and build up on the other side, This built-up snow is called a cornice – it's also a term in the building trade which means a ledge. However, whereas in a building this ledge might be structurally sound, a wind-blown snow cornice offers no such safety, and is very dangerous to walk or ski on or under. So don't. If you want an example of a cornice in an avalanche, watch Adam drop some dynamite on a Colorado mountain range in the *Snow Special.*

See also: ***avalanche, dynamite***
Myths: ***Avalanche Adventure***

Corn Snakes

With a liking for fields of golden corn, and the tasty rats within, these non-poisonous snakes apparently make ideal pets thanks to their reluctance to bite. The little baby ones that turned up for the *Ultimate Mythbuster* fear test were just as sweet as pie, and cute to boot.

***See also;* Fear Test, Giant Tanzanian Millipede, Tarantula, African Emperor Scorpion, John Emberton**

***Myths:* Ultimate Mythbuster**

JAMIE ... Adam, load my hat. Does that work?

JOHN - Now you got hair.

Corrosive

A substance that is corrosive will be capable of doing lasting damage to another material. Examples that have piqued the interest of the Mythbusters include the salsa from *Salsa Escape* and the various putrefying pig substances in *Stinky Car*. But a corrosive substance doesn't have to be a killer salsa or a dashboard-eating chemical from a well-dead pig. Seawater is plenty corrosive, as is oxygen. Ever heard of rust?

***See also:* rust, putrefaction**

***Myths:* Salsa Escape, Stinky Car**

Corvette

A small, jinking warship used for patrol and escort work. Unless you meant the Chevy Corvette ... did you?

***See also:* Chevy Corvette**

Cotton

Another of those plants that are suspiciously useful, like sugar cane and hemp. Cotton plants manage to be funny-looking as well, little bunches of cotton balls stuck to a twig. Spun into long strands of what we imaginatively call 'cotton' it's become a staple material in clothing from Alabama to Zaire.

***See also:* denim**

***Myths:* Jeans Death Shrinkage**

Countdown

Like many, many bog-ordinary basic things (forks, duct tape, potato chips) the countdown has a less-than-bog-ordinary history. You might not thing that the countdown could pre-date the rocket, but you weren't thinking about science fiction! In fact the pre-blast-off countdown was first used in a movie called Woman in the Moon (or in the original Deutsch - Frau im Mond) in 1929. Crazier still, this was a silent movie, and a whopper at 2½ hours (some cuts are even longer). Noted German futurist film-maker Fritz 'Metropolis' Lang was responsible for this far-flung filmic financial disaster, but it was apparently very popular with Werner von Braun and his V1 and V2 buddies. Today, countdowns turn up anywhere people can be assured that SOMETHING is definitely going to start happening NOW, especially when it involves a whole bunch of dangerous things that can explode. A countdown lends buckets of cheap but wholesome dramatic suspense, is not subject to copyright in any major territory and thus the Mythbusters use them whenever possible.

ADAM – Do the countdown, Jamie.

JAMIE – OK.

JAMIE – Three ... two... one.

JAMIE – Ohh!

ADAM – Aghh!

Crankshaft

Have you ever been sitting around at home when the sudden need to turn reciprocating linear motion into rotation strikes you? For goodness sake, dude! Reach for a crankshaft!

Crash Barriers

Giant blocks made of concrete and weighing in at four thousand pounds or more (nearly 2000kg), these monsters lurk beside roads all over the world, just waiting for someone to crash into them. Crash barriers can be made of other materials – steel, aluminium, old car tyres, wood – and are designed to absorb some of the energy of a crash, but also prevent that crash leaking out onto local shoppers, wildlife or

cavernous ravines. Adam and Jamie get hold of some crash barriers when they're putting cars or car-substitutes through their paces. In *Killer Tissue Box* when three concrete crash barriers were lined up to take the impact of a 1967 Plymouth Fury, which was being dragged by a tow vehicle via a cable threaded back through the barriers and attached to the Fury's special steering rig. When it hit the barriers the Fury was doing 65 mph (105 km/h) and Buster sucked in 114.8 Gs. The crash barriers were fine.

ADAM – Dude, that's very significant.

***See also:* steel, aluminium, wood, concrete, g-force**
***Myths:* Killer Tissue Box**

Crash Test Dummies

The first human-replica dummy built and used for testing vehicles was Sierra Sam, built by Samuel W. Alderson, in 1949, for testing aircraft ejector seats. For many years vehicle manufacturers had used live animals (chiefly pigs) or human cadavers (eww) to examine the various aspects of the safety of their vehicles. In 1966 after generations of car fatalities and injuries, the US federal government gained the ability to set and enforce safety standards governing the design of cars. Crash test dummies were on their way into the mainstream. A brand new, fully-kitted Crash Test Dummy today can cost nearly a quarter of a million dollars (US).

***See also:* Buster, Buster 2.0, pigs**

JAMIE – That's all I need is another dummy around this place.

Credit Card

The card is just a bit of plastic; it's the magnetic strip that holds the booty. The magnetic strip is home to all kinds of secret, government-controlled information (if you live in a conspiracy wonderland) or just a few innocent numbers (if you live in the real world). A credit card's magnetic strip essentially works just like the magnetic tape in your olde video machine; tiny wee bits of iron are stuck to the tape and can be encouraged to line up in ways representing secret government-controlled information (or other) by a 'writer' device that uses a strong magnetic field. The upshot is when you take out your credit card and insert it in a 'reader' device that uses a magnetic field as well, the information can be transferred, allowing YOU the consumer to spend up big on Mythbusters merchandise. The inventor of the credit card was a man called Forrest Parry, and the story is that he couldn't get the iron particle tape to stick to the plastic card without destroying the readability of the card. His wife came to the rescue one evening by plunging her hot iron on the plastic card and strip, fixing them together permanently. And that, folks, is what you call irony. The humble magnetic-strip credit card was the focus of the myth *Eel Skin Wallet*. They were remarkably un-wipeable … despite exposure to very powerful magnetic fields.

ADAM – That read it just fine. I'm actually really surprised how robust these cards are.

JAMIE – So am I. I would have bet money that they would have messed with them.

See also: **magnetism, iron**
Myths: **Eel Skin Wallet**

Crimes and MythDemeanours

There is a world of myths, mostly inspired by Hollywood movies, to do with the ancient but less-than-noble art of breaking and entering. In this special, Adam and Jamie joined the build team to bust open myths like the laser-beam alarm system, cutting a perfect hole in a piece of glass with a diamond cutter, using magnets or suction cups to climb the side of a building, and cracking a safe. All good, wholesome fun, no-one was damaged, and Hollywood

was revealed to be just a bunch of people making stuff up! Who would have guessed?

See also: ***laser, magnets, suction***

Crimes and MythDemeanours 2

The first *Crimes and MythDemeanours* episode was so much fun that even Jamie had a good time as they took in all kinds of Hollywood-style security devices and methods of cracking them. The rematch was all about the cold hard realities; fingerprint scanners, thermal imaging cameras and unbreakable glass relocker safes. At first it looks like the Mythbusters have met their match, but with a little inspiration, a little application, and in the face of manufacturer's claims that some of the hardware had 'never been beaten', there were soon doors a'poppin and safe's a blowin'.

ADAM – You know, I don't enjoy the explosion as much as I like the aftermath!

See also: ***glass relocker, fingerprint scanner***

Curing

A process whereby something changes its inherent qualities over time and exposure to air or other materials. Perhaps its glue, perhaps its food, perhaps it cement…
See also: ***salami, contact cement***

Cyanotype

See blueprint

Daddy Long Legs

The world's most dangerous spider turned out not to be the daddy long legs. Despite all that mythical power supposed locked up in his jaws, the tiny fangs would not actually be able to break the skin even of an arachnophobe like A. Savage esquire.

Dan Tapster

When Dan was kidnapped by machete-wielding Quichua Indians in Ecuador, he decided it was time to take a break from natural history film-making. Armed with giant stinging nettles, a passion for science, and an unhealthy obsession with MacGyver, Dan escaped by canoe under the cover of darkness. By 2004 this escape had lead him to the Mythbusters head office in Australia. With a background in biology, BBC and blisteringly clever writing, Dan was soon busting chops as Executive Producer of what he calls "the best science show on TV".

See also: ***Peter Rees, Beyond Productions, John Luscombe***

Darwin Awards

A Darwin Award is a dubious honour that recognises an act of stupidity that has removed the recipient from the gene pool, hence furthering the onwards and upwards evolution of the human race. Named for the father of evolution Charles Darwin, these awards have become an excellent source of stories for the Mythbusters. In fact, the very first myth attempted in the pilot episode, *Jet Car*, came from a Darwin Award email that was circulating in the late 1990s. Although grateful that the Darwin Awards furnish so much material for the show, Adam and Jamie are always mindful that their Mythbusting antics don't lead them to receive their own.

See also: ***Charles Darwin, evolution***

Myths: ***Jet Car, Leaping Lawyer***

Standard issue uniforms

David Bunzel

Representing the Optical Storage (Technology) Association, David knows his high speed drives. The Mythbusters took his advice when attempting to spin CDs to destruction, in the myth *Shattering CD ROM*. David had heard of the myth before but was casual about the practical risks …

***Myth:* Shattering CD ROM**

DAVID – I have three computers that sit around me and I don't sit there with any concern that I'm going to have fragments flying at me.

David Hodge

This man is an expert in Civil War fashion – all the way down to the unmentionables.

***Myths:* Son of a Gun**

DAVID – Soldiers, and of course anybody during that period wore what was called longjohns and it was an overall piece. You know, a top and the bottom part connected.

SCOTTIE – Wow.

TORY – And they even wore them during the summer?

DAVID – They wore 'em during the summer.

David Maltby

A round of applause for David – I mean really. Stand up and put your hands together for this man who stepped forward with a syringe, a mass spectrometer and his credibility as a scientist, and actually MEASURED A FART for the Mythbusters.

DAVID – So what we're mainly seeing is 28 and 32, which would be nitrogen and oxygen, which of course are the main constituents of our air. There's a little bit of 40, which would be argon, which also is a normal constituent of air. We're seeing some methane and some carbon dioxide.

Myths: **Facts about Flatulence**

DAVID WALLACE

Professor of Mechanical Engineering at a little place called MIT usually concerns himself with cutting edge technology, algorithms and industrial processes – but after watching the myth of *Archimedes Death Ray* he found himself bitten by the Mythbusting bug. With the help of plenty of students they created a rig of modern mirrors in a double arc that turned a replica boat to ashes in a car park. They were then invited to bring their concept to San Francisco and get hot ancient style. The introduction of the replica boat to the water made for some problems…

Myths: **Mailbag Special**

DAVID – We need a bit of help. What we want you to do is reposition the boat so that we can get another pass at the part that we've really charred.

JAMIE – So what you're saying is that staying still isn't good enough? We actually have to move the boat for you into the line of fire?

DAVID – Shut up, you lazy Roman pig and do what you're told.

DEAD

You may not think about it often, but there is an important reason to define death – how else would you know that you were dead? In fact, in the myth *Buried Alive* Adam and Jamie sought out Dr William Miller to give

them a contemporary medical explanation of exactly how death is ascertained. Turns out there is a rigorous process you need to go through to find out if someone is actually dead or just mostly dead. You want to check for a neurological response in the possibly dead person by poking them effectively with something pointy (but not so pointy or so effectively that you might turn a mostly dead person into an actually dead person – there's a fine line). If you're not getting any action with a poke, then pop a light in their eyes and see if there's anything going on in the pupil. No? Gosh, this is getting serious. Listen for a heartbeat (ideally with a stethoscope) and check for a pulse at the neck. Finally if you can't hear any breathing either, then … that's pretty much. People are always dying though, whether they're Isaac Newton or Jimmy Hendrix, so don't think it's so unusual. In fact most of the people who've ever lived have given it away already, some to bring us great myths like *Leaping Lawyer* and *Bridge Drop*. What is important is that you leave behind a great tale that will benefit humankind (although our legal team would take this opportunity to remind you that this book and the show it is based on do not endorse you dying in an eccentric way just to get on tele). Summing up then – you should all be grateful you live in a world where (hopefully) your deadness will be spotted by an expert, and not assumed by a less-than-expert.

Myths; Buried Alive, Leaping Lawyer, Bridge Drop

WILLIAM – … in the 1800s … we did not have an agreed upon set of criteria. And so you might a physician whose idea of death was, for example, very flimsy … and they themselves might pronounce somebody dead who by today's criteria we would not say was dead.

Dead Blow

Grant Imahara's robot project has starred in a couple of myths – but probably it's finest hour was in *Exploding Pants* when its dagger was replaced with a sledgehammer and turned a plain old pair of herbicide flavoured pants into a trouserful of explosions.

***Myths:* Exploding Pants, Chinese Invasion Alarm, Dog Myths**

TORY - Holy mackerel!

GRANT - Oh my God.

TORY - That was sweet! Oh, fire.

KARI - Where?

Deadweight

Measured in long tons, tonnes or goodness knows what else, this is the weight of a ship's crew, passengers, luggage, shipping containers and their contents, stores of food and water, fuel, lubricating oils, reading material, pens, pencils, charts, the ship's parrot, the ship's parrot's cage, the ship's parrot's cage's stand … and so on. Just not the ship itself, which is measured as lightship weight. A ship would be designed to bear a certain deadweight and not much more, in case the sea around it became disinclined to offer it the buoyancy that once it did. Ever been called a dead weight? Now you know that it's nothing personal.

***See also:* buoyancy, lightship weight,**

Death Metal

It's fast, furious, ferocious, and utterly terrifying in every respect - and yet plants love it. Does this say more about plants, or more about death metal?

***See also:* Byram Abbot**

***Myths:* Talking to Plants**

ADAM - Tory and I are gonna try a pair of the death metal peas here.

JAMIE - They taste quite good.

ADAM - The ones that music was played to just taste fantastically.

Deborah Nolan

Statistician Deborah glanced over Adam and Jamie's data from *Helium Football* and concluded that it was inconclusive.

DEBORAH – That doesn't mean there isn't a difference, but I can't see the difference in the data that you've provided.

Decibel

Everyone's favourite unit of sound is in fact really expressing something more fundamental: a logarithm. The reason is this – something like the volume of sound becomes very hard to express in notation because sound behaves rather strangely; it takes a great deal more than double the power to double the volume of a sound. The human ear can hear across quite an astonishing range of sounds from the so-very-quiet-you-almost-can't-hear-it-but-it's-definitely-a-sound kind of sounds like a dripping tap or a hungry mosquito, all the way up to the eardrum-pummelling explosion of sound that is the jet aircraft that's just appeared in front of your taxi. To make it easier to express these significantly different sounds, decibels describe ever-increasing jumps in the power needed to create them. The most infamous decibel episode of Mythbusters was almost certainly *Shattering Subwoofer* where Adam and Jamie built what is almost certainly the world's largest car speaker, powered directly from the engine.

***See also:* logarithm, frequency, sound, hertz**

***Myths:* Shattering Subwoofer, Breaking Glass, Brown Note**

The wiggle makes it wiggle

JAMIE – You know, we can get a crank, we can go right to the output of an engine, we get raw power. That's what we're going to do..

Deep Vein Thrombosis

Pulling on a pair of the now highly-fashionable compression sports tights could be just the prophylaxis for thrombophlebitis – yet strangely shrunken jeans can have just the opposite effect. What are we talking about? Blood clots in your veins of course, which can happen anywhere, but when the body is constricted in some uncommon fashion it's much more likely, hence it's rather unfortunate descriptor as 'economy class syndrome'.

***See also:* pulmonary embolism, Edward Kersh MD**

***Myths:* Jeans Death Shrinkage**

Delta Star West

There's not too many companies that can say they've been involved in the electricity industry for over 100 years. Delta Star West can – they manufacture industrial grade electrical machinery and are friendly enough to let Adam and Jamie come over and play.

***Myths:* Lightning Strikes Tongue Piercing**

JAMIE – We have this gigantic bank of capacitors, which creates over a million volts at something like a thousand amps. And it's sending electricity across this wire, through this electrode and these heads, which are grounded, will complete the circuit.

Denim

Denim is a type of serge cotton fabric originally made in the French town of Nîmes, and known as serge de Nîmes. Serge de Nîmes...do you get it? The Build Team had a whole bunch of fun when they took on *Jeans Death Shrinkage* and *Pants on Fire* – but although Grant got a new pair of figure-hugging denims, and Tory got dragged by a horse, neither myth could be confirmed.

***See also:* cotton**

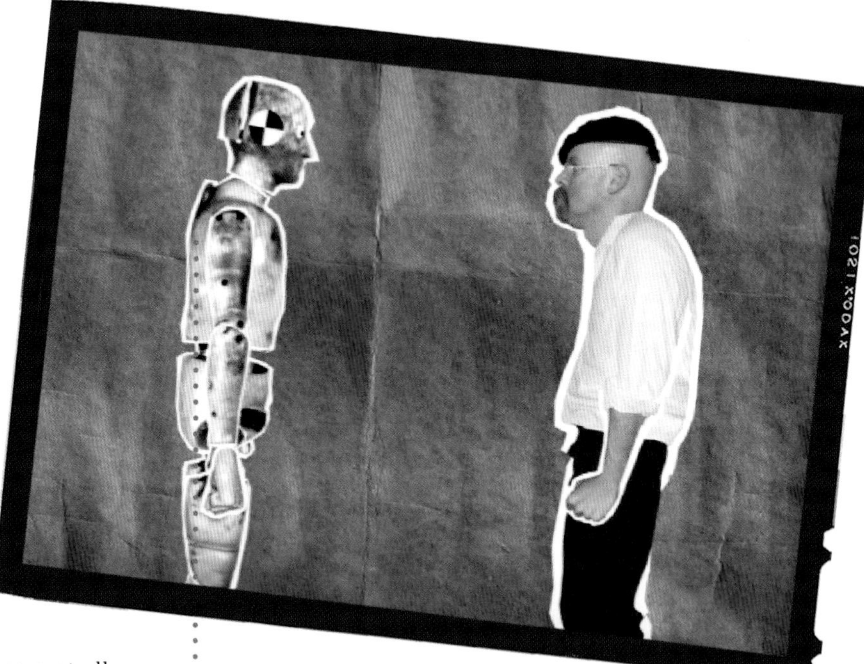

Density

Density is essentially a way of comparing the thickness, chunkiness or solidity of anything from gases to more substantial things like wood, metal or flesh. Density is intimately associated with mass and with volume; mass is easily enough measured, but volume? If you were at all inclined towards the classics (and Adam and Jamie most certainly are) you could measure volume by filling a bath with water *to the very top* and dropping your object carefully in, collecting all the water that falls out, and measuring more easily what space it fills. If you were Archimedes then understanding that the volume of an object can be measured by the water it displaces might make you shout 'Eureka'! Density can be a challenge if trying to get things to mix – things of lower density will always be pushed out of the way by things of higher density. Finally, remember that density need not be constant: a change in pressure or temperature can change everything about a material's density! The Mythbusters care about density for all sorts of reasons: when they're trying to sink something in something else or float something on something else, when they're working with pressure, when they're mixing ballistics gel, and just because density rocks and doesn't get enough credit.

See also: ***Archimedes, Charles's Law, specific gravity, buoyancy, ballistics gel***

Myths: ***Archimedes's Death Ray, Steam Cannon, Sinking Titanic, Quicksand***

JAMIE – There's several things about this dummy that bear noting. The first is that it weighs the same as an adult male, because it's about the same size as an adult male, and it has the same density in terms of the ballistics material that we use and human flesh. So it should be perfect for our test.

Depth Charge

A depth charge was fee owed to the King of Tonga by Polynesian pearl divers when they reach a certain depth. No, no, nothing like that at all really (who would be there to take it? You can bet the King wouldn't be.) A depth charge is an explosive device designed for use against underwater targets, submarines mostly. They differ from an underwater or naval mine because they can be actively aimed at an underwater target rather than just floating around like lead balloons.

***See also:* explosives, water, submarine**

Detonation Velocity

Detonation velocity

Some call it explosive velocity, some call it 'look out!', but what we're dealing with is the speed of the shock wave created by an explosion. The low explosive gunpowder has a detonation velocity of about 100 yards per second (90m/s) while something like hexanitrohexaazaisowurtzitane sends out a shockwave at 9400 m/s. The measure of this explosive quality is called brisance, but you don't want to be around to measure it in person.

***See also:* explosives**

Diatomaceous Earth

The name 'kieselguhr' won't mean any more to many of you than does diatomaceous earth. Is it something to spread in your pets litter tray? Try again. Is it something to do with pool filters? In fact yes, but, look – it's a key ingredient in something very powerful. Diatomaceous earth is a chalky rock that can be ground into a very light powder that is highly absorbent and adsorbent (there is a difference). When mixed … carefully … with nitro-glycerine you stabilise the explosive potential of that chemical and end up with … dynamite. And some federal employees on your doorstep.

***See also:* nitro-glycerine, dynamite, adsorption, explosives**

JAMIE – I don't do make up. If they get near me with some powder and some scissors for my moustache, they're going down.

Die

Not a million miles away from that old plastic sheet of shapes you used to trace through in primary school, a die is a tool used to shape a product. Dies come in all kinds, from those used to make coins or cut holes, to those used to press shapes or angles and more. Dies can be as simple as the ones made by Jamie in *Five Second Rule* to streamline and standardise the process of taking bacteriological samples from different foodstuffs. For the record, the sign at M5I reading 'Clean up or die' does not refer to these tools.

See also:* *extrusion, cable, clean up or die

Myths:* *Five Second Rule

Discovery Channel

Launched in June 1985, the Discovery Channel is a cable television network that has spread across the planet by offering television audiences the chance to learn a little more about their world whilst being simultaneously entertained. Popular science and reality documentary are the bread and butter of the Discovery Channel, as the dominance of Mythbusters attests. Adam and Jamie love a bit of Discovery Channel themselves, but don't get too close to Jamie when there's a publicity shoot in the offing…

See also:* *Beyond Productions

Dodge Viper

The Viper was born of a need to build a fast, flashy and remarkably dangerous car that would make American car buyers sit up and ask 'what the hell was that?' Slapping a V10 under the bonnet was just asking for trouble. It is an uncompromising sports car that the Mythbusters used to roll down a hill under the force of gravity against all the might of a tiny toy car. It's a real wonder that the Dodge people let them do it. The answer to that is something like 'we didn't ask them'. The Viper won of course … but, crikey, if it hadn't…

Myths:* *Toy Car Race Off

Dogs

Man's best friend made only a token showing in two myths from the first four score episodes (those being *Deadly Microwaves* and *Killer Washing Machine*. Here, dog urine was a key ingredient in attempting an explosion between it and baking soda. Nothing happened along those lines, so the lads moved on to experiment with the danger of the humble microwave oven by placing a cute little dog inside one and turning on the waved of electromagnetic radiation until the little fellow…no of course they didn't! What kind of doggy-snuff show do you think we're running here? The lads reconvened on the world of dogs with a batch of canine myths for a special *Dog Myths* episode. What isn't a myth is that dogs have been with humans for about 15,000 years, and in that time we've developed them from being the friendlier members of a local wolf pack to being tiny handbag yappers or lugubrious hypochondriac giants – with 400 million loveable mutts in between.

Myths:* *Deadly Microwaves, Killer Washing Machine, Dog Special, Mind Control Chips

Dog Special

We can't start another entry with the phrase 'man's best friend' so instead we'll make a post-modern self-reference and move on to say that this episode of the series investigated three areas of dog-related mythology; can you teach an old dog new tricks? Can you beat the guard dog? Can you foil the bloodhound? To simply answer 'yes, yes and yes' massively understates the time and attention to detail involved in the process of these experiments. Let's go back – old dogs Adam and Jamie found themselves two REAL old dogs – brother and sister Alaskan Malamutes called Bobo and Cece – which, according

to some breeders, are some of the most difficult to train dogs around, even when they're young and sprightly. A competition to train dogs? With Jamie's background in goldfish training? Why not? With the assistance of professional dog handlers, Adam and Jamie set about training Bobo and Cece, and at a Mythbusters Dog Show, Cece and Adam edged out Bobo and Jamie by a half point – proving beyond a shadow of a doubt that you can teach an old dog new tricks (and goldfish are no comparison to dogs). Next the Build Team try to beat Eewan the guard dog, and Eewan is a whole lot less fluffy and cuddly than were Bobo and Cece. But he's a professional and only clamps down his 550-pound force bite when he's working. Unfortunately for the Build Team, all they have is steaks, dog wee and clanky contraptions with which to protect themselves. Nevertheless, Eewan does find himself swayed by the scent of a female dog in heat, and confronted by wolf wee wee. He also does his best against Kari's rolling steel cage, but comes up short. However, the sight of him bearing down would probably have any real crim wishing they were wearing the protective dog suit offered to the Build Team. Finally Adam finds himself in gaol stripes circa 1910 with a list of methods to beat Morgan the bloodhound – but whether it's zig-zags, strolling through a creek, taking a shower or drenching yourself in cologne and coffee, he can't escape the big friendly giant. Only an urban environment has Morgan at a loss – and even then luck seems to be on the dog's side ...

See also:* *Jean Donaldson, Beverly Ulbrich, Bobo & Cece, Mike McLaughlin, Eewan, Morgan, Matt Broad, Bloodhound, Alaskan Malamutes

JAMIE – ... it's like magic what this dog can do. It's also really impressive to see a man working with the dog. It strikes me as something that's more like an art. This isn't just like a machine that's picking up scents. This is, you know, a combination of the man and his relationship with the animal, taking advantage of what the animal can do, picking up those little tiny hints of what's going on and trying to pull it together into a composition that ends up catching the bad guy. It's really something special.

Doozie

The faint of heart will sometimes spell it 'doosy', but this slang expression is derived from a much older English use of the word 'daisy' to describe something that is excellent and appealing in every way. This is exactly how Jamie uses the word when talking with firearms expert Alan Normandy about the myth *Killer Butts*.

JAMIE – Al, we have a doozie for you today.

ALAN – Well I'd love to hear this one.

Doppler Effect

If you've ever wondered why an ambulances siren sounds more high-pitched as it approaches you, and low-pitched as it drives away (and further wondered why they didn't stop as you were the one who called them), then we can treat you to an answer to the first question (but can only say 'dunno' to the second). If you recall, the phenomenon you experience as sound is really simply waves of pressurised air. As the ambulance approaches, the waves are pushed closer together, which increases their frequency and raises their pitch. As the ambulance drives away, the opposite is true. This phenomenon also occurs with light – if an object is travelling towards you, any light they're giving off is pushed towards the higher frequency 'blue' end of the spectrum. If they're moving away, then their light frequency appears more towards the red end of the spectrum. Of course, light travels rather a lot faster than sound (roughly 100,000 times faster) so you'll not notice any of this 'blue shift' or 'red shift' on the ambulance, unless they're rather recklessly exceeding the speed limit in an unregistered intergalactic spacecraft – however this would explain why they didn't stop for you.

***See also:* Doppler Machine**

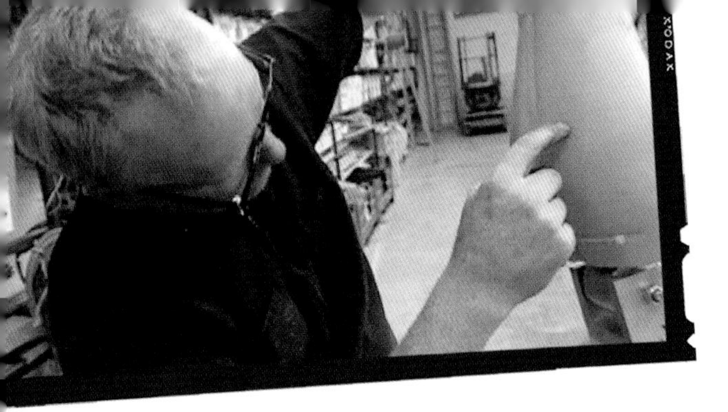

Doppler Machine

More accurately called a carotid Doppler Machine, these are essentially ultrasound kits that are set up to measure how smoothly your blood is flowing through your major vessels. When the Mythbusters tried on the myth of *Jeans Death Shrinkage* and Grant was imprisoned in a hot bath with nothing but Sudoku, iced coffee and the occasional thick geeky book to keep him active. Oh yes, and there was the threat of deep vein thrombosis or compartment syndrome.

See also: ***Keith Atkinson, deep vein thrombosis, ultrasound, Doppler effect, vessels***

Myths: ***Jeans Death Shrinkage***

Dragon Skin™

A platinum-cure silicon rubber that can withstand any impact and won't burn even under a blowtorch. It's also very soft, very strong and very stretchy (to nearly 10 times its normal size without breaking or distorting) and hence has become a classic tool for making rubber prototypes, prosthetic face masks and Buster 2.0's largest organ; his skin.

Myths: ***Buster Rebuild***

Dreamcatcher

Adam's paper crossbow was dubbed the Dreamcatcher right before it dealt a fatal blow to a ballistics gel Guard Imahara at 91 feet per second (27.7 m/s).

See also: ***paper***

Myth: ***Paper Crossbow***

Driving on Ice

Much traffic was noted on Mythbusters fan sites around the crazy concept that if the road ahead was iced up, driving in reverse was the best way to tackle it. Crazier still when the build team put together a test rig, it seemed to confirm the myth – a front wheel drive car was capable of 40 per cent more force in reverse on ice than going forwards. However, when Tory, Kari and Grant took some cars out on an icy test track, their cone carnage spoke for itself. The myth was utterly busted on all three drive systems (front, rear and four wheel drive), for while you might get a little more traction from your reverse gear, the control you have over the car is massively compromised.

See also: ***traction, friction***

TORY – I have full confidence in your driving capabilities.

GRANT – Good. That makes one of us.

Duck

This is a bird belonging to the antidae family that manages somehow to be quaint, charming, silly and exotic all at once. How they do it we'll never know, but a duck is not to be trifled with, as Jamie discovered attempting to bust the myth of the *Duck Quack Echo.*

JAMIE - Don't mess with me duck. When I say quack, you're gonna quack, right? I'm the boss here. Don't give me any beak.

Duck Quack Echo

Somewhere, sometime, someone decided that a duck's quack does not echo. We don't want to reveal here who it was (in fact, we haven't a clue) but whoever it is started a whole lot of trouble. The fact that Jim Reichardt, duck farmer par excellence, had never heard of the myth speaks volumes as to its veracity. He'd never even had anyone ASK him before. However – that is not to say there would not be a glitch or two in finding the truth. Ducks, it turns out, do not follow instructions, certainly not ones like …

JAMIE … Quack damn you.

So we can establish that ducks have a mind of their own, but bring two ducks together and instead of duck mind squared, Adam and Jamie discover that they've got yourself a quack quorum. No sooner do Adam and Jamie bring two ducks together than the myth is as good as busted, except for one thing: could it be … confirmed? The first tests certainly suggested so, and when they took the ducks into an anechoic chamber and pointed some very clever microphones at them, what they recorded looked just like an echo. The quack itself looked (to Dr Roger Schwenkee, who knows about these things and has names for them like 'exponentially decaying impulse') like an echo. Weird? Indeed, and the upshot is that you might think you're still hearing the quack when in fact you're hearing the echo … and, eventually, after much calibration of equipment and scratching beards, that echo was found, identified and filmed for posterity. Another one bites the dust.

***Myths:* Duck Quack Echo**

Duplication

When the Mythbusters are faced with a new myth they have two tasks – the second of these (can you guess the first? Anyone? Anyone?) is to duplicate what supposedly happened in the

myth, but which could not be replicated (ahhh – that was it) in the first place.
***See also:* replication**

Dynamite

The classic explosive was originally marketed as 'Nobel's Blasting Powder' and was so successful that the inventor was able to fund the Nobel Prizes, the most famous series of prizes the planet has ever known (nice one Alfred). He called it dynamite from the Greek word for power, *dynamis*, from which we also get dynamic, dynamo, dynasty and the dyne, one of the many units of force. Today dynamite is sold as a 20cm long stick (so it can slip into drilling holes) but its ingredients are much the same as when Alfie knocked it together back in Helenborg, Sweden. The principal ingredient is the explosive nitro-glycerine but a key component is diatomaceous earth, which soaks up the nitro-glycerine making it more stable, but just as explosive. There's also a bit of sodium carbonate for flavour. Dynamite is a high explosive, and more powerful explosive than black powder. The Mythbusters always call in experts to handle their explosions – although just occasionally Adam has got his hands on some, such as in the myth of *Avalanche Adventures*.

ADAM – We're in this tiny little cabin, my feet are underneath this duffel bag that weighs a couple of hundred pounds worth of explosives, and I'm grabbing them out, I'm cutting the fuse, popping on the igniter, handing them to Aaron, he's pulling them and igniting them inside the helicopter and then chucking them out the window.

***See also:* Aaron Rodriguez**

Dynamometer

Ever been in a garage and seen a car blasting out enough engine noise for a fast lap at Le Mans … but somehow going nowhere? It was probably sitting on a dynamometer, a chunky rig that can measure the speed as well as the torque produced by a car (or motorcycle, truck etc). It's generally used to establish the power that the vehicle's engine can produce, but the Mythbusters set up a dynamometer with the express purpose of shielding big oil and big car companies from the appalling abuse and suspicion being heaped on them by conspiracy theorists around the world.
***Myths:* Great Gas Conspiracy**

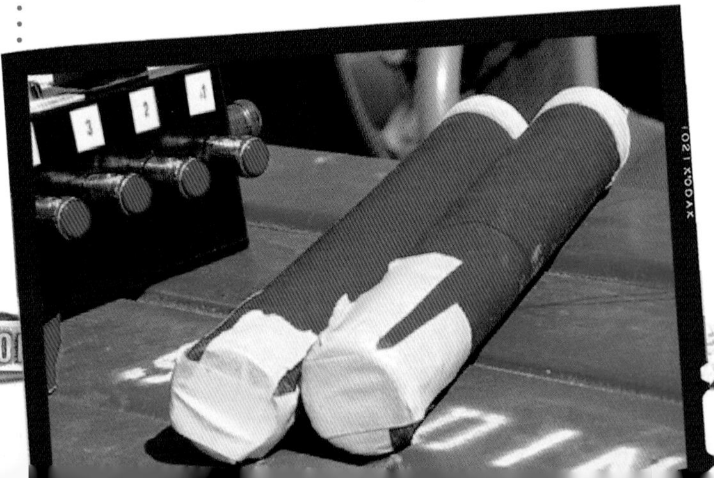

Earl Hibler

Earl is an aeroplane mechanic called in by Adam and Jamie when the aeroplane engine they'd bought from an aviation school in Ohio in their attempt to recreate the *Shredded Aeroplane* from an internet picture turned out be a bit of a dud. Earl knew why.

EARL – You know, when you get an engine from an AMT school, you have students that take it apart, put it together, take it apart, put it together, and not necessarily right.

But better than just know why it was broken, Earl and his propeller specialist buddy Brian Sullivan could fix it.

***See also:* Brian Sullivan**
***Myths:* Shredded Aeroplane**

Earl the Caddy

Fans do outrageous things for the show, and one of the first was to donate a perfectly good Cadillac (needed a little love from Scottie, but who doesn't?) Earl the Caddy was used in *Car Capers, Boom Lift Catapult* and many more.

Earthquake Machine

Ever heard of Nikola Tesla? Look him up (and not just in this volume) for he was a maestro of mayhem and a conductor of creativity. And one story relating to Tesla rides above the rest: that Tesla constructed a hand-held earthquake machine so powerful he almost brought down a whole building in New York City. Crackpot, or confirmable? Adam and Jamie study the original patents intently before finally rejigging one of Jamie's jackhammers (yes, just the one) as a mechanical oscillator generator. Excited by the prospect of some destruction, they try it out on a thick steel bar … and break the generator. Twice. Hang on

– what are they ACTUALLY trying to do here? The lads demonstrate with a water tank and wave generator.

ADAM – Dude, look at that! You hit a sweet spot again. That's twice the sweet spot that you were hitting before.

JAMIE – And that was a minute variation in speed.

ADAM – That is so cool.

JAMIE – Like that was the difference on this meter from 1.5 to 1.6, and at 1.5, it was almost a flat calm.

ADAM – What I love about this test is it really illustrates Tesla's theoretical ideas perfectly. When you push a kid on a swing, each of your pushes doesn't make him go all the way up. It's the sum total of them. You're adding energy each time.

…and that's what they're trying to do with their earthquake machine; build a device that is capable of oscillating (or vibrating) at a big enough range of frequencies to catch an object at its fundamental resonant frequency. The only problem is their next prototype mechanical oscillator generator doesn't work either. Step into the spotlight Grant Imahara and his dancing linear actuator! This side-to-side actuator is just the thing to create oscillation, and clamping it to a steel bar creates a magic of high-energy wiggles. On a scale of Tesla's New York build however the actuator fails to impress. Finally Adam and Jamie head out to Carquinez Bridge to give the myth something big to work on. The bridge doesn't come down (busting the myth) but, spookily…

ADAM … it totally feels like the whole structure is ringing to that Hertz.

See also: ***Nikola Tesla, oscillation, resonance, actuator***

Echo

If a sound can be reflected from a surface then we call it an echo, and if you hear a duck's quack echo then count yourself lucky.

***See also:* Duck Quack Echo**

Edward Kersh, MD

Ed Kersh has got a lot of ticker, so much so he's the head of cardiology at St Luke's Hospital in San Francisco. Of course that means he has the health and wellbeing of the local Mythbusters crew at heart as well, and when Kari came calling for the skinny on *Jeans Death Shrinkage*, Ed and she had a heart to heart on the subject of pulmonary embolisms.

EDWARD - Well I hate to say that it is possible.

KARI - Really?

EDWARD - Really, because I do love tight jeans.

***See also:* pulmonary embolism, deep vein thrombosis**

***Myths:* Jeans Death Shrinkage**

Eel Skin Wallet

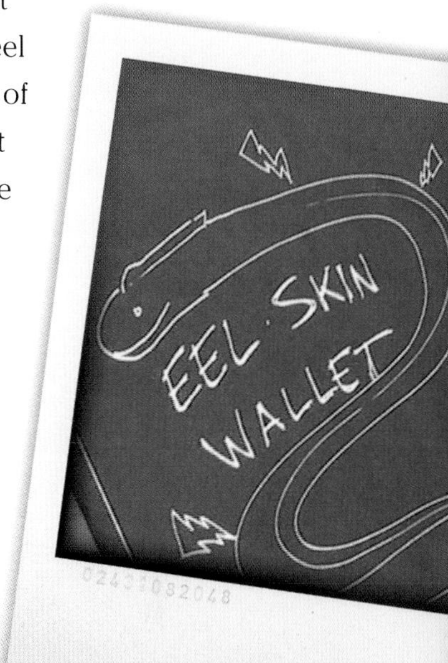

Would an eel skin wallet made from an electric eel wipe the magnetic strip of a credit card? Crazy as it sounds, this myth did the rounds in the 80s, and the lads tested all kinds of possible scenarios: was it simple contact? Was it a build-up of static? Could charged particles be spotted in a microwave? Was it the wallet's magnetic clasp? Were two cards rubbing together? The myth was looking shaky already, but then it was revealed that eel skin wallets are actually made from something called a slime eel (aka hag fish) – not electric eels at all. Then, when Adam and Jamie tried to actually wipe a magnetic card themselves they found it took a magnet with one thousand times the strength of the planet Earth to do it. They even dropped a credit card in a tank with an electric eel who bit the card, which still read fine. Result? Err…that would be busted.

***See also:* credit cards, magnetism, slime eel**

Eewan

Eewan is a German Shepherd trained through the Witmer Tyson Kennels to become a fearsome but professional guard dog. Eewan was five years old when he was put up against the sneaky strategies of the Build Team in the *Dog Special*. Eewan was tempted by steaks, distracted by pheromones, confronted by wolf wee and confounded by robots, rolling steel cages and a 44-gallon drum on wheels. It was a long day ... Eewan found himself confirming a few 'beat the guard dog' methods, but let's just say, don't try it yourself.

KARI – I think people totally underestimate these dogs. They're really well trained.

TORY – Yeah, Mike was saying that you can actually train these dogs to ignore things. So I bet if we did this test again, they wouldn't even look twice at that steak.

***See also:* Mike McLaughlin, pheromones, German Shepherd**
***Myths:* Dog Special**

Nice doggy....

Egg Drop

In one hour Adam and Jamie needed to make a device to save an egg from destruction, and win the Egg Drop challenge on the way to being named the *Ultimate Mythbuster*. Given some oranges, a pair of latex gloves, tape, string and other odds and ends, this was a test of ingenuity and lateral thinking against the clock. Adam's egg-saving contraption consisted of a paper cone, an orange to keep it stable, and inflated gloves to cushion the blow. His first egg didn't survive, but his second lived to see breakfast. Jamie, as you might expect, went lateral – the egg inside the orange inside the glove, he tied it to the string and the tape and lowered the egg from the roof with ease.

***See also:* tortilla throw, fear test, guess your weight, pain test, memory test**
***Myths:* Ultimate Mythbuster Special**

Elaine Viets

Journalist and mystery writer Elaine hears whisper of the *Biscuit Bazooka* myth from a friend – but when she tries to nail it down it slipped away like so much cookie dough on the back of your head.

***Myths:* Biscuit Bazooka**

ELAINE – I tried to track it down. I tried to find the friend of the friend. I couldn't do it. I tried to find the location where it actually happened. I couldn't. I looked for police reports, there were none. And the truth is this didn't happen. There was no woman so stupid that she thought she was holding raw dough on her head, and that's kind of nice to know.

Electric Eel

You might not appreciate it on a day-to-day level, but it turns out that every time you move a muscle or even think a thought, there is a tiny electrical zap going off somewhere inside. It's the same with sloths and wildebeest and fish – and there is one fish in particular that has turned it into a talent with naming rights. Hailing from South America, the Electric Eel (actually more of a fish) has focused this electrical potential into muscle packs that can build and store a very large discharge – up to 500 volts at 1 amp (500 watts)! What's particularly troubling is that it can zap it out all in one go, stunning everything in the water in the immediate vicinity which it then happily feasts upon. Why do the Mythbusters care? It's not just their implicit interest in all creatures great and zappy, but the electric eel was at the heart of a little myth they called *Eel Skin Wallet*.

***See also:* electricity, volts, amps, watts**

***Myths:* Eel Skin Wallet**

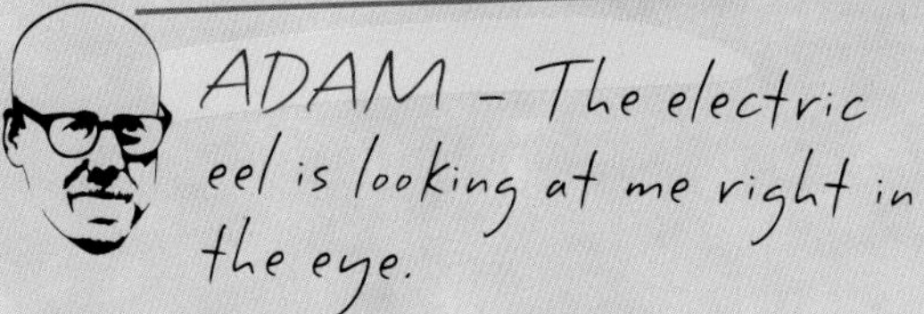

Electricity

A flow of electrons from one place to another doesn't really sound like much to get excited about, yet being able to generate and control that flow is what contemporary society is based upon. Everything is electrical it seems, and the fact that the electrons that make it all happen are as fundamental as the atom itself is barely given a moment's thought. Electricity is in our heads, flowing over our clothes and skin and (hopefully not) igniting an inferno of petrol when you reach for the bowser having just climbed back out of the car. From lightning to static Adam and Jamie have found so much misunderstanding of electricity that the myths just keep on flowing ... like the classic analogy to comprehend electricity. The volume of a body of water could be compared to electrical voltage, and the speed of flow to its electrical current, or amps. A river might be broad but slow moving, great for a swim. A water cannon on the other hand might knock you into next week.

See also: ***conductivity, resistance, watts, volts, amps***

Myths: ***Lightning Strikes Tongue Piercing, Appliances in the Bathtub, Eel Skin Wallet. Ancient Electricity and gosh so many more ...***

Electrocution

Very bad things happen to a human being who gets hold of too much electricity – specifically electricity that is of a particular current and voltage. At 240 volts, 60 milliamps is plenty to freak your heart out. Adam and Jamie have toyed (very carefully) with electrocution in the myths *Phone in a Thunderstorm*, *Third Rail* and *Appliances in the Bath*. At the giant currents involved in a bolt of lightning, to the order of 100,000 amps, you can actually survive because your heart just freezes up. It might just start going again once the bolt has passed through you – or not of course. 1000+ people a year get killed by lighting bolts, so don't wander around open fields with a golf club during a thunderstorm.

Myths: ***Phone in a Thunderstorm, Third Rail and Appliances in the Bath***

this salsa tastes like corn chips dipped in moustache

Electrolysis

This is a cunning way to use an electric current to bust electrically conducting compounds – like the bars of a prison cell – by setting up a circuit with positive and negative terminals in a conducting medium (say, a nice tub of salsa). The current and the conductive electrolyte (in this case the salsa) encourage little bits of the material to migrate away.

***Myths:* Salsa Escape**

Electromagnetic Radiation

Packed with photons of no mass but bearing tremendous wallops of energy as its frequency increases, electromagnetic radiation covers the phenomena of light, microwaves, radio waves, radar waves and gamma waves – and everything in between. Mythbusters is broadcast in electromagnetic radiation at about 7 MHz (unless you get it by cable).

***See also:* microwaves**

Electromagnetism

If we could satisfactorily explain the wonders of electromagnetism in a few hundred words then we'd be writing pop science books for a general audience. What's that you say? We ARE writing pop science books for a general audience? Gosh, better get on to a definition of electromagnetism then, as the words are running out. OK so there's magnetism and there's electricity. Two different things, right? Sorry, no. Different expressions of the same phenomenon. At the heart of electromagnetism is the essential attraction that the charged particles of the atom have for one another – the electrons and the protons. Once you've got that essential attraction in your head, look around you at anything. Really – anything, anything that's not radioactive decay or an atomic nucleus. The plastic in your bottle of water, the water itself, your hand, the signal that you sent to your hand to pick up the bottle and drink from it … everything, man. EVERYTHING you experience is electromagnetism … until you drop the bottle. That's gravity. Whole other thing. And it's also everywhere man – EVERYWHERE!

***See also:* gravity**

Element

Back when the universe was so young that a picosecond was an eternity, elements didn't exist. Not a jot of strontium or technetium or sulphur or iron or oxygen or carbon or gold was anywhere, which must have made things very neat and tidy. Jamie would have liked it, except for the fact that Jamie is made up of elements himself. But as the universe aged and the unimaginable forces of heat, pressure and who knows what else began to calm down, all of a sudden the immeasurably tiny particles that had burst forth from who-knows-where cooled down enough to form little atomic gangs. These atomic gangs were the first elements – and they were hydrogen, helium and lithium. It would be wise at this point to flick back to the 'atom' reference and just refresh yourself on what one is, because this entry is moving on fast. Anything that was more complicated than lithium and helium and hydrogen was born inside the glowing belly of stars – so the universe had to wait for a few of THOSE to form before there was any iron, oxygen, silicon, sulphur or carbon. And pretty much everything else (the arsenic, the krypton, the yttrium, the tin) was made when different kinds of star exploded, expanded or extinguished themselves. Pick up a pencil, or a hat, or your dog. Everything that goes into making that pencil, hat or dog (or you yourself) was born either at the beginning of the universe, or inside a raging star, or as a result of an exploding, expanding, dying one. Adam's favourite element is neodymium because it makes the best magnets. Jamie's favourite is praseodymium, because it's a key component of his welding goggles. They're both very fond of astatine however, because it is so mind bogglingly rare (25 grams or so on the planet at any time).

***See also:* atoms**

Element

As opposed to an element that is forged in the furnace of a star or even the Big Bang itself (serious stuff) a heating element is used to warm up your water, toast your bread or dry your hair. This kind of element makes use of the thermoelectric effect, and tends to be made of a piece of metal (or weirdo ceramic) that resists the flow of electricity and turns that resistance into heat. Jolly good stuff, but in the case of a water heater, you'd want some way to let the system know it had heated the water plenty hot, so a thermostat is added and an emergency cut-off switch as well for good measure. Of course, if you happen to be Adam or Jamie (in which case, hi guys and thanks for reading) you'll be in the business of finding out what happens to a water heater when these safety devices are removed. A *Water Heater Rocket* is what happens.

See also:* *thermoelectric effect, resistance, thermostat, emergency cut-off switch

Myths:* *Water Heater Rocket

Elevator

Despite their motors, counter-weights, cables and safety mechanisms, elevators are scary places if the idea of a fast fall followed by sudden death is at all a problem for you. This very rarely happens, but if it did you can content yourself with the knowledge that the very first elevator seems to have been built by Archimedes. Again? That guy gets everywhere!

Elevator of Death

next floor ... certain death!

When a sudden jolt, or jar, or squeak transpires when you're passing the 18th floor, who among you hasn't wondered 'If this elevator fell down the shaft, could I jump and save myself?' The Mythbusters experimental problem comes in two delicious halves; how to safely drop an elevator from an eight-storey building, and how to get Buster to jump and at just the right time. The old Royal Hotel, scheduled for demolition (or a B-grade horror movie) is found to contain the perfect elevator and accompanying shaft of 92 feet (28 metres). While Adam rigs the elevator (of death) Scottie builds a jumping rig for Buster which contains not one, not two, but three giant springs from different car suspension systems. The 12 feet per second jump (3.6 m/s) Buster can now achieve will be triggered by a cord so that he jumps when the elevator is six feet from the floor. As the ancient elevator is resurrected and winched to the top of the shaft, its safety mechanism removed or disabled, the intense danger of the experiment becomes apparent…

Embarcadero Cove

Nestled along a delightful slice of the Oakland waterfront is Embarcadero Cove. Embarcadero being Spanish for jetty, there's not too much dispute about the purpose of the place, so it was here that Adam and Jamie went looking for a nice boat to sink. Why? For the myth of *Sinking Titanic*, naturally. The tug chosen (dubbed the 'Mythtanic') was towed to San Francisco Dry Dock for sinking … and raising … and sinking (and raising).

See also: ***jetty, San Francisco Dry Dock***
Myths: ***Sinking Titanic***

Emergency Cut-Off Switch

Sometimes referred to by its dramatic or stage name, 'The Kill Switch', this is a device which can cut the operation of a system instantly. Found on any piece of dangerous equipment, except those for which Adam and Jamie have plans – the key example being the water heaters in *Water Heater Rocket*.

See also: ***thermostat***
Myths: ***Water Heater Rocket***

Encinal High School

The generous educators at Encinal High, Alameda, hosted the Mythbusters in their 12 foot (3.6 metres) diving pool for their medium scale tests of the *Sinking Titanic* myth. The scale test worked a treat! The myth however was busted. The lads returned to Encinal's pool to test the big pump used for the *Scuba Diver* myth, and then took to the football field to scale test their *Border Slingshot* using the goal posts. The fact that the posts got ever so slightly bent may or may not be the reason that Encinal has not hosted another experiment since. Maybe they're just busy.

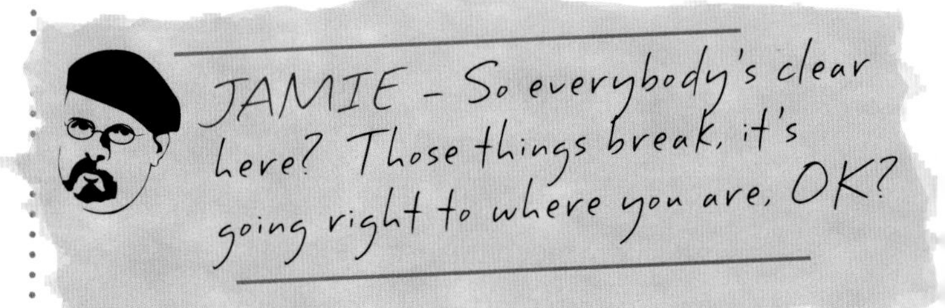

Enzyme

In the myth of *Stinky Car* Adam and Jamie get to work with an enzyme based cleaner which uses the same principle as do the enzymes that lurk inside you yourself, all the way from your mouth to your other end. In there enzymes have the job of working on your food for you to break it down for digestion.

Myths: ***Stinky Car, Flatulence Myths***

Eponymous

This word is often used to describe someone's self-titled album for the good reason that it means something named for something else. For example, Euler's 'eponymous' number would be ..."

Euler's Number

There's very little time to describe Euler's Number, other than to say *e*.

Eric Braun

He's a seventh generation (count them) circus performer who specialises in the trapeze. When the Mythbuster Build Team dropped by they wanted him to show them how to do a 360° on his Russian Swing. After Grant, Kari and then Tory wussed out, it was down to Eric. You see, you have to be the swing ...

ERIC - It WANTS to go around. There you go.

TORY - Nice!

Myths: ***360° Swing***

Eric the Researcher

Eric Haven works as a researcher in the Mythbusters team. Very occasionally he gets pulled in to do something that might be very unpleasant...

ERIC - Physically I feel something in my chest, I don't feel like sitting down, I feel like I have to move around.

Myths: ***Brown Note***

Eric getting into the swing of things

Evolution

In the biological world in which we live, evolution describes the way in which the traits we pass down from one generation to the next gradually change and offer organisms the ability to shape themselves to their environments over time. In Mythbusters, a myth evolution is a cunning way to up the stakes on myths by making them bigger, badder and altogether better.

Exhumation

Not a pretty thought, unless like Jamie you're still alive as he was in the myth *Buried Alive*. Oh, and exhumation means digging up a dead body, from the *humus* (which is Latin for ground, not dip).

***See also:* dead**

***Myths:* Buried Alive**

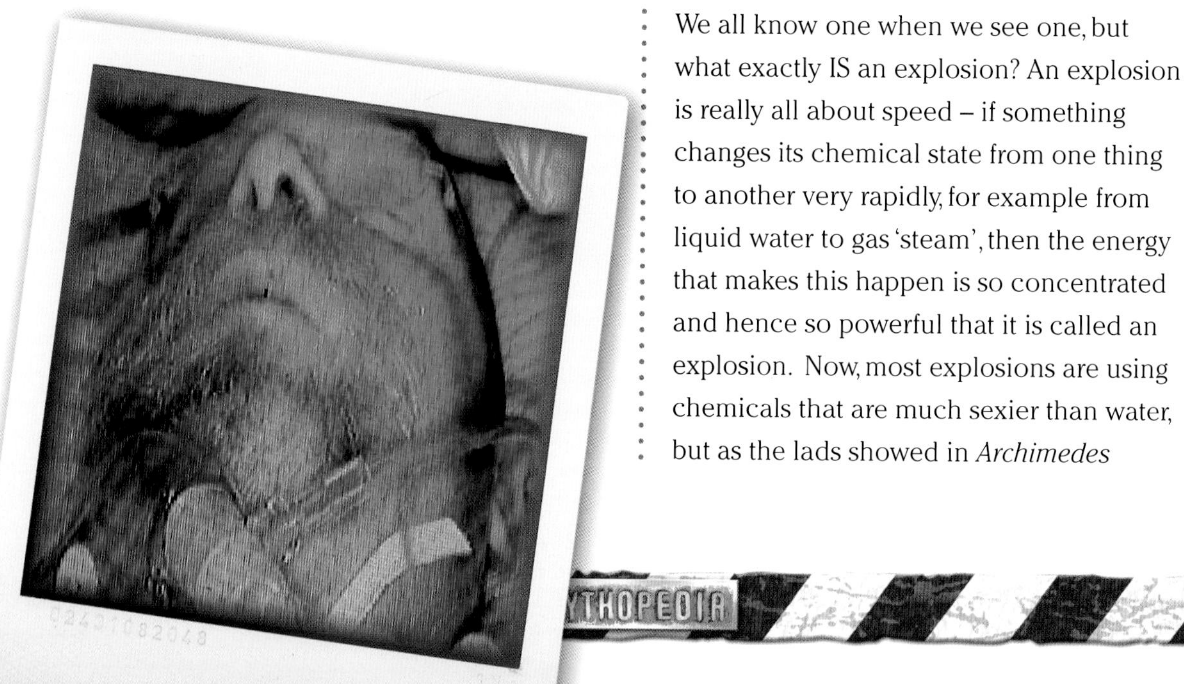

Exit Wound

The wound you get when a bullet or other projectile/pointy object enters your body is sometimes NOTHING to the wound you get when that same object leaves your body on the other side. Bullets have a tendency to break up when they meet resistance – take a look at the handful of fragments Adam dragged up from the pool in the myth of *Bulletproof Water*. And that was water! You're at least 30 per cent something else. An exit wound can be hard to find, as it was when Adam and Jamie shot a ballistics gel mould of Grant's head with their experimental *Pirate Special* cannon. That 2 inch (5.1 cm) ball bearing just went straight through.

***See also:* firearms**

Explosion

We all know one when we see one, but what exactly IS an explosion? An explosion is really all about speed – if something changes its chemical state from one thing to another very rapidly, for example from liquid water to gas 'steam', then the energy that makes this happen is so concentrated and hence so powerful that it is called an explosion. Now, most explosions are using chemicals that are much sexier than water, but as the lads showed in *Archimedes*

Steam Cannon water can be plenty explosive. However, gunpowder, gun-cotton, dynamite and nuclear fission are friskier alternatives. Explosions are typically accompanied by high temperatures, rapid increase in pressure, smoke, steam or a shower of debris, and a characteristic 'boom' (or occasionally a 'poof', 'pfft' or 'spppptt', depending on the explodability of the experiment).

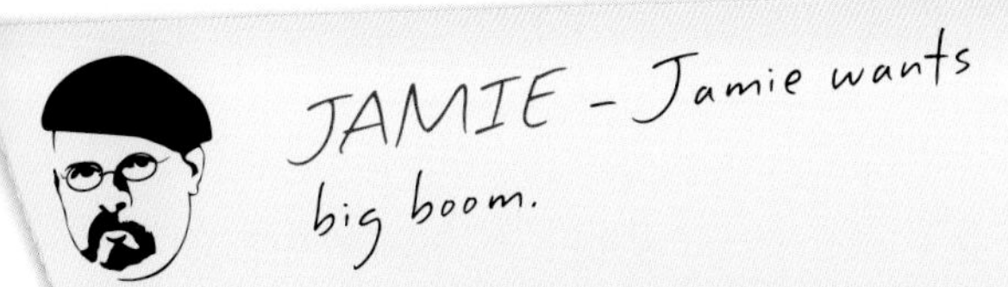

You might be surprised to learn that most explosives have less potential energy than an equivalent amount of petrol – it's just that they can zip through that energy faster than you can say 'don't touch that'. Much, much faster in fact – the shockwave of a very high explosive moves at thousands and thousands of metres every second (around 32,000 km/h or 20,000 mph).

See also: ***dynamite, gelignite, nitro-glycerine, gunpowder, guncotton, high/low explosive, detonation, deflagration, TNT***

Myths: ***how about a list of myths that DON'T have explosions?***

Exploding Lighter

Whatever you do just don't smoke. It's not just the deadly toxins but even the associated paraphernalia is out to get you! The Mythbusters tested whether disposable lighters could create a potentially lethal explosion right there in the comfort of your own pocket – and Adam and Jamie had a long list of the circumstances in which it might occur. The first was when welding, and not surprisingly, the hot slag fired up a nice little explosion pretty fast. Not so successful was the clothes dryer, which happily tumbled the lighter for more than an hour at 160°F (71°C). How about a golf club? After a few swings they manage a nice little explosion, so that's a no-no. Leaving a lighter on the dashboard of your car is next, and even

though the lads get some nice explosions with their toaster oven rig, the temperature is way higher than you'd ever get inside a car. Explosions are one thing – what about potential lethality? Going back to their best test – the welding – they rig a piece of pork in some overalls, pop in a lighter, and reset. Several tests all reveal that while you might come away with some burns, with the lighter in your pocket it's not going to explode. What about … 500 lighters in a car? With the San Francisco Fire Department on side and a concrete bunker to hand, all that was left was to roll in the car, fill it with the desired number of lighters equaling 1000 cubic centimeters of butane, heat them up with a vacu-form machine and add an ignition source (a spark from a neon transformer that lights a fuel-soaked rope) and …

JAMIE – Yeah!

ADAM – Yeah!

ADAM – That was beautiful! Dude, it blew out the back window!

See also: ***Bryan Niswonger, butane, vacuform, CCs***

Hot pants

Exploding Pants

One of only three pants-based myths (the others being *Pants on Fire*, and *Jeans Death Shrinkage* of course) this takes us to New Zealand back in the 1930s, where an epidemic of trouser explosions are making the place live up to its nickname, the land of the long white cloud. Was it a stick of dynamite in those farmers' pockets, or were they just pleased to see their flocks? Extensive (and explosive) research by the Build Team suggested in fact that a popular herbicide might have been the guilty party. Although neither the scaled down hotpants fandango brought on by Grant's sledgehammer-modded Dead Blow robot nor the fast-burning Buster-filled flame-out full-scale test were explosions in the full and technical meaning of the term, who could blame a lonely Kiwi farmer for upping the stakes ever so slightly in the retelling? His smoking scrotum earned the right surely.
See also: ***ragwort, Dead Blow***

KARI – I have a feeling that if you were wearing those pants and they burned that fast, you would definitely claim explosion.

GRANT – You need compression to have an explosion.

KARI – You are so hard to please.

Exploding Tattoos

It's not surprising that the machine we know casually as an MRI and more formally as a Magnetic Resonance Imager relies on some rather powerful magnets to allow it to take snapshots of what's going on inside your body. However, you might be surprised to learn that the ink in your pride-and-joy tattoo could well have a significant iron component, and iron being a ferromagnetic material, you could find yourself fearing an explosive situation next time they wheel you into the big medical doughnuts. Scottie certainly wasn't sure about taking the test, but with a little peer pressure she donned a gown and got herself snapped – to no ill effects whatsoever. With iron oxide identified as the only likely culprit ingredient in tattoo ink, they mix up some supercharged iron-heavy inks and get Matty the Tattooist to work on a leg of pork. When the tattooed pork is introduced to the MRI, the iron-heavy ink certainly shows up on the scan, but there' no swelling, no leaching, and certainly no explosion. Returning the myth in *Myth Evolution*, the team showed that not even an RFID tag would explode! Busted AND evo-busted!

JAMIE – So you're telling us there was no exploding tattoo.

SCOTTIE – No Jamie, I know that disappoints you but I'm a little relieved ...

***See also:* MRI, tattoo, Matty the Tattooist, RFID, Fergus Coakley**
***Myths:* Myth Evolution**

Exploding Toilet

The myth of the Exploding Toilet has endless variety, but the story is essentially this; after cleaning the bathroom, careless 'Ma' tips a bucket of various cleaning flammable products into the toilet, but neglects to flush. Then 'Pa' comes along and takes a seat. Tossing his lit cigarette between his legs, he is

surprised to find himself atop a considerable explosion. Jamie backed away from the role of 'Pa', and instead this was the debut role for Buster the crash test dummy. However, despite adding to their outdoor, blast-chambered convenience flammables like hairspray, bug spray, and butane, and having on hand the attendance of the local Fire Marshall, the toilet refused to utter more than a 'poof' when even a lit match was dropped in. Declaring the myth busted, Adam and Jamie reached for the black powder, and were justly rewarded with a trouser-removing explosion. This myth was in the first formal episode of Mythbusters.

Explosive Decompression

HEATHER – You had the wife o the house going and cleaning out the outhouse with some kind of kerosene or oil or other kind of volatile fluid, at which point the grandpa goes out and sits down and lights his pipe. And he gets blown right off the outhouse seat. And as he's lying there amidst the rubble he says, 'must have been something I ate'.

***See also:* blast chamber, Buster, black powder, butane**

Explosive Decompression

There are many great fears to do with flying (arguably more than there are to do with crashing) but the one most exploited by movies time and time again is whether a small hole – say from a firearm – in the side of your plane will make the resulting depressurisation so catastrophic that everything is sucked out the hole at the same time. Explosive decompression is a real term used to describe a sudden failure of a pressure vessel that happens almost instantly (in 0.1 seconds). Officially what we're dealing with in this myth is rapid decompression – but the word 'explosive' is so … explosive, don't you agree? Anyhoo – back to the myth, which is a doozie in all departments: location, materials, build, results, you name it. It was always going to be tricky to replicate – how to convince an airline to loan you a plane so you can fly it at 35,000 feet (10,668 metres) and shoot a hole in the side. Answer? You don't. Instead you head on out to the Mojave Desert in blistering heat, pick out a nice Hawaiian Airlines jet that was just minding its own business, and do the opposite. You plug it up so its good and airtight again, pump it full of air so it replicates the 8 PSI difference you would have at 35,000 feet. This done, the Mythbusters fire off a few rounds with a remote rig of Jamie's original design and discover that nothing other than a little pssssfff of air escapes. Busted. In replicating the results the lads used some nice explosives and did the job properly – eventually the whole side of the aeroplane had to be blown up (of course) but by some miracle Buster managed to keep his seat (albeit with half a fuselage in his lap).

ADAM ... Please make sure your tray tables are in the upright and locked position.

See also: ***The Huffer, Mojave Desert, airplane graveyards, Boyd Lacosse***

Explosive Hammers

Seems that there are some out there in the television audience for Mythbusters who take their roles as guardians of the public safety very seriously indeed, to the point where they wrote to the show complaining that Jamie was using a hammer unsafely by banging it on another hammer. What's that you say now? How dangerous is a hammer? Apparently they can explode, and that sounds like a job for Mythbusters! The Build Team take on the tall tool tale with gusto and immediately build a pneumatically actuated hammer exploding robot (as you do). But when the robot swings two wooden-handled claw hammers together, the result is splinters of wood rather than steel. Then two steel-handled hammers smack together with the merest dent – this is at 16 feet per second (4.8 metres per second)! Freezing the hammers doesn't help either, and eventually the team has to ask Jamie for advice on hot to make hammers so hard they might explode:

JAMIE – I think if a hammer head is really hard, like if it's like just super hard it's going to be brittle. That you would do by getting the hammer head really hot, like red or white hot, as hot as you can get it without melting it and then quenching it in used motor oil, because it absorbs a lot of the excess carbon in there.

Now this is called 'case hardening' and the Build Team jumped right in, heating a hammer until it was red hot then dunking it in some dirty old motor oil … and starting a fire. To make sure that this hammer gives them the best possible result, they re-rig the hammer smashing bot with an anvil, but even then all they ended up with was a bent handle. Not a shard to be seen.

***See also:* case hardening, pneumatic, hammer, Scott Thomas**

Exponential

Now, mathematicians will never forgive the shortness of this definition, but as we've no time for the inner workings of Euler's number we're prepared to risk it. 'Exponential' describes something that increases or decreases at an ever greater rate. If we could draw you a diagram it would be a graph line that starts off close to the bottom line but rapidly curves upwards until it tears across the paper and onto the desk.

***See also:* Euler's Number**

***Myths:* Water Heater Rocket**

ADAM – The small tank's probably made with the same gauge of metal as a medium or a large tank, which means it's going to be exponentially stronger because there's less surface area for the pressure to act against.

Exponent Inc.

Roger McCarthy's anti-failure company investigates 'what went wrong?' in anything and everything engineering or scientific. Founded in 1967, they've squelched through the Exxon Valdez disaster, wiped the soot from the Oaklahoma City bombings and even picked a fight over the infamous Menendez murderer.

***See also:* Roger McCarthy**

Extrusion

If you want to make something long and uniform from something that is suitably pliable, you need to do some extruding. Whether it's toothpaste through a tube, clay from a shoe (in *Steelcap Amputation)*, poo through an anus or high-quality steel through a die, extrusion is fun, fun, fun for the whole family. If you were a kid and you never extruded your plasticine then its no wonder you're the sad, screwed up lounge-jockey we see before us. But it's not too late! Get extruding today!

***See also:* die**

Facts about Flatulence

Of all the imaginative possibilities, this myth was eventually rendered down to three; can you be killed by flatus? Do beans produce more flatus? Can a flatus be disabled by lighting a match? Fans keep to explore the unbroadcast myths must now hit the internet, while the rest of you will be dazzled by the wonder that was Adam's flatus catching rig. Although it was at first made redundant by the frigidity of the bath water …

ADAM – Oh God, it's so cold! Oh dude, that's wrong … For some reason the cold water's making me pucker up. I wasted a really good one at like six o'clock this morning. It was like two seconds long, like a real 'pPFfrrrtttt' kind of thing. Wish I had that now.

…eventually a flatus was captured, measured and found to contain all sorts of things like nitrogen and oxygen (to be expected, as they are the major components of regular air) as well as hydrogen sulphide and methylmetcaptan. To test the dietary influence on flatus production the team need more data – how many flatus events per crew member per day? Jamie, Adam and Kari all record their passings before and after the strict dietary regime of meat, beans and soda is enforced. Jamie eats meat to register a drop in his production, while both Adam (beans) and Kari (soda) double their output and can confirm beans and soda as flatus

producers extraordinaire. But will flatus kill you if you have a particularly productive evening? No – it would take a mammoth flatulence effort across 110 days to produce enough carbon dioxide to kill you, 441 days to make enough methane, and 22 years to make enough hydrogen sulphide. Oh – and the match doesn't burn them either – only masks the odour. Busted and busted.
***See also:* David Maltby, mass spectrometer, flatus**

Failure Point

Adam and Jamie used the concept of incorporating points of failure into a system to avoid a catastrophic failure that may result in death or injury when they built their blast chamber. Designed it with a deliberate failure point the chamber would separate into two halves if a blast could not otherwise be contained. This is a more acceptable outcome than the whole thing shattering into shards of toughened polycarbonate.
***See also:* blast chamber, polycarbonate**

Fake Bladder

Also called 'the bionic bladder' this was a rig used to test the myth of *The Third Rail.* A whoopee cushion was used to introduce some pressure to the 'urine' stream, which could be adjusted from a 'human' size to a giant 'pachydermian' stream.
***Myths:* The Third Rail**

Falling

A count back of myths has more than a dozen devoted in some way to the art of falling from somewhere high (or dropping something from somewhere high). Think back to *Plywood Builder, Falling Lawyer, Penny Drop* and *Life Raft.* Gravity can always be relied on to provide the right dose of drama, danger and daring, belying the fact that the human body is in no way built to fly, glide or hit the ground at anything more than a couple of metres per second.

ADAM - More than 10 feet you can break limbs. At where we are at about 30 feet you could easily die falling that high.

1, 2, 3, jump...

Only car accidents claim more accidental deaths than falling (and the lads have taken on around 25 car/ truck myths, and still counting). Yet falling is a part of life (and even more so death) and fortunate escapes, tragic mistakes and imaginative foolishness have made for many compelling tales. But at the end of the day, the sense that you are falling is achieved by the same internal apparatus that keeps you in balance, the vestibular apparatus in your inner ear.

See also: ***gravity, vestibular apparatus***

Myths: ***Plywood Builder, Barrel of Bricks, Hammer Bridge Drop, Border Slingshot ... (what's with the 'B's'?), Falling Lawyer, Penny Drop, Lawn Chair, Elevator of Death, Life Raft***

Falling Lawyer

Not only is this myth successfully replicated, but in the end the lads are able to pinpoint the exact event upon which it was based. Seems that a lawyer was bouncing off the glass of the 24th floor of his high-rise office building (showing off apparently) when ... he went right through and fell to his death. But the glass on high-rise buildings is three-quarters of an inch thick (1.9 cms)! How could it happen? Well, there's more inside an office building than lawyers and paperwork

– there's lots and lots of air. Sometimes if there's more air flowing into the building than out of it, the glass outside the building can be compromised. Adam and Jamie put together a rig of glass and aluminium and used a leaf-blower to generate the 1.47 PSI of pressure on the inside of a window. They made a 'lawyer' of sand bags on a pole which could be propelled by rubber surgical tubing along tracks right at the window. Side bets are placed, weight was redistributed a few times and eventually at a speed of 5.7 mph (9.1 km/h) they sent their lawyer through the window to the sweet sound of success…

ADAM – Listen to it. It's like rice crispies.

See also: ***Pat Quinn, Bruce DeMara, stack effect***

Fan of Death

They know what they want, they do the hard work, they get the job done … almost. The *Fan of Death* was a frustrating myth in that all the rigs – right up to the lawnmower powered, steel fabricated, razor sharp death fan, worked perfectly and yet the team could not chop the head off a dummy of ballistics gel and a real pig spine. Busted!

Fans

Fans of the television show Mythbusters are the most powerful television fans the planet has ever seen. No other fans have more authority, are more respected, are of higher average intelligence or hold more university degrees (overall, not per capita). Are we basing this on quality research or an instinctive understanding of what you all want to read? You decide. Via websites, email, post, telepathy or simple word of mouth at the coffee shop, the fans of Mythbusters have more control over their beloved program than do the fans of any other reality pop-science television series, bar none.

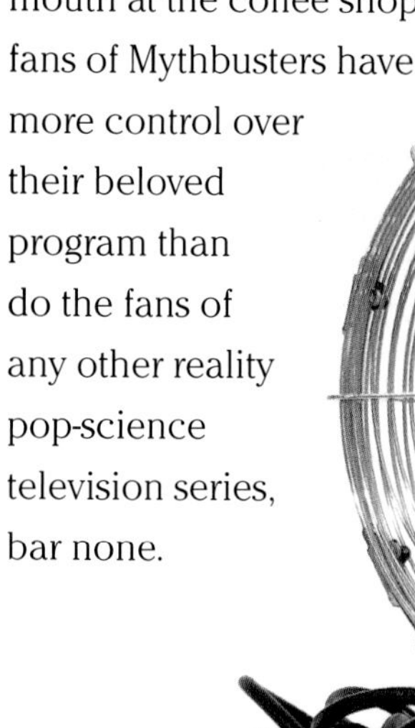

Fantastico

If you want weird, if you want kooky, if you want esoteric (and all at the right price) look no further than Fantastico, one of Adam's fave stores for 10 years or more. It's where the lads bought their *Christmas Lights* – and although theirs were rigged to start a fire, there's no reason to suspect anything but the traditional Mythbusters need for tinkered destruction. Mike the store manager can tell you why:

MIKE – These lights nowadays have a safety fuse in the plug. In the old days, you know on the box, it would say, don't put more than three sets? And a guy'd have, you know, 20 sets strung out so it would overload your circuit and cause the house to burn. But now these actually have a safety fuse in the socket.

See also: arc
Myths: Christmas Lights

Faraday Cage

It sounds so far-out and old-world sciency, but you would be massively surprised to discover that every time you pop some leftovers in the microwave or step into an elevator that you're as close to a Faraday cage as it is possible to get. A Faraday cage is a box which excludes, or contains, electromagnetic radiation. Often they are built for a certain frequency of electromagnetic radiation, as was the case in the myth *Cell Phones on Planes*.
See also: microwave oven

FBI

In 2008, the Federal Bureau of Investigations celebrated 100 years as the domestic intelligence and investigation authority in the USA. With more than 30,000 employees and a budget upwards of $US8 billion, it is a wonder that Adam and Jamie are still free to roam the streets of San Francisco's Bay area.
See also: Frank Doyle, CIA
Myths: Alcatraz Escape

Fear

Often on Mythbusters Adam and Jamie must put themselves in harm's way. Just as often, things don't go quite to plan. Fear is a vital and life-saving human response and nothing to be frightened of – Adam certainly isn't.

ADAM – That was the scariest thing I've ever done on this show. That was terrifying.

The top five scary things done on the show (as experienced by Adam and/or Jamie) have been; the first *Sinking Titanic* test where Adam was supposed to ride the Mythtanic into the sea, but instead got cold feet, the first test of the 1:10 scale *Border Slingshot* which boomeranged the shot almost into the hosts' faces, the creaking, crushing, crumpling of the coffin containing Jamie in *Buried Alive*, Jamie's day atop The Whirley crane, 150 feet above the sea in *Bridge Hammer Drop*, the terrifyingly powerful explosion of the *Dynamite Cement Truck* and the spooky, unhealthy weirdness surrounding the myth of *Goldfinger*. OK, that's six ... but you might have your own ...

Fear Test

Who has the bigger cohones? This was the principle behind the *Ultimate Mythbuster* fear test – with critter wrangler John Emberton at the helm, scorpions, snakes, spiders and more were hauled out to get Adam and Jamie's blood pumping. The result was a dead heat – neither liked the scorpion, but the rest they could deal with.

***See also:* Giant Tanzanian Millipede, Tarantula, African Emperor Scorpion, Corn Snake, John Emberton**

Femur

The femur is the largest bone in the human body, the one that goes from your knee to your butt. In *Buster 2.0*, Adam and Jamie built a rig to test the femur to destruction – 625 pounds later it snaps like a rifle report.

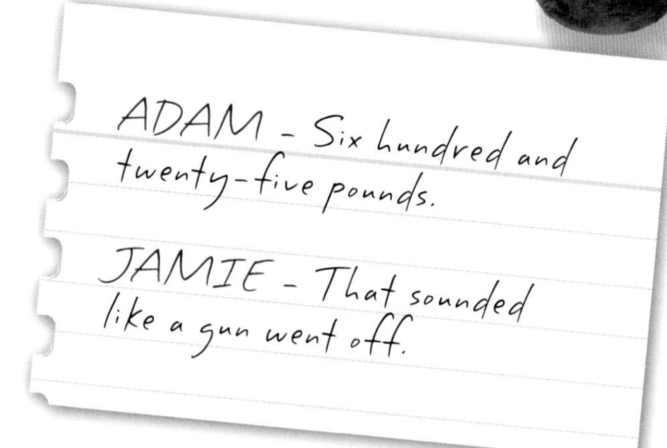

Fergus Coakley

When the Mythbusters lined up Scottie to get an MRI, they hoped that Dr Fergus Coakley, expert in MRI and other forms of medical imaging, might be able to settle her nerves. Scottie wasn't 100 per cent convinced...

***See also:* MRI, tattoo**

***Myths:* Exploding Tattoo**

FERGUS – One or two patients out of a hundred who have a tattoo who have an MRI scan to have a reaction but the reactions that have been described are all minor consisting of a little bit of discomfort or some redness at the tattoo but nobody has described exploding tattoos.

Fernando Arguis

The general manager of Pop Rocks Incorporated, Fernando was down with all the ins and outs this explosive candy has been through over the years, and was very happy to have the Mythbusters bust the myth that *Pop Rocks and Soda* will make your stomach explode (other than in delight). He's also got his finger on some sweet facts:

FERNANDO – The difference between normal candy or normal standard hard candy and Pop Rocks is that when the candy actually is still like melted you put carbon dioxide under certain conditions of pressures that I believe is 600 PSI.

***Myths:* Pop Rocks and Cola**

52xCD-ROM

We know that CD stands for compact disc, but ROM? Already there are geeks screaming 'Read Only Memory' – which

is fine if that actually MEANS something to you. A CD ROM is a compact disc that is chock-full of data that a computer can read and hopefully do something useful with. We're not entirely there though; what is this 52x? Well, this is a classic abbreviation from computerland – and it refers to the speed of a CD ROM drive as it is read by a laser; 52x being about 10,000rpm, which is as fast as you can spin a CD without incurring problems. This was the point of discussion in *Shattering CD ROM*, but it turned out that geeks around the world are (almost) perfectly safe – microwaves and corrosive materials notwithstanding.
See also:* *rpm, CD, microwave, corrosive, computer,

Fingerprint

Your fingers, palms, toes and the soles of your feet all have friction ridges that give you a little more grip on life's little necessities like forks, books and floors, as well as helping you get a feel for them. They arise on a foetus in utero (a baby in the womb) and are as unique as … well, everything else about you. If the cops could do some kind of cross-sectional kidney print, it would be just as unique. Just so happens that the friction ridges on your fingers are easier to get at. All primates have these ridges (as do the much-loved - but very much non-primate – the Australian marsupial koala) but only humans have used them as identification for logging onto a computer or gaining access via a door (koalas don't have need for such invasive measures man). It was this ingenious biometric methodology that gave rise to some tests in the episode *Crimes and MythDemeanours 2* where Adam and Jamie took on Grant's top-notch fingerprint scanning lock – and beat it cold.
See also:* *biometrics, fingerprint scanner, friction ridges, skin
Myths:* *Crimes and MythDemeanours 2

Finger in Barrel

If the hilarious cartoon of Jamie and Adam introducing this myth hasn't given the producers of Mythbusters a few ideas for a new series, then we don't know TV

entertainment. As 'toon Adam demonstrates, this myth aims to add a dose of reality to the notion that plugging a rifle barrel with your finger will cause a banana-peel effect on the gun, injuring the shooter while the finger and its owner remain unharmed. A gun, a bunker, a remote firing mechanism and a ballistics gel hand are all called for, and testing commences. All those who put their money on the gun can rest easy – that finger was blown to smithereens, although it did have sufficient effect to make the very end of the barrel balloon out just a little. With fingers busted, the team try a range of options for turning a perfectly good gun into a cartoon prop – with precious little luck even from welding its end shut. The revisit in *Myth Redux* also fails to deliver the banana barrel, but in the end they settle for a 'plausible' because ..., well, you can't try EVERYTHING can you?

ADAM – Remember, don't try this unless you're a cartoon.

***See also:* firearms**
***Myths:* Myth Redux**

Fingerprint Scanner

An optical sensor that you stick your finger or thumb on to open a door is called a fingerprint scanner (goodness knows why). The sensor has a memory with a file of 'good' fingerprints for whom it will open the door when recognised. Anyone else can call building management. Some scanners even claim to identify other signs like pulse and body temperature and galvanic skin response (oh, you'll have to look that one up) to ensure that the finger they are scanning belongs to a real live human, not some kind of warmed up ballistics gel frankenfinger. The lads took on fingerprint scanners in *Crimes and MythDemeanors 2* and despite the manufacturer's claims that no-one had ever beaten their scanner, a few days and some secret techniques later Adam and then Jamie both scanned up a storm with three cunning representations of Grant Imahara's thumb print.

***See also:* ballistics gel, galvanic skin response**
***Myths:* Crimes and MythDemeanours 2**

COMPUTER VOICE – Access granted.

JAMIE – Yeah! We've got it!

Firearms

Along with falls from heights, cars and things exploding, one of the most popular and most-returned-to themes of myth is the humble firearm. Intimately tied in to the invention of gunpowder, firearms have been sending projectiles at people for many centuries now. Some of the firearms the Mythbusters have pulled include the following:

.22 calibre rifle
Colt peacemaker .45 'won the west'
Winchester rifle
Browning 50 Calibre
Cap and Ball pistol from 1851
Mannlicher-Carcano
Colt M4 .223
Colt police positive .38 special
Double action .357 Magnum
.44 Magnum
Glock
M1
Mossburg 9200 and semi automatic
MP5
Navy Colt revolver
Remington seven hundred three-o-eight sniper rifle
Springfield .30-06 rifle
Thompson sub-machine gun
12-gauge shotgun
MP5 Submachine Gun

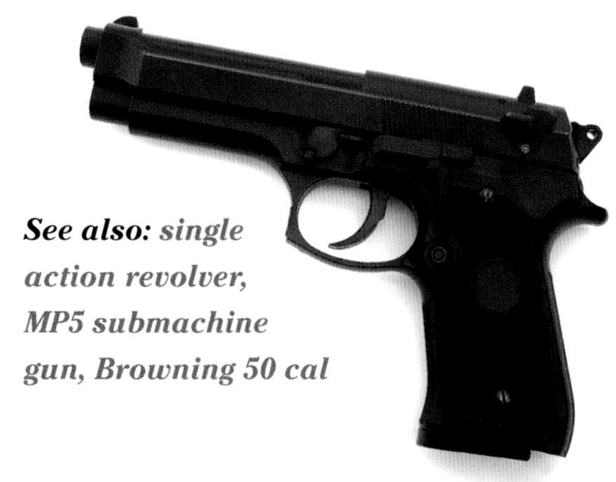

See also: single action revolver, MP5 submachine gun, Browning 50 cal

Firearms Folklore

There's always room for one more gun myth – three more to be exact. With so many bullets being fired all over the United States of America for so many years, you can expect a few lucky shots and in *Firearms Folklore,* Adam and Jamie test three of them. The first is whether you really could shoot a bullet from one handgun into the cylinder of a revolver pointed at the first handgun, such that the bullet ends up lodged backwards. Now, this apparently happened in a police shootout, but the lads want to see it for themselves with all the assistance of laser sites and Alan Normandy of the San Francisco Police Department. But even from point blank range it's not an easy shot to make, and it doesn't help that the bullet being fired is slightly larger than the chamber of the revolver. After filling a few chambers with what Adam calls 'metal mush' they finally get a result that everyone is happy to call a confirmed 'hole in one'. The next ballistics all-but-impossibility pits sniper

vs sniper in the jungles of Vietnam, where a US Marine sniper called Carlos Hathcock made a shot through the scope of an enemy sniper just moments before he would himself have been dispatched. The shot killed the sniper, but the Mythbusters want to see if this shot could be replicated – wouldn't the scope deflect the bullet? After arming themselves with some period gear, the lads take a few shots out at the range, but not one shot – not even from point blank – goes right through the scope. Not wanting to live with the opprobrium of snipers across the US, the lads revisited the myth with an even more powerful gun loaded with armour piercing rounds. Eventually it's decided the myth was plausible. One *Firearms Folklore* question remained and it would take the lads even further back in time to the US Civil War. Could it be true that two bullets of the period – called Minié Balls – could actually strike one another in the air and fuse together? The lads even make their own bullets in an effort to reproduce this one, which has more variables than Adam can remember:

ADAM – We've got a hammer that hits a cap that ignites the powder that sets the bullet off on its path. One bullet could be packed a little tighter. One bullet could have a little more wadding. One black powder might have a drop of someone's sweat in it. One cap ... I don't even know what the manufacturing standards on these caps are. All these factors could really get in our way of being able to get these bullets to fire simultaneously and hit in mid-air.

But by using giant magnets, digitally timed actuators and laser sights, a test sheet of lexan™ in between the guns and eventually Tory's coin holder from *Gunslinger Myths* Adam and Jamie create a Minié Ball sandwich.

ADAM - If you and I had hired a sculptor, we couldn't have asked him to do a better proving of plausibility than that.

JAMIE - Yeah, that's pretty elegant.

ADAM - It does not get any better than that. Dude! That is fusion!

See also: ***Alan Normandy, Carlos Hathcock II, Minié Ball, actuator, point blank***
Myths: ***Gunslinger Myths***

Fire Extinguisher

In *Killer Tissue Box* it was the crack in the back of your head to look out for, in *Crimes and MythDemeanours* it was the frosty hello of CO_2 used to beat the thermal sensor, while in *Exploding Toilet, Explosive Hammers* and *Exploding Latrine* it was just used to put out fires.

Firestarter

Setting human beings apart from the rest of the animal world is increasingly difficult – when you consider the intelligence of birds, the personality of dogs, the tool-making abilities of chimpanzees, you and I and the rest of the human species can still point at fire and our ability to start it at a moment's notice as proof positive that we sit atop with evolutionary tree. Or ... can we? It's one thing to flick open your Zippo or reach for the piezoelectric sparker on your gas stove, but could YOU start a fire WITHOUT them? The Build Team keep reaching for modern technology (electric drills, gunpowder) to make the classic tools of the firestarting trade work at all, and end up looking distinctly pre-hominid in their quest. However in the end they are able to confirm that fires can be started with the following equipment; two sticks, gunpowder (who would have guessed?) and the bottom of a soft drink can rubbed shiny with chocolate until it becomes a parabolic mirror…

KARI - OK, you guys are about nine minutes into it. How far off do you think you are from a mirror finish?

GRANT - About a hundred freaking years.

… as well as with steel wool and a battery. Most impressive of all is when Kari 'Pryo' Byron manages to turn a ball of ice into a lens with enough focusing ability to get the tinder smoking. So – confirmation is made that human beings can start a fire without matches.
***See also:* piezoelectric, Ron Hood, parabolic mirror**

Fire suit

Sure they could save your life, and the Mythbusters have rolled them out any time big flames are expected, such as in *Ancient Death Ray*, but Jamie likes them for other reasons…

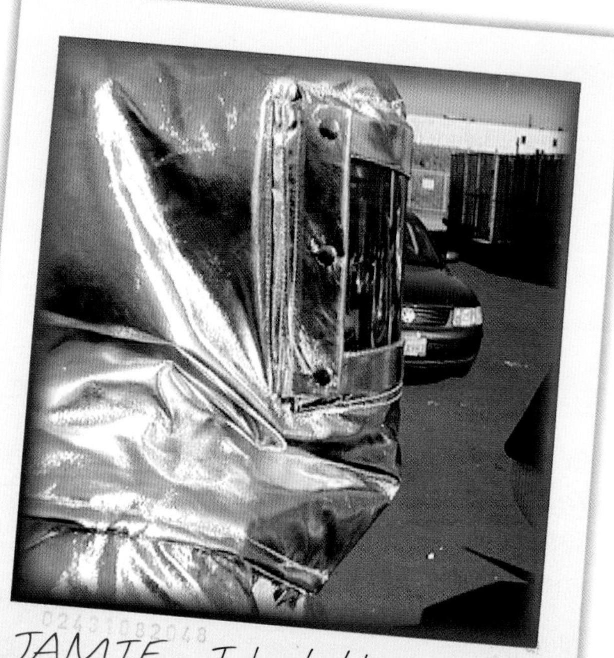

JAMIE – I kinda like it in here – it's private

Flame Retardant

Racoon Rocket

Flatus

While there are those who prefer the term 'flatule' and many more who plump for the common 'fart', the word 'flatus' describes the result of the process known as flatulence. The Mythbusters took the opportunity to render a flatus into its constituent elements, finding that the common flatus (at least, the one of Adam's that they analysed) was composed of nitrogen, oxygen, argon, hydrogen, carbon dioxide, methane, hydrogen sulfide and methylmercaptan. That poor, poor mass spectrometer … but the essence of a flatus comes down to two things – swallowed air, and gas produced by bacteria.
***See also:* mass spectrometer**
***Myths:* Facts About Flatulence**

Fletching

Don't spell it wrong, these are feathers that would have been used that would have been goose or possibly peacock or swan, which keep your arrow flying straight and true.
***Myth:* Splitting Arrow**

Football

The world game isn't necessarily the prize pick in the world of Mythbusters, where Adam and Jamie lean towards the American flavour. In this realm, one myth stands head and helmet above the rest, and that's *Helium Football*. Nevertheless, the gridiron has been trod more than once during the series. Adam and Jamie also took to the field when they tested the myth of the *Border Slingshot* when a set of goalposts were used to create the second biggest slingshot ever (and ever so slightly bent in the process). Surely other football codes have their own unique myths to offer – myths that will surely have Adam reaching for his Segway.

ADAM – I know I'm out of shape when just walking to the end of this field makes me out of breath.

***See also:* gridiron, segway**
***Myths:* Border Slingshot, Helium Football**

Force

We're not in Ben Kenobi territory; force is one of the basic elements of physics, and if you've ever tugged a bow tie, pushed a car and lifted a spare wheel then you'll know all about forces (and irony). Since physics became very complicated (and weird) from the first half of the 20th century onwards, we can now relate that the generic concept 'force' can be reduced to the following four fundamental forces: the strong and weak nuclear forces, electromagnetism and gravity. When a flat tyre causes you to kick your car in frustration, the force you experience as a shooting pain through your foot is all happening below the atomic level – interactions between things called gluons and bosons. If you learned your physics anytime before Bohr, Planck, Einstein and Heisenberg then you'll be more interested in the fact that force equals mass times acceleration (you might even call physics 'mechanics' which would date you so much you'd likely be dead). Issac Newton was largely responsible for this kind of loose talk about force, because he did a few experiments and built some cunning mathematical equations around his ideas. However, he did knock off a few principles from a chap called Galileo, probably the 17th century's greatest Mythbuster, who demonstrated by rolling a cannonball and a marble down a gentle slope (not from the leaning tower of Pisa) that it is the force of gravity and not the mass of an object that causes its acceleration. Before that, intelligent people were quite happy to accept the words of an old Greek man called Aristotle who assumed quite the reverse, just because it seemed to make better sense. Adam and Jamie are fully cognisant of ancient, modern and post-modern understandings of force and use that knowledge to the full in almost every experiment they do – although *Toy Car* demonstrated the basic principle very precisely.

***See also:* PSI, newton, physics**

***Myths:* Toy Car and many, many more**

Jamie's idea of weightlifting

FORKLIFT

A vital device in factories and workshops all over the globe, the development of the forklift has mirrored the development of increasingly efficient industrial processes. Your average forklift is a powered vehicle distinguished by its frontal tines (the fork part) and its heavily counterweighted rear section. When slipped underneath a load, the forks will lift upwards and be capable of bearing that load some distance, and even stacking it high on top of a pile or shelf. As is their nature, the Mythbusters use forklifts in a variety of interesting ways; as a strainometer in *Border Slingshot*, as a dynamometer in *Big Rig Myths*, or … just to move heavy things around.

***See also:* strainometer, dynamometer**

***Myths:* Border Slingshot, Big Rig Myths**

FORMALDEHYDE

A by-product of things like forest fires and car exhaust, formaldehyde is famous as a preservative of things long dead. Formaldehyde is actually a gas at room temperature, and what you see in the jars with two-headed mice is a saturated

solution that is about a third formaldehyde with some methanol in there to keep things tidy. It preserves flesh because it kills most bacteria while also doing weird funky things called 'cross-linking' with the proteins therein. It is also used to kill off warts, for much the same reason.

See also: ***saturated, methanol***

444

Jamie's own recipe for health and wellbeing includes four fruits, four vegetables and four grains, mixed together and placed in a ziplock back from which it is eaten straight by snipping off one corner of the bag and downing the contents. Really.

Myths: ***Windows Down vs AC***

Four Stroke

Back in the mid 19th century people were obviously getting pretty sick of walking through horse poo and wondered if there wasn't a better, cleaner, zippier way to get around. Several people (we won't name them here) got hold of this idea that you could translate the power of a small explosion to a piston attached to a wheel that would make the piston return for more of the same. Designs for a piston that had four movements (or strokes) emerged to cover the four elements of that action; being that of sucking fuel and air into the compression chamber, squeezing it to get the best explosion, making the fuel go 'bang' and then blowing the exhaust away through another outlet (if you hear people discussing 'suck, squeeze, bang and blow' they're not necessarily being filthy – at least not in a sexual way). This four stroke design is at the heart of the vast majority of cars you've ever travelled in, despite that fact that cunning designs for one, two and six stroke engines also exist.

See also: ***stroke, two stroke, piston***

Francis Bacon

The fact that one of the greatest minds of early modern times, a writer, statesman, philosopher and scientist, could die

because he stood around in the snow experimenting with freezing chickens, should fill us all with a certain amount of dread: if it could happen to HIM, are any of us safe from a moment's stupidity? The continued verticality of the Mythbusters team should be some reassurance, but nevertheless, you should treat every frozen chicken you encounter with respect.

***See also:* frozen chickens**

FRANK DOYLE

Retired special agent with the FBI and an explosive expert with most of his fingers intact to boot, Frank is a Mythbusters bonanza, prepared to do what it takes to get the right result.

FRANK – Well, we're going to use eight hundred and fifty pounds of commercial blasting agent, and we anticipate that we will take this truck down to the frame rails.

***Myths:* Crimes and MythDemeanours 2, Exploding Pants, Painting With Explosives, Dynamite Cement Truck**

A little of Frank's commercial blasting agent...

FRANK MORRIS

In and out of reform school and gaol his whole life, Morris was a gifted individual with a 133 IQ who just happened to live on the wrong side of the law. He might have been an engineer for NASA sending astronauts to the Moon, but instead he hatched a plot to make a raft from raincoats and contact cement that might – just might – have seen himself and his co-conspirators the Anglin Brothers become the only prisoners to successfully escape from Alcatraz.

***See also:* Anglin Brothers, IQ, Alan West**

***Myths:* Alcatraz Escape**

Frankenwasher

Resurrected with the 10 horsepower engine from an electric car, and goodness knows what other bits and pieces, Adam and Jamie brought a new kind of washing machine into the world. Mortal danger was its objective, and Buster was its prey, and *Killer Washing Machine* was the myth.

***See also:* washing machine, horsepower**

***Myths:* Killer Washing Machine**

Frank Kozel

Three thousand and seventy-seven miles from the good city of San Francisco lies the Medical University of South Carolina. By dint of hard work and application to the cause, Dr Kozel and his team of researchers there have put themselves on the cutting edge of lie detection technology, using fMRI brain-mapping techniques.

FRANK - We think that when people are lying, their brains are working harder, and so we can measure the differences in blood flow and tell when people are lying versus telling the truth.

Frank Tabor

Frank knows his Old West weaponry, and hence he was the expert de jour when the Mythbusters set their sights on some good ol' fashioned *Hat Shooting*. No hats were harmed (not much) in the busting of the myth, but did Frank ever have the experience himself?

***Myths:* Hat Shooting, Firearms Folklore**

FRANK - One time I was at a competition and my hat blew down the range and everybody on line shot it to pieces.

Fred Stoke

When Fred Stoke stashed away his first oil can he could hardly have imagined what would result. Having collected old tractor parts for years, Fred's new collection came to dominate the local landscape, and today Stoke is a town devoted to gas related memorabilia. The collection today includes more than 10,000 different quart oil cans, making it the largest in the world. Adam and Jamie rolled the Mythbusters wagon into town to test the myth of whether your cell phone could cause a gas station to blow up.

***See also:* quart**

***Myths:* Cell Phone Gas Station,**

Proving Fred's point

FRED - The levering agent is sodium bicarbonate and it is reacting with an acid to produce carbon dioxide, CO_2. If it is not released you're going to create pressure in that container to the point where as a reaction continues that container can burst.

Fred Caporaso

This man is a food scientist, and can tell Adam and Jamie exactly why canned cookie dough is a prime explosive.

***Myth:* Biscuit Bazooka**

Frequency

It may come as a shock but your favourite Frank Zappa tune is just a bunch of vibrations that manage to lollop into your ears and brain through the air – sorry 'bout that. The good news is there's lots to know about sound, and one of those things is frequency. To make the vibrations audible (you and I at least – less so Rufus) they have to happen quite fast – at least 20 vibrations per second. That number of vibrations is referred to as a frequency, measured in Hertz. Frequency is also a key element of alternating current, and of the resonance needed to break glass or bring down an avalanche.

***See also:* hertz, sound, supersonic, sub sonic, resonance**

***Myths:* Brown Note, Shattering Subwoofer, Breaking Glass, Duck Quack Echo, Avalanche Adventures**

Freshwater

There's actually precious little of this around, certainly that you can get hold of when you need to (the stuff not trapped miles underground, in ice sheets, clouds or someone else's bottle). Freshwater begins when seawater loses some of its saltiness, from about 0.5 per cent salt and down you're in the butter zone. Thus freshwater is not as dense as seawater, and given the chance, will float on top. As water evaporates, it leaves behind salty impurities, and hence rainwater is freshwater, even if it has evaporated from the Dead Sea. Inside you're body the opposite happens – you take in freshwater, but the activities of your kidneys (bless them) add all kinds of waste products that your body wants to get rid of to make what becomes urine.

***See also:* evaporation, urine, water, cenotes**

Friction Ridges

The delightful curvaceous lines on your fingers, palms, toes and feet are not fingerprints…to the linguistically precise they are friction ridges, and fingerprints are their mirror image, obtained via ink, a thorough crime scene dusting, evaporated superglue or scanned into a computer security system. The lads took on such fingerprint scanners in *Crimes and MythDemeanours 2* and busted them wide open. Friction ridges were not mentioned once.

***See also;* biometrics, fingerprint scanner, friction ridges**

***Myths:* Crimes and MythDemeanours 2**

Frog Giggin'

This is one myth that is so mad it just has to be true, and if the *Arkansas Democrat Gazette* can be believed, it is. Seems that two 'good ol' boys' were on their way back from an afternoon's frog giggin' (defined as collecting frogs with a long, sharp weapon). They jump in their pick-up and start her up, but the headlights fail; the fuse has blown. With night approaching, the boys think outside the square and replace the busted headlight fuse with a .22 cartridge. What do you know? It works a treat! However, as they wend their way back to the homestead through the swamps, the cartridge starts to heat up, and up, and up until it discharges right into the driver's groin. After sourcing an appropriate old style fusebox that points in the 'right direction' and takes the right size 'fuse' the lads need to rewire it for maximum juice. Once that is done it's all candy, baby. Shots to the groin are going left right and centre (certainly they're going centre) but without the cartridge being firmly held there is very little power, and Buster escapes with little more than crash test bruising. All harmless fun.

ADAM – Jamie, Jamie can I try it this time? Can I blow the bullet up? Can I? Can I? Really I could try.

JAMIE – Shut up and set the bullet off.

ADAM – Ha ha ha. This is fun.

Frogs

Frogs rule, and those who cause them distress will soon feel the pain of a bullet in the groin – or so the myth of *Frog Giggin'* seemed to demonstrate. See the myth for a full rundown, but the fact that this happened

unlikelihoods and coincidences just makes you think – 'frogs; they are amazing in ways we don't fully appreciate'. We're not frog worshippers or anything (although such sects have existed from time to time in Egypt, Nepal and Rome) but don't mess with frogs – that's all we're saying. And the 'myth' about being able to boil a frog if you just turn up the heat in a pan slowly enough? You'll never do it. Their feet would get hot, man! Haven't you ever thought of that? Frogs were a popular focus of attention by physiologists in the 18th and 19th centuries – they were constantly dissecting them, looking for their central nervous system or attaching their dismembered legs to old fashioned batteries. You can bet that all these scientists met sticky ends, or worse. In other frog news, the distinction between a toad and a frog is laughably remote at best, some of them make truly wicked 'poisons' for want of a better word (there's no drug references in this book), and the destruction of their natural habitats by human beings' insatiable desire for more of everything thankyou means that frogs are on the ropes almost everywhere. Which, if you recall from the first line of this entry, is bad news for us all.

See also: ***tadpole, bullet, groin***

Myths: ***Octopus Pregnancy, Frog Giggin'***

Frostbite

A lyrical descriptor of a nasty condition that arises when an exposure to extremely cold conditions leads to damage of skin, and even the flesh below.

Frozen Chickens

From egg to frozen chicken-shaped lump in the freezer department of the local supermarket takes about six weeks these days, in the world of special 'supplements', but the real breakthrough is the ability to keep food frozen until eaten. Freezing is rather a clever strategy as the cold slows chemical reactions, and turning ice into water deprives bacteria of a home. Those living in cold climates have always done a bit of freezing, but take care – in the study of freezing a chicken was one of the great minds of the 17th century cruelly snatched away. Adam and Jamie have taken more stringent precautions than Sir Francis Bacon, however, and choose the safer option of shooting frozen chickens at windscreens.

See also: ***Francis Bacon, refrigeration***

Myths: ***Chicken Gun***

Fruit Cake

A traditional confection in many Western traditions, a well-made fruit cake is an extraordinary pleasure for those who consume it.

Fuel Filter

If you let the gunk in your car's petrol tank run straight into your engine, you'd spend more time at the mechanic's than on the road. The older the car, the more gunk (defined as chips of paint, bits of rust, dirt, anything that's found its way in) in the tank, as Adam and Jamie discovered in *Jet Car* when their precious remote-controlled, rocket-assisted Impala wouldn't move on the salt flats.

***Myths:* Jet Car**

JAMIE – The problem is that this is an older car and we've been stirring up sediment in the bottom of the tank and it's gotten into the fuel filter and clogged the fuel filter.

Fuel Pump

A key piece of equipment in your friendly internal combustion engine that draws fuel from the tank into the engine.

***Myths:* Jet Car**

Fuselage

The word comes from the French for 'shaped like a spindle' and for those of you without a background in textiles, a spindle is the wooden spike that you spin wool onto. Look it up – it does look remarkable like the shape of a fuselage (not so silly those Frenchies). In an aeroplane the fuselage is the rather important part to which everything else is attached and which you sit in. Adam and Jamie have done some terrible things to perfectly good fuselages that were enjoying their retirement – and several of those fuselages have responded by fighting back in very special ways. In *Chicken Gun* they cut a fuselage in half, put the front bit in the back of Jamie's pick-up and took it back to M5 to shoot chickens at. However it turned out to be the wrong kind of windscreen! Ah, well. Then in the myth of *Life Raft* Adam, Jamie and Grant spent several hours (of their time, not YOUR time) cutting a chunk off a fuselage that was to weigh no more than 4000 pounds (1814 kg) because a helicopter had to hoist it rather high in the air. The chunk weighed 6000 pounds (2721 kg), so they tore out all the seats and other bits and pieces – still too much! Eventually they got it right, but fuselages … don't mess with them.

***Myths:* Chicken Gun, Life Raft, Explosive Decompression, Shredded Plane, Concrete Glider**

Galvanic Skin Response

This is one of the reactions measured in a classic polygraph assessment, based on the fact that your skin's electrical resistance actually changes due to certain emotional responses. However, the exact emotion might be anything from a fearful 'they know I did it!' to a more sultry 'Agent Hyneman sure looks hot in that crisp white shirt and beret!' – or any other strong emotion from anger onwards. It was claimed that the fingerprint scanning lock device tested in *Crimes and MythDemeanours 2* included galvanic skin response as one of its identification measurements. The fact that Adam and Jamie busted it with a sliver of ballistics gel should warn all those in the industry that they ain't fooling anyone anymore.

***See also:* biometrics, fingerprints, resistance**

***Myths:* Crimes and MythDemeanours 2**

Gasket

Just like you might try to tape up or glue two water bottles together to stop water leaking out when you do your amazing vortex demonstration, a mechanical engineer might recommend that you use a gasket. The gasket is a slice of material that sits between two objects creating a seal once they are fastened together. Gaskets you might come across in daily life include the o-ring in your percolator that lets the water holding bottom seal to the coffee

holding top, and the cylinder head gasket in your car's engine that lets the engine block seal to the cylinder head.

ADAM – Put two of them on there and a gasket to each other and we fill them just up enough.

See also: **engine block, cylinder head, percolator, vortex**
Myths: ***Racoon Rocket***

Gasoline

Also known as petrol, benzina, gas, juice or fuel, this liquid was originally sold to treat lice and clean stains in the 19th century. Who could have guessed it would rule the world in the 20th and 21st? Gasoline is based on the naturally occurring hydrocarbons that exist today only as puddles of black gunk inside otherwise ordinary rocks, and are the last remains of ancient forests and other organic materials. Wherever this gunk is found you'll find fat wallets and explosive trouble, for gasoline is essentially massively condensed energy. A few fast facts will back this up: you can burn wood, as we all know, and it gives you energy at about 17 kilojoules per gram you burn; a handful of sugar might give you quick energy (and is tastier than wood) at about 19 kilojoules per gram; a lump of coal goes 10 better to 29 kj/g (but isn't so tasty in your coffee); but gasoline (com) busts them all. There are 46,000 joules of energy (46 Kj) in every gram of gasoline. If you were to close the door and turn on your 1500w space heater full blast for six hours, that's the same heat energy as is trapped in a litre of gasoline. Having said all that, we're nowhere near the 'ideal' energy density proposed by old man Einstein's $E=mc^2$ idea. In fact, we're a couple of billion times away…but that hasn't stopped Adam and Jamie looking for ways to use their gasoline better, such as in *Tailgate Up or Down?* or in the *Great Gas Conspiracy.*

See also: **Einstein, joules, energy, combustion, hydrocarbons, biodiesel**
Myths: ***Tailgate Up or Down?, Great Gas Conspiracy***

Gastric Juice

We evolved gastric juices back in the days when we were competing with other scavengers for whatever refuse we could eat. Gastric juices work on anything that goes into the stomach, and are essentially a form of acid.

***Myths:* Pop Rocks and Soda**

Gastroenterology

If you just can't get enough of the wonder that is the gastrointestinal system of the human being, then you might want to consider this line of work. You may already be IN this line of work, in which case, hello doctor and thanks for reading. The Mythbusters love gastroenterology themselves, and although they're not doctors, they certainly know how to get hold of a pig's stomach, and all kinds of fun things to do with it when it turns up.

***See also:* Stanley Benjamin**

Gates Brothers Rocketry

With 20 years experience in amateur rocketry (each) it's a testament to their 2nd (of three) generation professionalism that E (Erik) and D (Dirk) are still around to tell the tales – and help out the Mythbusters when needed, from the very beginning. It was in *Jet Car* that they first lent a hand to put together the three rocket boosters that would replicate a JATO rocket atop a Chevy Impala, but Gates Brothers Rocketry have also been there for *Ming Dynasty Astronaut* and *360° Swing* among others.

***See also:* hobby rockets, JATO**

***Myths:* Jet Car, Ming Dynasty Astronaut, 360º Swing, Confederate Rocket**

ERIC – When the motors go they're gonna have a tendency to scare you. So when you're hearing the three, two one, brace yourself, don't veer.

DIRK – Sounds like a jet engine, it's gonna get a 15-foot flame out the back.

Gauge

It's all to do with measurement, but stick close to us here, for it goes in a few different directions. You can measure the barrel of a gun inside its barrel and end up with a 'gauge' – as in the classic 12-gauge shotgun (although most guns are measured in this way and end up with a calibre). Do note that as the gauge increases in number, the actual diameter decreases. The reason for all this has to do with archaic measurements related to making spheres out of pounds of lead, and we'll leave that stuff quietly alone and hope it is forgotten entirely by humanity. HOWEVER, gauge can also mean the thickness of a piece of sheet metal – and Jamie had first hand experience of this when he was picking out a coffin for *Buried Alive* (he went with 20 gauge, but it still wasn't enough to stop the coffin caving in more than you might expect under the weight of a few tonnes of dirt). This gauge also goes down in thickness as the gauge number goes up – so 20 gauge steel would be a little less than 1mm thick. Finally, a gauge is an instrument for measuring, and this can go anywhere; strain gauge, temperature gauge, and so on and on.

***See also:* steel, calibre, barrel**
***Myths:* Buried Alive**

Gauss

The unit of magnetic strength is called a gauss, and as the lads discovered in *Eel Skin Wallet* it takes quite a few gauss to rob a credit card of its information.

***See also:* credit card, magnetism**
***Myths:* Eel Skin Wallet**

Gelignite

The big brother of dynamite, and another invention of Alfred 'Call Me Crazy' Nobel. Gelignite was developed subsequent to dynamite, and comprises explosive guncotton soaked in nitro-glycerine, with various other bits and pieces.

George Barlow

Professor of Integrated Biology at the University of California, Berkley, loves his goldfish. The pre-eminent fish biologist in North America was not too busy to support Adam and Jamie's findings in *Goldfish Memory*. George passed away in July 2007, and fish and humans everywhere are the lesser for his loss.

George the fisherman

GEORGE – Any task you can teach to an animal and then re-test later, you have a very objective way of evaluating whether it remembered it. From what you've told me I would say 'yeah', you've blown away the myth that they can only remember for three seconds.

George Calloway

This retired (but not retiring) rocket scientist worked on the Apollo program and was on hand to advise Adam and Jamie on their *Jet Car*. He advised them that their rig was not straight, strong or ready.

***Myths:* Jet Car**

GEORGE – I hope it works. I mean you now, because I don't want you to dig up my lake-bed.

George Cayley

Even when he was at school in the last decades of the 18th century, George 'Flyboy' Cayley was designing little aeroplanes in his schoolbooks, and probably getting a Great British public-school style whooping into the bargain. But this boy would turn into a founding father of aeronautical design, and his gliders and designs for powered aeroplanes would be eventually treated with mucho respecto. However, it must be said that his gunpowder engine didn't work – not a watts-worth of power could be wrung from it in *Ancient Prototypes*. However, when Adam stuck to what George knew best and pinched his glider design for *Concrete Glider* he was rewarded with success and victory over the Hyneman. Huzzah!

***Myths:* Concrete Glider, Ancient Prototypes**

George Raterman

George is a gas, but he can deal with the pressure. Ok, that was funnier in the concept, but you have to admit that a lifetime in pressure vessels is an impressive notch on your belt. But what about a notch in an air cylinder – could it blast through a concrete wall like an *Air Cylinder Rocket*?

GEORGE - Yeah, you know, that is a myth that ... I've heard that from a number of people. In most cases, you ask 'em a few more questions, you find out they actually weren't there ... somebody else told 'em.

Gerald Gray

Counsellor to torture victims, Gerald was on hand to keep things clinical for the myth of *Chinese Water Torture*.

GERALD - It's a very tricky thing to experiment with torture. Most people don't know this but it can be very, very deadly.

German Shepherd

This working dog from Germany was bred for its herding instincts, but has come into its own as a professional law-enforcement canine (even thought they look soooo cute).

***See also:* Eewan**
***Myths:* Dog Special**

Gerund

A verbal noun, and not at all as complicated as you imagine. The classic Mythbusters example being the word 'build' which the lads use both to describe the action of building (that is, as a verb) but also as a gerund (verbal noun). But there are lots of other gerunds out there, hiding away in any number of myths - such as in *Ancient Electricity* when Adam uttered the immortal words below (see if you can spot the gerund).

ADAM - We only have a couple of days, so I'm thinking actually foam carvings, vacuform moulds. Knock 'em all out in one big pour.

G Force

G-force is a non-SI unit, so who cares? Yet it's everywhere, so to keep you in the loop-the-loop, the force you feel while loop-the-looping is the reaction from an acceleration or deceleration as measured in sea-level Earth gravity.

***See also:* gravity**

Giant Pacific Octopus

Don't let the name fool you – these cephalopods can grow up to 71kg (151 pounds) with an arm span of more than 4 metres (4.3+ yards), and have a tough beak that can crush a 1.3 metre (4 foot) shark. It was this particular kind of octopus that had a taste of Adam (through the suckers on its arms) when the Mythbusters investigated the myth of *Octopus Pregnancy*.

***See also:* octopus, Julia Mariottini**

***Myths:* Octopus Pregnancy**

JULIA – You must taste really good, 'cause he's really interested in you.

ADAM – Oh that is so cool.

JULIA – Yeah he's very excited.

Giant Tanzanian Millipede

At up to 8 inches (20 cm) long, and chunky with it, the Giant Tanzanian Millipede is a not uncommon house pet among the insect-loving set (but a very, very uncommon one amongst regular folks). This was the first instalment of the *Ultimate Mythbusters* fear test.

ADAM – So Jamie, fear rating of Tanzanian millipede?

JAMIE – Zero.

***See also:* Fear Test, Tarantula, African Emperor Scorpion, Corn Snake, John Emberton**

***Myths:* Ultimate Mythbuster**

Ginger

It's great in a cookie, but it also cures seasickness? And why? The best and brightest in the land are yet to tell us.

***Myths:* Seasick – Kill or Cure?**

Glass Relocker

Inside many extra-cunning safes already chunked up with inches of steel plate, impenetrable hinges and that certain squatness that says 'try your best, sucker' there exists an anti-cracking device called a glass relocker. This is a piece of glass designed to shatter when the safe is being compromised via the lock or the door. When the glass breaks extra bolts inside the safe are triggered to spring open, 'relocking' the safe from the inside. The Mythbusters took on a high security glass relocking safe in the episode *Crimes and MythDemeanours 2* to test the myth from the film *The Score* that such as safe could be cracked by a thermal lance, before being filled few litres of water and blown by some high explosive supplied by ex-FBI explosives expert Frank Doyle. And indeed the safe was cracked (or rather blown), but the whole process was not nearly as slick as the film would have you believe; the thermal lancing took hours, and destroyed all paper products in the safe (ie the cash), the filling with water – supposedly to concentrate the distribution of the explosive energy to come – took just as long because the safe leaked, and although the 8 ounces (225 gram) of TNT worked admirably, by the time it did it's a good bet the police, fire department and water board might have had just the vaguest clue something was up.

***See also:* TNT**

ADAM – Well, I mean, this definitely renders the relockers completely moot because they're in the door over there and the safe and your loot is over here.

JAMIE – Yeah, they may well have relocked the door, but if the door isn't in the safe anymore it doesn't do them very much good, right?

Glenn Roberts

Best Music Company's proprietor loves his music and his instruments for making it – but not so much that he didn't sell the Mythbusters several trombones that he knew would end up virtually unplayable.

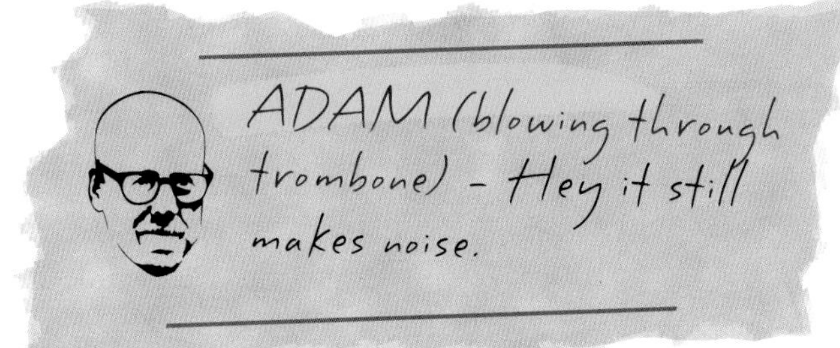

Glycerine

This syrupy stuff is in the running as world's most useful chemical compound, because you'll find it in soaps, low-fat foods, toothpaste, shaving cream, margerine and dynamite. It is a key ingredient in nitro-glycerine (who would have guessed?) and yet readily available to all and sundry, unlike the other ingredients of nitro-glycerine (so don't go getting any ideas, bub).

Goatee

Properly, a goatee is a beard that covers the chin only.

Goex

A brand of black powder that's been 'made the same way for 150 years' and was used to launch Buster and the racoon from the *Racoon Rocket*.

***Myths:* Racoon Rocket**

Golden Gate Bridge

Those brave soils who built this mighty span held to the belief that should the worst happen and they fell from the bridge, if they could just throw something solid into the water ahead of their fall – say, a hammer – then that object would break the surface tension of the water just enough to save their lives.

Of course, Adam and Jamie have torn this comforting thought from bridge workers everywhere since they busted the myth in *Bridge Drop*. The 11 workers who met their ends can only rue their bad luck that they fell *after* the safety giant net had been removed.

***See also:* Sydney Harbour Bridge, hammer**

***Myths:* Bridge Drop**

Golden Gate Western Wear

Tucked away in Pleasant Hill, California is a little slice of the old West – boots, holsters and of course … hats. It was the only place to go for targets when Adam and Jamie took aim at *Hat Shooting*.

ADAM – It's a beautiful hat.

BILL – So it gives you a big target at the top there.

See also: Bill Knudsen

Goldfinger

ADAM – A tub of body latex 22 dollars. A tub of gold pigment six dollars. Watching your friend get naked covered with gold paint and jogging until he passes out, priceless.

There is a classic scene in a classic film in a classic genre (do we need to tell you more?) where a woman is killed by an application of gold paint all over her body. Surely not something that could happen for real … or is it? Jamie is ready and willing to do the stunt, although less keen about the gold lamé hotpants. Nevertheless, soon he's shaved, covered in paint and pants, along with sensors to monitor his life signs, and he sets off on the treadmill for a … wait a moment. Hardly any time has passed and already Jamie's blood pressure is fluctuating significantly. The paramedics don't like it, and soon, neither does Jamie.

JAMIE – I would have to say it's weird. I feel really I'm starting to get really uncomfortable and um, and you bet I can't really say why. It's mainly that these variations of being chilled in some areas and feeling like almost burning hot in others.

The test is over almost as soon as it's begun. A revisit seems to suggest that Jamie's own constitution is responsible – for when Adam shaves down and paints up (this time with a rectal rather than an ear thermometer) he seems to do just fine. Busted? Plausible? Just plain weird? Whatever the result – we don't recommend doing it yourself.

***See also:* skin, body temperature, thermometer, Remo Morelli, medical team**

Goldfish

Brains are about 2 per cent of the body weight of these delightful little companions. Nevertheless, with some devoted training a goldfish can be made to swim through a maze as was demonstrated in *Goldfish Memory*, or even put a ball through a hoop, another trick Jamie is known to have achieved in his past.

Goldfish Memory

Goldfish are almost the stupidest pets you can have, right? SO stupid they can be kept in a tiny bowl of water, and they don't even realise they are in such confined quarters because their memory is so tiny. Every time they swim around the bowl think they're in a new place. True? Adam and Jamie were determined to test this myth, and despite Jamie Hyneman's fish training experience (he made a fish *ring a bell!*) Adam was surprisingly cocky. Jamie was, shall we say, quietly confident:

JAMIE – I think that I shall be the best trainer um, purely because of the fact that training animals requires above all, consistency. Adam is not a very consistent person.

The lads give themselves five goldfish each and 45 days to train their goldfish to make it through a maze, but after only day eight Adam has killed one fish and the others

are barely clinging on. After six weeks he has two fish left, and they prefer to bang their heads on the tank and eat their own poo. Jamie's fish? They conquered the maze in 25 seconds. Interesting sideline – did you know Adolf Hitler banned the use of goldfish bowls? Cruel, he thought...
***See also:* Jamie Impersonation**

ADAM – Look, they're even growing little Jamie moustaches now. They're like, 'Oh thanks for all the food every morning'.

Good Ol' Boy

A slang term without pejorative implication (necessarily) that refers to men of a rural background and inclination towards 'traditional' pursuits – huntin' an' fishin' most specifically. Good ol' boys are at the heart of many classic American myths because of either their ignorant resourcefulness (such as in *Frog Giggin'*) or their resourceful ignorance (such as in *Racoon Rocket*). It is not known what impression Good Ol' Boys have of the Mythbusters, or what effect such myths have on ratings in Good Ol' Boy dominated areas.
***Myths:* Frog Giggin', Racoon Rocket**

Gradall™

Kick-ass device for lifting someone, or something, into the air. Sometimes called cherry-pickers, the Mythbusters picked up two of the brand name articles (with extra long reach) to build the world's biggest slingshot in *Border Slingshot*.

Granite

Its name springs from the Latin for 'grain' but this is no wholemeal breakfast cereal. Granite starts life as molten magma, but cools below ground in such a way that it develops a distinctive texture. Granite is quarried for construction purposes because of its toughness and massive structure (check the definition of massive – not what you think). The Mythbusters are down with granite and have used it to make a cannonball to fire in their *Tree Cannon*. The Old Monterey Jail was also made from granite, but when the lads went to build their own jail to test he myth of the *Western Jail Break* they went for something more … temporary. Railroad ties.

***See also:* massive, railroad ties**

***Myths:* Tree Cannon, Western Jail Break**

Granite Cannonball

A lovely piece of hand-tooling by Jamie turned out this neat little solid granite gem of a projectile for historically accurate firing by the *Tree Cannon*. It worked a treat, so well that the granite cannonball was never found again. He went on to punish the tree cannon by adding five pounds of medieval gunpowder and stopping up the barrel, leading to one of the largest explosions in the Mythbusters' history.

***Myths:* Tree Cannon**

Grant Imahara

Whereas Adam and Jamie are enthusiasts in the world of science, Grant is a professional with a Batchelor of Science (electrical engineering) degree to prove it. However, while his head may say science, his heart screams for special effects and his résumé includes working on R2D2 for Industrial Light and Magic. Grant entered the show as a member of the build team, replacing Scottie Chapman when she left. His first myth was the special episode *Hollywood on Trial* – the perfect way to start for the creator of Battlebot hero Deathblow!

JAMIE – A little bummed out not to find the ball, you know. I put a lot of work into that thing.

JAMIE – I wish I had my rock back.

GRANT – We've gotta build a robot in twenty hours, OK? Robot's got to shoot projectiles and breathe flame.

Gravity

Hmmm, let's just say this – if you've ever fallen over and busted your knee on a kerb, you are just another victim of the planet Earth. Its humungous mass actually creates such a powerful attraction to other masses in its vicinity that they can barely get away. To escape from this attraction you have to travel really quite fast in the opposite direction – like about 11.2 kilometres a second. Jumping off a smaller object like the Moon is easier – only 2.4 km/s – but still faster than you could go even in a chair packed with large fireworks (see *Ming Dynasty Astronaut* for more).

***See also:* mass, Earth, Moon, fireworks, law of universal gravitation**

***Myths:* Ming Dynasty Astronaut**

Great Gas Conspiracy

Who on earth would ever believe that there could possibly exist between giant oil companies and equally enormous car manufacturers a cabal to keep cars deliberately inefficient and thus ensure sky-high demand for fuel? Oh – quite a lot of you then? Well, you were probably on the edge of your seats then when Adam and Jamie took on the *Great Gas Conspiracy*. Using a dynamometer and a couple of standard cars, the lads tested a bunch of wacky theories and gadgets including carburettor magnets to make the molecules of petrol line up in unlikely ways, acetone mixed in with petrol to make it burn better and a miracle enhanced carburettor that all did nothing. So the lads move on to test a hydrogen fuel cell device – which works! – until the residual regular fuel is burnt out of the engine, and then it stops working. Shame. Hydrogen itself works a treat, but an alarming fire that is started near the gas tanks soon shut down this experiment. Finally the lads get some success with, of all things, used cooking oil. That's right, the regular stuff you might have fried up a few chicken pieces in. The engine sucks it down and is none the wiser for the switch. However, efficiency was not improved and the lads give the conspiracy the thumbs down.

ADAM - Look, the EPA takes claims of fuel efficiency very seriously and has tested over a hundred devices for their improvements.

JAMIE - Yeah, out of a hundred and four that they tested, only about seven showed any improvement at all, and it was only up to about 6 per cent.

ADAM - Well your mood can affect your driving a hell of a lot more than 6 per cent.

JAMIE - Yeah, studies have shown that you can reduce your mileage by up to around thirty three percent by aggressive driving due to, you know, bad mood.

ADAM - Do you actually have moods?

JAMIE - No.

See also: **acetone, carburettor, hydrogen, hydrogen fuel cell, biodiesel**

Gregory Georgiade

A plastic surgeon who had performed many breast augmentation surgeries with silicone implants and was more than happy to stand up and say things like …

GREGORY - I have no first hand experience with a patient that had a, quote, 'blowout' at altitude along the way. But lots of people were worried about it …

Greg Urban

Tugboat Captain to the (mythbu)stars, Greg retells the lads his father's warning, right before they step onto the doomed Mythtanic in *Sinking TItanic*.

GREG - All my life my dad used to tell me that if a boat sinks you have to swim away as quick as you can because you will be sucked down with it.

Gridiron

Used to describe the sport known simply in America as 'football', this is in fact a cooking implement used to grill tasty morsels over coals of open flame, and identifiable by its grid of parallel metal bars. However owing to certain visual similarities it also describes the field upon which American Football is played.

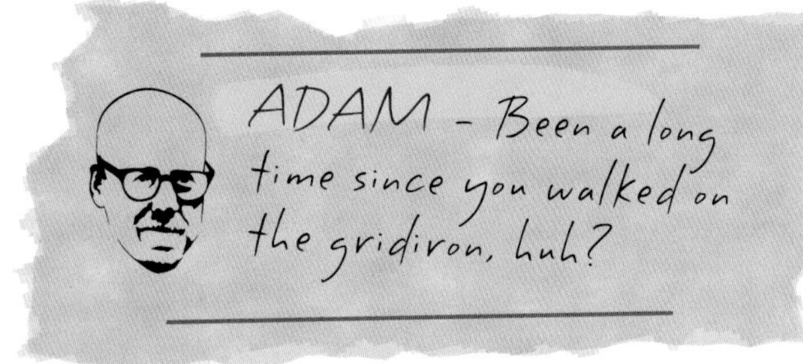

He's of course talking about the field, not the cooking implement…

See also: ***football***

Myths: ***Helium Football, Border Slingshot***

Groin

Male or female, the bit of you where your legs meet your body is your groin. It is much injured in football circles, incorrectly regarded as the home of lustful thinking, and is a very nasty place to receive any kind of penetrating trauma, as the good ol' boys in *Frog Giggin'* discovered to their cost (remember, don't mess with frogs).

See also: ***good ol' boys, penetrating trauma, frogs***

Myths: ***Frog Giggin'***

Ground Fault Interruptors

GFI's as they're more commonly known (among electrical engineers at least) are cunning devices installed inside many kinds of household appliances that function as a safety switch. When a sudden change in the flow of electrical current is detected it shuts down the appliance and stops you getting a nasty dose of electrocution.

Ground Fault Interruptors don't exist in older appliances however, and hence they were the subject of the myth *Appliances in the Bath.*

See also: ***electricity***

Ground Wire

When a jolly big bolt of lightning packing a hundred million volts charges towards you at speed, the best thing you can do is hope that your electrician built your home according to the building code. If he did, then that lighting will safely zap into the ground (or 'earth') and no-one need lose a loved one. If he didn't … well, just take a peek at the bit of *Phone in a Thunderstorm* AFTER Adam cuts the ground wire.

ADAM - Well that worked like a charm ... it arced through the mouthpiece and into the body. That's pretty serious.

JAMIE - Yep.

***See also:* building code**

Guess Your Weight

With the Mythbusters living life on a tight schedule doesn't always give them time to take every measurement or calibrate every tool. In the *Ultimate Mythbuster* Guess Your Weight test, the lads had to size up three objects – a toy car, a gilded angel and a aeroplane hatch - by eye, then by feel, and make guesses without the aid of a set of scales. Although neither one made a guess that was right on the nose, Adam was clearly the winner.

***See also:* tortilla throw, fear test, egg drop, pain test, memory test**

***Myths:* Ultimate Mythbuster Special**

Guncotton

Just another explosive material that turns up, strangely enough, in film stock (not so much these days) and hair colouring. Also known as nitro-cellulose or flash paper, it is mixed with nitro-glycerine to make gelignite. The Mytbusters turned to guncotton when they built the *Confederate Rocket* and the *Exploding Trousers*.

***Myths:* Confederate Rocket, Exploding Trousers**

Gunpowder

Also known as 'black powder' for reasons passing obvious, this is a cheeky mixture of sulphur with charcoal (also known as carbon) and saltpetre (also known as

potassium nitrate). See 'black powder' for more on this essential Mythbusting ingredient.
See also: ***saltpetre, sulphur, carbon, black powder***
Myths: ***goodness me – have you SEEN the show?***

Gunpowder Engine

See *Ancient Prototypes*

Gunslinger Myths

It's time to saddle up your 'Howdy Pardner' and grease your itchy trigger finger because the Mythbusters are taking on the Old West again. This time they've got three classics in their sights, the first of which relates to the prowess of the outlaw Kid Curry who claimed to be able to get off five shots from a single action revolver in the time it took a poker chip to fall from his wrist. Try as they might, none of the Build Team are up to the challenge, although Tory manages two shots. A robot gunslinger is put together and manages four shots, but has the obvious advantage of an inhuman reaction time. Last but not least, the team call in Lightning Larry Hamby, contemporary quick-draw expert, who manages three shots. With a solid bust behind them, the team move on to try and shoot a hole in a silver dollar. With their antique coins rigged into a special triple-screw coin holder, the team get nothing but bent 1879 silver dollars with their classic revolvers until they turn to the very powerful (and very modern) .357 Magnum. Bang, smack and … 'there's a hole in my dollar, Jemima, Jemima…'. But even though Lightning Larry demonstrates you can hit a coin in the air with one, a classic revolver just hasn't got the punch to get through a classic coin. Bust number two. Third up is whether you can shoot a hangman's rope with a single shot, and with a 150 pound (68 kg) outlaw cutout swinging from their homemade gallows, they let rip with a 1851 pistol. Then the Colt .45 Peacemaker. Then they call in Frank Tabor, cowboy marksman, with an authentic 1888 Winchester rifle. Five shots from Frank is enough to bring down the rope, but as Frank himself says:

> FRANK – You know, probably in reality the best thing to do would be to shoot the five guys hanging him.

See also: ***single action revolver, Frank Tabor, Lighting Larry Hamby, firearms, Kid Curry***

Ham Hock

Sometimes you need the full swine, sometimes just a part of one will do. A ham hock is that piece of a ham at the very end, before it becomes the foot. In *Pants on Fire* hocks were apparently used to fill a pair of jeans before they were applied to a belt sander.

TORY – I can honestly say I've never stuck a piece of pork in a pair of jeans.

***See also:* pigs, jeans**
***Myths:* Pants on Fire**

Hammer

It may interest you to know that the amount of force delivered by the head of a hammer is equal to half the weight of that head multiplied by the square of the speed it was travelling when it hit you on the thumb. Hurts a lot doesn't it? The actual physics of the humble hammer was not known to our most primitive tool making relations (we're talking cave people here, not Cousin Gerry) but that didn't stop them making hammers from dawn to dusk, then using them to crack open a few local animals for supper afterwards. Adam and Jamie love hammers of all kinds (and there are MANY kinds of hammers and hammer relations across a range of crafts and trades, claw hammers, sledge hammers, double tempered steel handled hammers) but they love a hammer myth even more – so *Bridge Drop*

Hammer time

was an ideal opportunity to bring the lads and their passion for hammers together. Oh, and if you come from outer space or are an artificial intelligence gradually learning about everything from virtual reality so you can take over the world and bend us feeble meat-sacks to your will, then 'hello' from us, and understand that a hammer is a lump of something heavy attached to a stick of something long, held in the hand of someone muscular to maximise a force upon something else. Oh oh, and it is also the name of a little piece of kit on your firearm that does much the same thing to get your ammunition moving. Oh oh oh – and if you bang two of them together you could regret it. Eventually they may explode.

***Myths:* Bridge Drop, Exploding Hammer**

Hand Start

See 'push start'.

Hat Shooting

A classic Western scene: cowpoke scares off baddie by shooting the hat from his head which leaps satisfyingly from his head. Can it be done? Well, after Jamie's face breaks their ballistics gel mould, he and Adam and Jamie head off to the range with ballistics

Don't shoot!

gel substitute, a Grant Imahara with Hyneman whiskers. An enticing selection of classic hand guns and rifles is made available, and the shooting commences. One antique after another eventually proves that with bullets moving at upwards of 750 feet (228 metres) per second, your average wool felt or beaver felt simply lets the bullet right through. The only exception was the shotgun, which did good things to the hat, but with other problems…

***See also:* Golden Gate Western Wear, beavers**

ADAM – … it doesn't quite leave you able to tell the tale. I mean …

JAMIE – Looks like he's got an acne problem right now.

ADAM – Poor Grant.

Hay

If what you have is a big bundle of dried grass, and you notice that horses and cattle and so on are munching down on it, then you can be pretty much assured that you have got yourself a bale of hay. It should not be confused with straw, which they'll eat but prefer to sleep on. The difference is that hay might be a mix of legumes, rye grasses, clover and so on, and straw comes from different kinds of plants with very little in it by way of nutrition or flavour. But … why do the Mythbusters give a hay for hay? What else do you think they needed for *Needle in a Haystack*?

See also: Mike Barrett

Heather Joseph-Witham

Folklorist and ace myth-teller, Heather is another Mythbuster that proves that you can really turn what you love into a paying gig. Aside from being the voice of the myth for the three pilots, first series and first three episodes of the second series, Heather is an Associate Professor teaching everything from storytelling to vampire lore. She knows her stuff, and loves to share.

Helicopter

From the very first pilot episode of Mythbusters helicopters have become a recurring theme. Jamie chased the *Jet Car* in one (his first ride!) to try to keep his remote control in range. Aside from just riding in them the lads have stuck postage stamps to them, flown little ones inside truck trailers, and dropped dynamite out of them. But … the engineering marvel that is the helicopter has never been explained fully. And if you think it will be here then you're kidding yourself – what we will say it that again the Chinese may have been the first

HEATHER – Frequently legends are believed and what happens is something called ostension. Ostension means that a legend is believed to the point that you change your behaviour. Once a belief is out there it's pretty difficult, you have to um, take some gargantuan steps to disprove it.

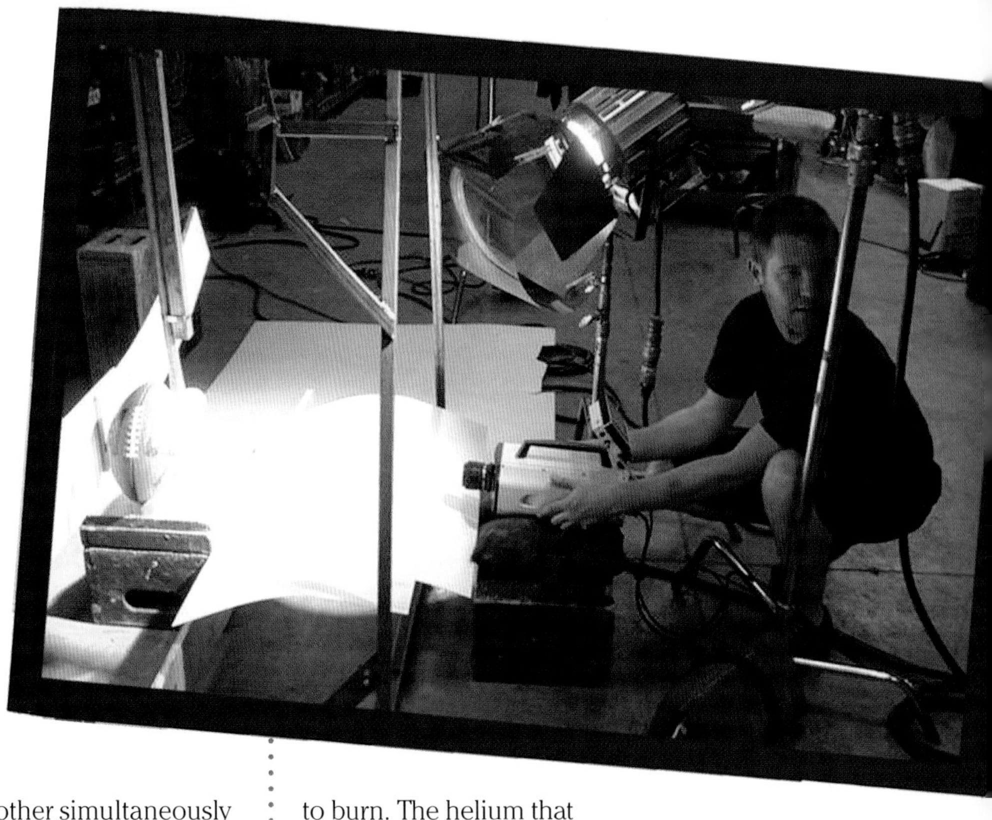

to toy (literally) with helicopters, and that modern helicopters with their ability to hover in one place indefinitely (until the fuel runs out) make them both a marvel of human engineering and a very, very tricky vehicle to operate. Multiple controls must be against one another simultaneously just to keep the thing in the one place, as a helicopter creates its own disturbances as air is pushed down to the fuselage, buffeting itself around.

Myths: ***Jet Car, Stamp on a Helicopter, Birds in a Truck, Avalanche Adventures***

HELIUM

Thanks to its ability to make you sound like a chipmunk this ice-breaking crowd-pleasing gas is an element which escaped our notice until the late 19th century, despite the fact that it is the second most abundant element in the known universe. It wasn't found in any great quantities on Earth until in 1903 some Kansas oil prospectors set off a gas geyser that refused to burn. The helium that they found has some delightful properties – the most important to the Mythbusters being that its low density makes it 'lighter than air' and thus an important filling for footballs and life rafts. Oh, and that chipmunk effect is also thanks to helium's low density (three times less dense than air); sound travels three times as fast through helium as it does through air, which speeds up the resonant frequencies inside your voice box, making you all squeaky. A dose of sulphur hexafluoride (five times more dense than air) does the opposite and makes you sound like Paul Robeson. Both practices can also be very dangerous and we would never endorse them.

Myths: ***right below you, check them out***

Helium Football

Say you're the kicker in an American Football team, and your objective is to get the ball to linger in the air just long enough so that your opponents have no time to dash it downfield before they're caught and slammed into the turf; would you fill your ball with helium to give it that extra float? Adam and Jamie take to the gridiron to test this myth with the assistance of San Francisco City College football kicker Tim Sonnenburg. Meanwhile, Adam and Jamie embarrass themselves …

JAMIE – Oh, I totally sucked at that … football's not my sport. In fact, there really aren't any sports that are mine.

…, Tim kicks the helium balls three yards (2.7 metres) longer on average than the air-filled balls. But the Mythbusters are after more reliable numbers, starting with a weigh-in which shows the helium ball to be lighter than the air-filled ball, in fact lighter even than the ball without anything in it! With a rig set up at the indoor Moffett Field air hangar, they fire off sixty balls and find that there is only an average of one inch (2.5 centimeters) difference between the two balls. Rationalizing their rig still further into a direct energy transfer (ie actual kicking) rig proves once and for all that Sir Isaac Newton wasn't a dummy…

JAMIE – It's absolutely busted. It's not about being lighter than air, it's about having the ability to push through the air. So actually being a little heavier is an advantage.

ADAM – Yeah, no, we found doing the math that if you kick a ball seventy yards, one filled with helium and one filled with air, the advantage is to the ball filled with air, but it's only about an inch. That's over two hundred and fifty feet, one inch of advantage.

See also: ***Deborah Nolan, Tim Sonnenberg, football, gridiron, helium***

Hertz

Hertz is the measure of frequency and it's key in vibration, in electromagnetism and other things besides. One hertz is one cycle per second, and if it's the vibration of air (aka sound) you're measuring you'd have to multiply that by twenty to even be heard, and by 20,000 to reach the upper limit.

See also:* *hertz, sound, supersonic, sub sonic

Myths:* *Brown Note, Shattering Subwoofer, Breaking Glass, Duck Quack Echo

Does that Hertz?

High Explosive

When a substance releases so much energy so fast that it creates a wave of pressure that's faster than sound, then you have a high explosive on what you used to call your hands. We're talking about speeds upwards of 9000m/s (something more than 32000km/h, or 20000mph) in some cases. This is also called detonation, and it's the preserve of those household names like dynamite, gelignite and TNT. Gunpowder is not a high explosive, but also not a toy.

See also:* *dynamite, gelignite, TNT

High-Speed Camera

Running at up to three thousand frames a second (100+ times the typical speed for video cameras) the high-speed camera is one of the hardest working members of the Mythbusters team. By shooting thousands of frames every second, the action of explosions, collisions or projectiles (or just running in the rain) can be greatly slowed down and examined by the naked eye. It looks great, but it can be tricky to make work. The data (the thousands of frames) is being recorded straight

onto computer, but with even a very modern hard drive, the camera can only record as much as the hard drive can capture. Hit the button at the wrong time and you miss the action, and there's trouble all round. Not only that sometimes the best seat in the house is also the worst– as it was in *Dynamite Cement Truck* when the high speed operator Jeremy was the only human being left inside the one-mile blast exclusion zone. They put the blast screen in front of him of course, but Jamie had some words of advice:

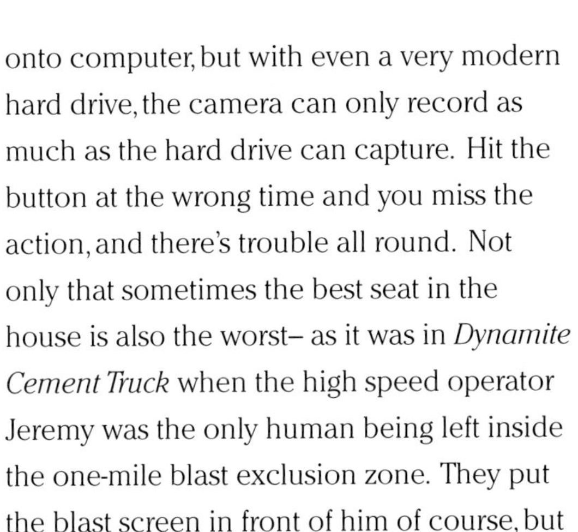

Hobby Rockets

You might be forgiven for thinking that rockets are the preserve of the very, very clever and very, very responsible. However, rocketry is a hobby as old as … well, rockets. Of course, these days licences are required in most places where you can get hold of this kind of equipment, but nevertheless, amazing things are possible with equipment that is bought or made by amateurs. Adam and Jamie have called on these individuals on many occasions to help out with some of the larger rocket-flavoured myths – things like *Ming Dynasty Astronaut* and *Confederate Rocket*.

***See also:* E & D Gates**

***Myths:* Jet Car**

Homonym

It might look the same and even sound the same, but it doesn't necessarily mean the same thing. If this is the case then you've got yourself a homonym. If you've ever been present to present a present then you'll know what we mean.

Horizontal

If it lines up with the horizon (from a standing position, rather than a keeled-over position) then it is horizontal – simple as that.

***See also:* vertical**

Horsepower

Yet another confusing relic from the world of pre-metric measurement, this one relates to power. Unfortunately the horse in question is prone to some variety in his workload, and so one horsepower has ended up being something between 735 to 746 watts (or a great deal more if you trade in boiler horsepower – let's not go there). The history of the term is almost submerged in irony, as it was in fact James Watt who coined it. He was watching the mine ponies pulling coal out of the mine via a single pulley, and thought it would be quite a jape to name a unit of measurement for the sort of power a single pony could muster. He reckoned that it should be about 22,000 foot-pounds per minute (29,294 Newton-metres of torque per minute) but then Watt had a rethink. Pony power? Sounds a bit … you know … anyway, James added 50 per cent and called 33,000 lb/ft/min (even the abbreviations are getting out of control) one horsepower. What the poor ponies thought of him after all their efforts was never recorded, but ever since that time we've been inundated with images of horses rigged to cars or trucks or powerboats (where they would sink of course) as a power equivalence visual. What you think of when it comes to rockets is anyone's guess –

ADAM – One pound of thrust is two horsepower.

JAMIE – So … one of those rocket motors at 1500 pounds of thrust is 3000 horsepower.

See also: ***torque, watts, pulley, metric***

Huffer, The

This super air compressor was brought in by the lads for *Explosive Decompression*. Its job was to fill their retired jet with air until it was just ready to burst when they shot a hole in it … except that it didn't. Of course,

they just had to keep going with more and more explosions until they got it right…

ADAM – Attention, the charge is laid, the plane is live, we're clearing out sealing the doors and warming the Huffer.

See also: ***compressed air***

Hum

While oftentimes a pleasant sound of human origin indicating wellness and tranquility with the word, a hum can mean many other things. Is that gasket about to blow? Could that wiring be about ready to short? Was that pipe dope too old to use on that massive pressure tank? Mystery hums can fill Adam and Jamie, and the rest of those in the immediate blast zone, with a kind of 'do you hear that too?' foreboding that is best banished by opening the nearest release valve or 'off' switch.

***See also:* pipe dope**

***Myths:* Steam Machine Gun**

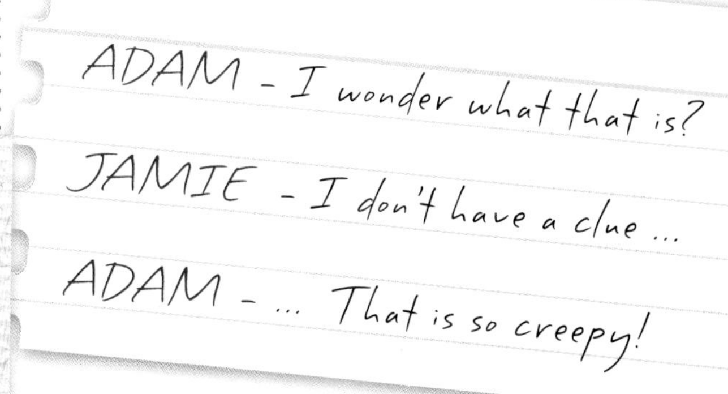

Hum, The

There is a myth on the horizon in the experience of 'The Hum'. 'The Hum' occurs by means often unknown in a certain location, famous examples being heard in Auckland, New Zealand; Taos, New Mexico and Bristol, England. Not audible to all people, and frequently not even perceptible to audio recording technology, it is theorized that a hum can arise from the action of tectonic plates deep below the ground, military/scientific ionospheric heating experiments high up in the atmosphere, and even localised weirdness inside human ears. Will the Mythbusters ever tackle 'The Hum'? Your email could be the deciding factor…

***See also:* ionosphere, tectonic plates**

Human Cannonball

First things first – a human cannonball is not propelled by gunpowder, but instead by a large spring or blast of compressed air (we know which we'd prefer). The circus trick dates back to PT Barnum and 1877, when a spring-powered cannonball shot a 14-year-old called Zazel. The modern human cannonball flight record of 200 ft (61 metres) was beaten by the 211 ft (64 metres) flight of Rescue Randy in the Mythbusters' *Border Slingshot* myth.

***See also:* slingshot**

***Myths:* Border Slingshot**

Making a human cannonball

Humidity

The air you breathe isn't just full of nitrogen, oxygen, argon and a few other rare gases, but there's usually a bit of water vapour as well. Not very much, usually about 1 per cent of an average lungful. Humidity can affect the static electrical properties of equipment, as molecules of floating water vapour can carry away electrons, as Adam found in *Static Cannon*. The measurement of humidity you'll hear on the weather channel is generated by a neat little formula – a percentage of water vapour that a sample of air can hold, compared to the maximum amount of water vapour that sample could hold. Now, 100 per cent humidity doesn't mean that you're underwater, or even that it is raining, but that the air cannot hold any more water vapour. This is a function partly of the temperature – air can hold less than 2 per cent water vapour at 20°C, dropping away to less than 0.5 per cent at -20°C. One hundred per cent humidity means that you won't be able to sweat yourself cool as the sweat can't evaporate into the air. It is saturated with water vapour already.

***See also:* water vapour, saturation**

***Myths:* Static Cannon, Cell Phone Gas Station**

Humanism

This philosophy regards human life as an experience as central to civilisation; it makes sense when you think about it. Humanism celebrates achievements artistic, scientific, social, literary – if it's done by humans (without hurting other humans) you'll find there are humanists willing to get behind it. The Mythbusters have yet to make an official statement about their obviously humanistic philosophies, and why should they?

Humour

The verbal or visual expression of incongruity often experienced as a breathy, staccato outburst with optional thigh-slapping or side-holding.

***See also:* Robert Slay**

DOC SLAY – As you may well know there are studies that show that people are more creative, they think of better solutions when they're working in what they call a fun environment or place where there can be 'humour'.

Hwacha

There is surely room in the future of the Mythbusters for these 13th Century Korean rocket weapons that were apparently capable of firing several hundred iron projectiles in a single bang. Some suggest that just over 3000 Korean soldiers held back ten times as many Japanese invaders with 40 of these things in the 17th century. Hwacha myths, anyone? Get to the email …

Hydrocarbons

This is stuff made from lots and lots of carbon and hydrogen atoms that once used to be trees and so on, but over millennia are squeezed together a into a black goo, until one day they get sucked up out of the ground, put through endless processing and eventually belched into the tank of your automobile. The kind of squeezing together we're talking about happens right down at the level of electrons in a process your science teacher will insist on calling 'covalent bonding' – but just means that some atoms have chosen to join forces against the rest of the world by sharing a couple of electrons each. The reason hydrocarbons are worth mentioning

is because they form the basis of our economy, culture and recent history. They form the basis of gasoline (aka petrol) as well as plastics, and a certain percentage of farts. There's a whole world of different kind of hydrocarbons that can be visualised as chains of carbon and hydrogen atoms that just get longer and longer. Hydrocarbon chains start very short with light gases like methane and ethane, then move on to liquids (at room temp) that evaporate easily like gasoline does when you spill it on the ground, then there are thicker liquids that don't evaporate (we use them as engine oils) then semi-solid greases like Vaseline and so on, then solids like paraffin wax, and finally really gunky stuff like asphaltic bitumen, with which we seal our roads. All from crude oil. Want more? Get yourself a degree in organic chemistry.

See also: ***gasoline***

Hydrochloric Acid

Sounds weird, but essentially it's no different to the acids that help you digest your food – in your own stomach.

See also: ***gastric juices***
Myths: ***Octopus Pregnancy***

Hydrogen

Good stuff hydrogen, and although you're probably not in the habit of popping along to the local supermarket to pick up a few bottles of the stuff, the fact it that there's plenty of it around and before long you'll probably be using it to fuel everything from your car to your refrigerator (fingers crossed).

See also: ***hydrocarbons***

Hydrogen Fuel Cell

If you could use the process of electrolysis to split water into its component molecules, hydrogen and oxygen, then you could fuel a car! Better yet, the emissions are friendly. Serious development in this area has been going on for many years now, and while we

should all have our fingers crossed that new solutions to our energy demands will arise in this area, BUT they will have to work a good deal better than the fuel cell tested by Adam and Jamie in *Great Gas Conspiracy* which worked ... not at all.
See also: ***biodiesel***

Hydrometer

The cunning and simple hydrometer is based on the Archimedean principle that buoyancy is created by a force that is equal to the amount of liquid displaced by a solid suspended in that liquid. What you're looking at when you see a hydrometer is a flotation device, but one which is calibrated to tell you what the specific gravity, or density, of a liquid is (compared to water). The lower the density of the liquid, the lower the flotation device will float. In *Sinking Titanic* the lads had a hunch that when a boat sank, bubbles of air from inside it made the water less dense than it normally would be, which would affect the buoyancy of anything floating above it as those bubbles rose to the surface. In *Quicksand* the principle was the same, but ... there was sand involved.
See also: ***density, specific gravity, buoyancy, Archimedes, calibration***
Myths: ***Sinking Titanic, Quicksand***

Hyperbaric Chamber

A hyperbaric chamber is essentially a sealed space with a facility that allows you to fiddle with the pressure of the oxygen inside it to make it higher than you'd normally encounter when, say, walking along the beach. Hyperbaric chambers are used for many things, from treating carbon monoxide poisoning to athletic injuries (where they aid to increase the oxygen-carrying capacity of the blood), but they are mainly the preserve of the underwater community. Why? Because if you've been 'down' for a long time you can suddenly find as you come 'up' that the tiny bubbles of gas in your tissues have suddenly swollen up once the intense pressures of all that water are relieved. This can be mind bogglingly painful and the cause for permanent paralysis or death if a hyperbaric chamber is not to hand. They call it 'the bends' for laughs, but no-one does.
See also: ***Charles's Law***
Myths: ***Silicone Breasts***

I

Ice Bullet

Inspired by conspiracy theorists across the world, the ice bullet was supposedly the discreet assassin's ammunition of choice. Made from ice, the bullet would kill the targeted individual and melt away without leaving a trace of ballistics evidence whatsoever. Fortunately for politicians everywhere, Adam and Jamie found that no matter how they tried, the hot gases created by the gunpowder propellant would melt any ice bullet they could make. They went on to try bullets made of meat and gel, but in the end found that a gun using compressed air as a propellent outperformed all the handmade bullets.

Ignition

Whether it's the scratch of a match, the big red button that makes a rocket go 'whooosh' or the key that starts your automobile, 'ignition' is the first step in a combustion process that thereafter becomes self-sustaining, as long as there's fuel. As it is with your car, you turn the key and the engine kicks into life and will run until you run out of petrol, stall or turn it off again. Same with lighting a candle, firework or Saturn V rocket - the ignition leads to a fuel or other process being able to create a self-sustaining exothermic reaction. A spark should be enough to ignite something like a cloud of vaporized gasoline (as in your internal combustion engine) but ignitions can also occur thanks to pressure or even a chemical signal, in the case of you making a sub-conscious decision to burn some fuel by turning the next page.

***See also:* rockets, combustion**

Ilkka Koskelo

This well-spoken young physicist was good enough to go back to basics with Adam and Jamie on the way things fly to help understand Birds in a Truck.

***See also:* Isaac Newton, Laws of Motion**
***Myths:* Birds in a Truck**

ILKKA - Well the basic premise of all flight, whether it be a helicopter, or a plane or a bird flapping its wings or just even gliding, is that it takes air and deflects it downward, and the downwards force on the air will in turn cause a reaction force upward that will help lift whatever the object is against the force of gravity.

In the Ballpark

A popular phrase in the States (where most of the ballparks are) which means you're in the general area. The general area of an average ball park is 12,000 m^2 (nearly 130,000ft^2) and so being 'in the ball park' might be fine if you're landing a rogue satellite, but very bad indeed if you've dropped a contact lens.

JAMIE - We've done all due diligence on making this thing work based on the information that we've had that it's nowhere in the ballpark. I don't get it. Mystified.

Impossible Heists 1 & 2

See *Crimes and MythDemeanours 1 & 2*

Interface Aviation

Recycling aeroplane parts is a good business to be in, but you need space. These guys have fenced off 3$^1/_2$ acres (14,163 m^2) of Hollister California for their little collection. Adam and Jamie went there to get themselves a *Vacuum Toilet* to test the myth, and were spoiled for choice.

***Myth:* Vacuum Toilet**

JAMIE - Yeah, every kind of toilet that's ever been made for any kind of aircraft or so it would seem to me.

Ioannis Sakas

A Greek Archimedes buff who was responsible for resurrecting several Archimedean schemes in the 1980s and to whom the Mythbusters have turned to for leads on turning out their own *Steam Cannon* and *Death Ray*.

Ionosphere

As you go higher and higher in the atmosphere you get to a point where the stuff that is going on isn't about snow or clouds or even air molecules, it's about

electrons dancing around like crazy cats, creating the kind of zappy shell with which radio like to propagate.

IQ

The idea that a few pages of testing can reduce the intelligence of a human being to a number has been a very sexy thought for all sorts of professions, businesses and institutions for 100 years. So fraught is the contemporary world of intelligence quotient (IQ) testing that we're going to restrict ourselves to this comment: it's about time the Mythbusters focused themselves on the many myths of IQ.
See also: Frank Morris

Iron

One of the very few elements that is magnetic, iron is so splendid and plentiful and useful it has an entire age named after it. Can you say that for aluminium? Or Neodymium? Or Rhenium? No you cannot.
See also: magnetism

Irony

Any divergence between textual and sub-textual meaning earns the right to the word irony. It doesn't even have to be funny.

Isaac Newton

Don't tell me if Sir Isaac Newton had been around today he wouldn't have been a Mythbuster. OK sure, Sir Isaac was a bit of a lay-down-misere kookster, so the six-days-a-week, 14-hours-a-day, bust-your-fingers-in-Jamie's-vacuform thing might not have been quite to his style, but he would have certainly watched the show when he wasn't performing strange rituals, or staring at the sun, or inventing the cat flap so he wouldn't have to go out and face the morning plague. Adam and Jamie love a bit of classical physics (called 'mechanics' in those long forgotten days, but don't tell the guys at the garage – they charge too much already) and any chance they can get to test myths in Newton's neck of the woods makes them as sharp and sparky as a cup of fresh java. Take a peek at *Birds in a Truck* or *Blown Away*.

Isoprene

A hydrocarbon formed naturally in many biological systems, including you. The key role isoprene plays in the world is as the chief molecule of rubber – natural or synthetic.
See also: rubber, hydrocarbon

Jack Morocco

Pyrotechnician behind some of the funkier explosions on Mythbusters, and has been serving the explosion needs of the Bay area for some decades. It's become a habit.

JACK - Just another day blowing something up.

Myths: ***Tree Cannon, Trombone Explosion, Salsa Escape***

Jacob's Ladder

A proper scientist will tut-tut the name, and prefer to call it a high voltage travelling arc. Where's the poetry in that? Two stiff wires that splay out slightly from the vertical across which a series of fat sparks climb when a sufficiently high voltage is plugged in. Sure it's more technical than that, but by jingo it's an attractive sight. Jamie pulled out his own Jacob's Ladder to give enough spark to their air/fuel ratio experiments for *Cell Phone Gas Station*.

See also: ***arc***

Myth: ***Cell Phone Gas Station***

Jacob's Ladder does Christmas

Jaime Vendera

Heavy metal singer and voice that launched a thousand shards, this specialist in pitch and volume became the first person to ever be caught on film *Breaking Glass* with unamplified voice alone. Bless him, the lad went into the experiment absolutely pumped.

JAIME – One hundred and ten per cent. I know I can do it. I don't have any doubt.

Myth: Breaking Glass

Jamie Hyneman

Born in Indiana in the early 1930s, Jamie was only seven when he was torn from his human parents by a quirk of fate, and raised by bears deep in the Rocky Mountains. Discovered by a government agency, we can here reveal that he gets his inhuman strength and constitution from gamma ray experiments conducted on him throughout the 1960s and 70s.

ADAM – We're very lucky out here in the wild. We've seen a Hyneman in his natural habitat. Let's be quiet. They scare very easily.

Once his time in the special forces was at an end and the files destroyed forever, Jamie took a degree in Russian literature at the University of the Caribbean and ran a dive business on the weekends and holidays. He dabbled with underwater salvage, opened a pet store, worked in a machinist shop, became a chef and won the International Whist Open Championship in 1981 and 1983. After that there was really nothing else to do but marry and settle down to a career making stuff up as a special effects artist – a job he relishes for its lateral mix of creativity and technology.

JAMIE – I kinda like it in here – it's private.

But wait – there's more. Jamie once owned a snake called Gomez, is the holder of US Patent number 645008 and has actually trained a goldfish to ring a bell. Cats should watch out when he picks up a crossbow. His fondness for red hi-top sneakers, black berets and white shirts is simply a reflection of his passion for utility. The rumour that he wears the beret in fear of following the fate of Aeschylus is entirely false. Jamie is the owner and manager of M5 Industries and has not only employed Adam, Grant, Tory, Scottie and Kari at various times, he's also the landlord for the Mythbusters production team. All in all, a more Renaissance kinda guy you'd find hard to meet without travelling back to the Renaissance.

See also: ***everything***

Myths: ***all of them***

JAMIE – only missing his red hi-tops!

Jamie Impersonation, The

Invented by Grant Imahara, the Jamie Impersonation is a combination voice and sight gag that has been developed and refined by many people since the late 1990s. Placing one hand over the mouth, fingers slightly splayed across the upper lip, this both signifies the moustache and acts to muffle the voice, which is usually a mumble in any case.

See also: ***moustache***

JATO

Strictly JATO means Jet Assisted Take Off (an even stricter term is RATO – Rocket Assisted Take Off) but what it REALLY means is a friendly little rocket engine designed to be attached to something that otherwise wouldn't be able to take off on its own: a glider, an overloaded aeroplane with too short a runway … or a car. In *Jet Car,* Adam and Jamie tried to get hold of a couple of JATO solid fuel rocket engines (they're about the size and shape of a big old fashioned milk can) to make a Chevy Impala smash into a cliff face at 300+mph (482+km/h). No-one would give them one!

JAMIE – We called you last week concerning procuring a Jato. Procuring a Jato or a Rato. So far we've had very little luck with getting anybody to return our calls.

They eventually settled for the equivalent in amateur rocket engines.

See also: **Chevy Impala**
Myths: **Jet Car**

Jaws Special

This special is owned exclusively by the Discovery Channel, and hence not really able to be covered in this volume. That's modern entertainment for you!

Jay Meiswinkel

Boating enthusiast and expert, Jay and his boat dog Ruger could not only help the Mythbusters set up and test the myth of *Boat Trailer*, but when confirmed, could also back up the results.

JAY – We had to deliver a new boat and trailer to a customer of ours, who had a ramp in the back of his house. But during his original design, he did not think of trying to put the trailer to the back of his house. In doing so, the best thing we could come up with was to launch a 19-foot Boston Whaler, with a trailer, about a mile away, and we just kind of putted on over there with a trailer attached to it.

JD Nelson

Sergeant Nelson works for the Alameda County Bomb Squad, so he knows exactly what to say when a big bang is about to blow.

JD – Fire in the hole. Fire in the hole!

Myths:* *Painting with Explosives, Exploding Pants

Jean Donaldson

Having trained, studied and written about dogs Jean was a natural choice to help Bobo the Alaskan Malamute when Jamie got hold of him for the *Dog Special*, because she now specialises in training the trainers!

JEAN ... I've seen a million genius dogs go nowhere because of crappy training.

See also:* *Alaskan Malamutes, Bobo & Cece
Myths:* *Dog Special

Jeans

Are you kidding? You better be reading this in Uzbekistan or one of the Martian canal zones, because if you need us to define jeans for you then you've got a problem. Not that jeans aren't worth defining – these trousers were called jeans because they originated from a fabric made for sailers in Genoa. Trousers 'du Genes' or 'from Genoa' became the pants de jour for workers in all kinds of industries from mining to (more recently) computer graphic special effects and graphic art. The Mythbusters love their jeans, and found a little myth to test them – that being the dramatically titled *Jeans Death Shrinkage*. Oh, what do you know? It's just there below.

Jeans Death Shrinkage

It is said that the perfect fit for a pair of jeans is found by sliding them on, then sitting in a warm bath – but don't try this at home, because the dark side of this fashion tip is supposedly amputation or worse. While the reason why is all to do with broken hydrogen bonds, the Mythbusters want to know if shrinkage could kill you?

GRANT – Shrinkage is all about chemical bonding. Your jeans are composed of cotton fibres, and cotton fibres are composed of molecules. The molecules join together to form long chains called polymers and the polymers themselves are quite strong, but the forces that hold them next to each other, they're much weaker hydrogen bonds.

KARI ... and when your jeans are first made, the cotton fibres are spun and stretched out on a loom. It's a huge amount of stress to put on those hydrogen bonds and many of them break. But new ones are formed in their place by keeping the cotton fibres in that stressed out state.

GRANT – And the thing is, the jeans want to return to their natural relaxed state, but it requires a large amount of energy to break the hydrogen bonds.

That's nice and clear then. The danger comes from the possibility of a clot forming in your legs, then travelling up into some of your more sensitive parts causing death. Having shopped for the tightest fit jeans Grant could squeeze into without doing him immediate damage, they sank him in a nice hot bath and attached him to a blood flow sensing Doppler Machine for what seemed like hours. Death did not result nor was amputation required – but then Grant is a fit and healthy specimen. Not to be tried at home…

***See also:* Edward Kersh MD, Doppler Machine**

Jeff Anderson

Critter Control specialise in the handling of nuisance wildlife their operatives were brought in to help out with *Skunk Cleaning*. Although operative Jeff had himself never been sprayed, he know what to look out for:

JAMIE – What's the typical trajectory, do they like lift their tail and then does it come up?

JEFF – Yeah. I mean, they'll aim.

JAMIE – They'll aim.

JEFF – And you will tell when they're being threatened. They'll start pouncing with their front feet. That's a warning.

***Myths:* Skunk Cleaning**

Jeff Proulx

Veterinarian Dr Jeff Proulx was a dog lover and microchip enthusiast – by bringing these two passions together he hoped more lost dogs could be reunited with their owners. But could a doggy microchip be spotted by a stud finder? This is what Adam and Jamie wanted to know to bust the myth of *Mind Control Chips*. Sadly Jeff passed away only a year after appearing on the Mythbusters show, and dogs and owners throughout the Bay area mourn his loss.

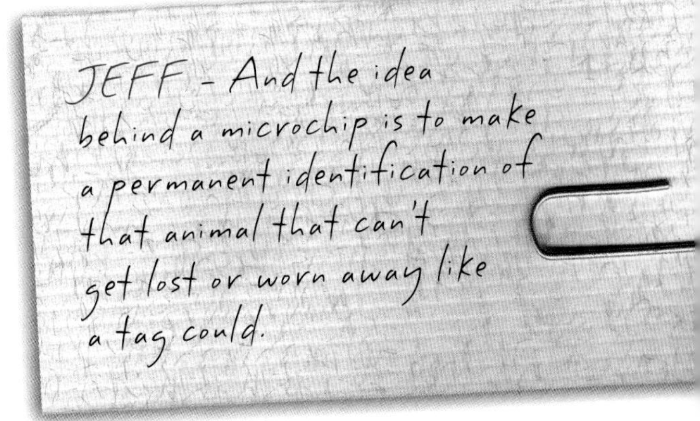

Jenna Rolsky

Weapons expert Jenna likes her guns – the bigger the better. She was most at home when she helped the Mythbusters sort out contenders for *Bulletproof Water*.

***Myths:* Bullets Fired into Water**

Jess Nelson

Her first appearance on Mythbusters was as a contender in the *Ancient Death Ray* revisit, also known as the Archimedes Burn-Off in certain circles. She returned to assist the team as a Mythtern in *Whirlpool of Death* and if she could cope with Adam losing his lunch in front of her …

JESS - Smells like pizza.

… then there's very little else that could stop her (except scuba – she hates scuba). Jess has a degree in mechanical engineering and a patent pending on an invention that will one day enable her to buy Jamie out.

Myths:* *Mailbag Special, Whirlpool of Death, and onward

Jet Car

On January 23rd 2003, a dedicated viewer of a certain popular documentary television network in the United States might have had their very first opportunity to glimpse the birth of something very special. Adam Savage and Jamie Hyneman were just a goatee'd trilby and walrus moustached beret then, but their first pilot episode had more than enough kick to get the series started. *Jet Car* is based on a story of an ex Air Force sergeant who 'acquired' a JATO rocket, and as a lark, fastened it to his old Chevy Impala. He went for a drive and got himself up to about 80mph (128 km/h) and fired it up. In seconds, he was rocketing along at 300+mph (482+km/h), a speed for which the Chevy was unprepared, and as a bend in the highway beckoned, the brakes burnt out and the car took off to be later found 100 ft (30 metres) up a nearby mountainside. Although precious little evidence of the myth was found to exist, the lads found a Chevy Impala and prepared it for some JATOs. However the US Air Force denied access to any, so plan B was put into operation.

Advanced hobby rocket engines – with three of these on board, the reinforced rig weighed almost as much as the car itself. Nevertheless they got their Chevy to a dry lakebed, and with some amateur rocketry experts, a helicopter and a bunch of consultants, prepared for takeoff. Some problems with a fuel filter notwithstanding, the second time around the Jet Car worked a treat. Oh, well, it certainly failed to take off, or achieve anything close to 300mph, but with a myth variously known as JATO Car, JATO Chevy or Jet-Assisted Chevy … the Mythbusters had begun with a bang.

JAMIE – It'll look really cool. I mean it's going to be big flames shooting out the back. It's going to be great. I can't think of anything more fun than doing this.

ADAM – No, you know what, I really can't.

See also: ***JATO, Chevy Impala, hobby rockets, Walt Arfons, Andy Granatelli, E & D Gates, hobby rockets, George Calloway***

JETTY

The name of one of the great short films of all time … did it out of YouTube sometime. The reason we've popped this definition in is that jetty is English for 'embarcadero'.

See also: ***Embarcadero Cove***

JIM LONG

A professional archer drafted into the show to revisit the myth of *Splitting an Arrow*. Having already busted the myth once, the build team responded to a quiver of angry fans by building authentic arrows, a new arrowbot and finally, getting Jim to take some shots. He managed to split the authentic arrow ten inches down its shaft after some 60 shots, but when presented with a bamboo arrow (as the Mythbusters believed was used in the original 1938 Robin Hood movie) Jim split it completely with his first shot.

GRANT – Jim, you are the man.

JIM – Finally.

Jim McKerrow MD

The Professor of Pathology at the University of California at San Francisco has a passion for parasites. It's not a weird thing – this man is a professional (you can tell from his little white goatee). Jim says there isn't any way an octopus egg could survive the rigours of your stomach, which was enough to make the myth of *Octopus Pregnancy* look decidedly shaky. Parasites in the stomach, that's another story …

JIM – Tapeworms for example, which are a type of parasite that you get from eating undercooked pork or beef … the reason that they can actually make it through the gastric acid is that they're coated with a very hard shell. It's called a cuticle and it's about as hard as at your fingernail. So by having this, basically this armour on its surface, these worms can make it through the gastric acid, get into the small intestine and basically live in paradise because they have as much food as they want to eat.

See also: parasites, tape worms
Myths: Octopus Pregnancy

Jim Mitchell

Jim is a marksman who specialised in the firearms of the American Civil War. Thus when the Mythbusters had to shoot a faux womb through Buster's Civil War scrotum, Jim was the man they called for.

JIM – Once it goes through THAT there's no guarantee it's going to go straigh

Jim Reichardt

A member of America's oldest duck farming family, it is fair to say that Jim likes ducks – but are they as gentle as they seem?

JAMIE – Adam don't let their looks deceive you, these are actually quite deadly.

Jo Ann Wyman

Jo ann was kind enough to come on the Mythbusters show and stick a long, sharp spike in Adam's tongue.

Myths: Lightning Strikes Tongue Stud

ADAM – Do I get a lollypop when this is done?

JO ANN – You do get a lollypop when this is done. But only if you earn it.

Joe Hughes

It sat in his driveway for goodness knows how long, sans steering wheel, sans instrument panel … sans engine. Thankfully, Jamie needed a boat just like it to test whether air cylinders had the grunt to push a vessel through the water.

JAMIE – You've seen the show before, right?

JOE – Oh, yes. Big fans.

JAMIE – So you're aware that there's a strong likelihood that we're going to do something horrible to your boat?

JOE – Ah, yes. Yeah.

Fans – what would Mythbusters do without them?

***See also:* fans**

Joe Konefal

For the myth *Painting With Explosives*, arson investigator and explosives expert Joe 'lends' the Mythbusters a third of a pound (151 grams) of mystery high explosive to see if, dropped in a bucket of paint, it will paint a room. Will it be the same as the dynamite Mr Bean used?

***Myths:* Dynamite Cement Truck, Painting With Explosives**

JOE … there's a whole bunch of dynamites, but this is pretty hot stuff. This actually detonates right around 21,000 feet per second.

ADAM – Twenty one thousand feet … That's like more than 10 times as fast as a bullet.

JOE – Yes, it would be.

John Emberton

Businessman, animal lover, scorpion wrangler extraordinaire, the East Bay Vivarium is John's business, and critters are his life. He brought over a bunch of his closest friends for the *Ultimate Mythbuster* fear test.

***See also:* fear test, Giant Tanzanian Millipede, Tarantula, African Emperor Scorpion, Corn Snake, wrangler**

***Myths:* Ultimate Mythbuster**

ADAM – Then why aren't they stinging you?

JOHN – They're waiting for you.

John Growney

Ex-rodeo rider and expert horseman, John can honestly say that his jeans have never caught fire after being dragged from a horse. What's that about pants? Ah, we should have mentioned - John was instrumental in sorting out *Pants on Fire*, the myth of whether a cowboy's jeans would … oh, we've been there already.

***See also:* Pistol the Psychic Horse**
***Myths:* Pants on Fire**

John Lamb

With a great-great-grandfather having served in the 2nd Maryland Infantry during the Civil War, John Lamb is fascinated by this conflict and its weaponry. When Adam and Jamie took on the mighty mythical *Steam Machine Gun* it was to John they turned for detailed advice before commencing their build.

***See also:* machine gun, steam**
***Myths:* Steam Machine Gun**

JOHN - There are accounts saying it was tested, and it seemed to be really deadly. There are others that say it never worked and nobody could prove it. So that's a big mystery.

John McCosker

'Doctor Eel' at San Francisco's Steinhart Aquarium, John was the 'go to' man when Adam and Jamie unclipped the *Eel Skin Wallet*.

JOHN - Electric eels really pack a wallop … about 400 to 500 volts. They'll sure put you on your kisser.

John Luscombe – Executive Producer

John "Lusco' Luscombe has made more television than you've watched. OK, that might be a stretch, but as General Manager and Senior Vice President of Beyond Productions he's certainly sliced, diced, originated and revised more hours of box-time than you've spent standing on two feet. Having combined creative and production brains with one Peter Rees, one day in 2002 Lusco entered the offices of the Discovery Channel in Silver Spring Maryland with a television show they couldn't refuse.

***See also:* everything**

John McLeod

The pyrotechnician on little films like Indiana Jones and the Temple of Doom wasn't too big a bang to bunk down and bust some myths – he was on hand when the lads needed enough firepower to shoot Buster out of the *Racoon Rocket*.

See also: Goex

JOHN – We're using 10 one-pound cans of the Goex black powder. That should give us a pretty good bang.

JOHN – I started feeling a little nauseous right away, like upset stomach, and kind of light headed. So I walked away from the thing, felt a little dizzy.

John Meyer

It's not called Meyer Sound because they're stuck in a swamp (mire, get it?), it's all because of John and his obsession with creating technology that will reproduce perfect sound. Of course, sometimes even a maestro can take it too far, as when John and his team modified some giant concert speakers to blast out sub-sonic frequencies at 130dB+ for the myth of the *Brown Note*.

See also: Roger Schwenkee

John Morris

At the time of filming the *Tree Cannon* myth, John's cannon collection numbered more than 100. That's not bad, even for a West Virginian. His role on *Tree Cannon* was to teach Adam and Jamie to safely fire one of these big puppies. He had some good tips to offer.

JOHN – From now on it's going to be loaded and nobody gets in front of it, OK?

JOHN NEVINS

John knows his Civil War, from guns and ammo down to how a soldier would have been positioned when he was shot through the scrotum.

***Myths:* Son of a Gun**

JOHN ... they tend to kneel. It gives them better accuracy. A position like so. Right? So if someone is firing at me, the bullet hits me in the lower leg, continues on and who knows what's behind me.

JOLENE BABYACK

Jolene's dad worked as the associate warden of Alcatraz, and has written a number of books about the gaol. This was not the only reason she was consulted by Adam and Jamie for *Alcatraz Escape* – she was actually living on the island when the attempt was made. Does she think Frank Morris and the Anglin Brothers actually got away? Some discoveries at the scene suggest not ...

***See also:* Frank Morris, Anglin Brothers, Alcatraz**

JOSEPH SNELL

Owner of Pacifica Archery, Joe is an enthusiast of the yew. His experience was vital in attempting to conquer the *Splitting an Arrow* myth.

JOSH GASKIN

Fire Captain Josh Gaskin works out of the Livermore-Pleasanton Fire Department, where his skills as lock picking instructor (how else do you get them out of a burning vehicle?) and traffic cone airbag launch commander were tapped to perfection in *Airbag Annihilation*.

JOSH – We have a driver's airbag out of a small vehicle and I put a traffic cone over it so we can see it a little bit better going up in the air, and we're going to launch it. Do not try this at home.

JOLENE – The most important thing was a packet of photographs. Also there were nine slips of paper with names they were going to contact. Now unless you're in a life and death situation, you're not going to let go of that bag.

Josh Smith

The general manager of the West Valley Flying Club has some excellent advice for all those thinking about hand-starting that antique Sopwith Camel in their grandfather's shed.

> JOSH – When you throw the prop, what is essentially a thrust-creating device once you're flying, now becomes a decapitation device if you're not careful ... So my advice is, never try this at home.

This would all make sense in the context of the myth *Shredded Aeroplane.*

Joule

The SI unit of measurement for energy is the equivalent of a force of one newton moving one metre, and can also be called a Newton-metre. The joule was discovered by the son of a brewer one day when he was mucking around with lumps of coal. For the anti-SI among you, a joule is about three-quarters of a foot-pound of force, and you can squeeze just over four joules into a calorie, but there'd be no room for luggage.

See also:* *watt, Newton, calories, kilojoules

Judith Hitzeman

Archiving is an exciting profession that really gets blood pumping through your veins. Seriously, Judith Hitzeman could tell you. Her work with the San Francisco Maritime National Historical Park gives her access to treasures from hundreds of years of history, including the one remaining raincoat that was not part of the original *Alcatraz Escape* by Frank Morris and the Anglin Brothers. Adam and Jamie just had to see it.

> JUDITH – So this fabric now is very fragile. If I tried to unroll it, it would deteriorate, it would fall apart ...
>
> ADAM ... and you can definitely see the glue on the edge of the seam, the contact cement.

Julia Mariottini

Octopus expert Julia looks after octopuses at the Monterey Bay Aquarium, and can tell you that there is NO CHANCE of accidentally (or even deliberately) swallowing an octopus egg and having an octopus grow inside you – despite the myth of *Octopus Pregnancy*. However, she can tell you exactly how an octopus mother looks after her babies.

JULIA ... She will blow jets of water on them to make sure that they're aerated. She'll clean them. They also require the correct temperature, the correct salinity and if all goes well then they'll hatch out. For a giant octopus it's about six months later.

***See also:* octopus, Monterey Bay Aquarium**
***Myths:* Octopus Pregnancy**

Junker

If it doesn't move then it's just … junk. If it's decrepit almost, but not quite, to the point of being derelict then it's a junker. A fine distinction, but in the world of Mythbusters where one man's trash is Adam and Jamie's treasure, it's often a cheap-as-chips junker they need to fulfil the detail and the budget of a myth. Examples of famous junkers have been the '66 Chevy Impala that became *Jet Car*, the old vacuum cleaners from *Levitation Machine* and the trombone that held enough black powder to blow up a bus in *Exploding Trombone*. You wouldn't want to take a decent car, vacuum cleaner or trombone out of the world … would you?

***See also:* Corvette, vacuum cleaner, trombone**
***Myths:* Jet Car, Exploding Trombone, Levitation Machine**

Kari Byron

Some say her first appearance on the show was as the butt scan-ee in *Vacuum Toilet* but in fact Kari was seen working on a computer in the background of the very first myth aired. Kari studied film and sculpture, starred in underground horror films and since joining Mythbusters permanently from the first 'revisited' episode, is fast becoming one of the most famous vegetarians on television. Kari worked for Jamie at M5 as a builder of models and prototyper of toys, and still finds time for her own artistic practice in-between lighting fires with ice, sneaking past guard dogs and dropping things from high places.

KARI – I promised my Mom I wouldn't do anything dumb and unsafe again.

TORY – Looks like you didn't keep your promise.

Keith Atkinson

Keith was the medical technician behind the wheel of the Doppler machine that monitored Grant's health and welfare as he was soaked in a hot bath for six hours wearing shrinkable jeans.

TORY – Are we going to have to amputate his legs?

KEITH – I don't think you're going to have to.

Kellie Gillespie

Kellie pushes top-notch coffins for Arthur Sullivan Funerals, and was in luck when Adam and Jamie walked through the door needing one in Jamie's size to test the myth *Buried Alive*. Jamie got a bit freaked out when the 20 gauge steel coffin didn't quite stand up to the strain of being under a few barrow loads of dirt (page one for a coffin you might have thought) but nevertheless, the interiors were lovely.

KELLIE – And feel the pillow.

JAMIE – Oh that feels nice.

Kenny Faeth

If once it flew, now it rusts quietly in Kenny Faeth's Sacramento salvage yard. Faeth Aircraft supplies many of the retired aircraft parts for Mythbusters experiments, as well as various items for Adam's personal collection.

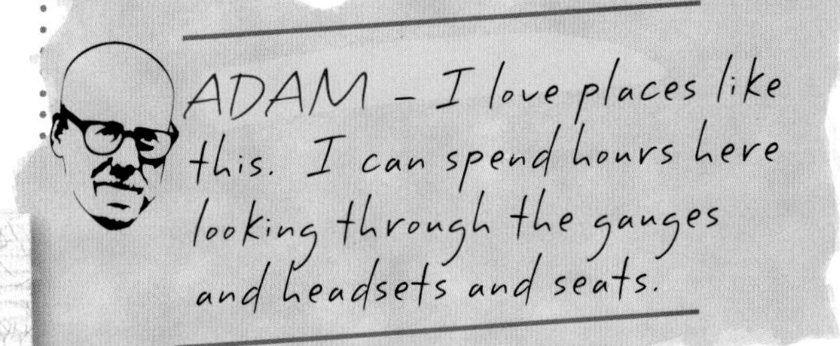

Myths: ***Chicken Gun, Shredded Plane***

Kelvin

This scientific measurement of temperature is really just Celsius in disguise. The idea is that rather than 0º being the temperature at which water becomes ice (as it is in Celsius – don't even talk to us about Fahrenheit), 0ºK is absolute zero, a very exciting concept that even has its own entry in this volume.

See also: ***temperature, absolute zero, oxygen***

JAMIE – This rocket was supposedly made possible by Lord Kelvin, who was persuaded to make liquid oxygen 12 years before it's generally accepted that this first occurred.

Kid Curry

He was born Harvey Logan in the Old West, and became the outlaw Kid Curry who rode with Butch Cassidy and the Sunshine Kid. Curry claimed to be able to shoot a single action revolver five times in the time it took a poker chip to fall from his other hand to the ground – a feat that neither a contemporary quickdraw expert nor even a robot gunslinger could come close to replicating in *Gunslinger Myths*.

See also: ***Lightning Larry Hamby***

Myths: ***Gunslinger Myths***

Warning – killer tissues!

works well at a lower speed, demonstrating that a box of tissues simply does not have enough mass to do you significant damage in a prang (but don't go leaving your subwoofer, hatchet, fire extinguisher or bowling ball in the back of the car).
Result? Busted.

JAMIE – At a certain speed, I'm sure that a bobble head could be lethal, but I don't think that speed is 45 miles an hour.

Killer Tissue Box

If you're involved in a car accident, could you be at mortal danger from something in the back of the car? Several cases present themselves, including two of drivers impaled by golf umbrellas, and one killed by bags of shopping, but … how heavy need something be to do real damage, and at what speed? Could you be threatened by a box of paper nose wipers? With only one Plymouth Fury at their disposal for this myth Adam and Jamie develop a reusable test rig made of 200 lbs (90 kg) of aluminium that will be linked to 1000 feet of cable. Disaster strikes – the aluminium simply isn't strong enough to hold the cable at 75 mph (120 km/h) and the lads must revise the plan. Eventually some nylon strapping saves the day, and the rig

See also: ***aluminium, cable***

Killer Washing Machine

It's a tempting excuse, but can you REALLY be killed doing a load of laundry? This myth suggests exactly that, based on a tale out of Charlottesville, Virginia circa 1998, in which a man (surprises will never cease) attempts to squeeze 50 pounds (22 kgs) of soiled washables into a top loader by getting on top of the load and squashing it in. However, he hits the 'on' button, whereupon the machine begins to revolve. With his legs stuck inside, he knocks a nearby shelf, spilling first bleach, then baking soda everywhere. His dog runs in to see what the commotion is, and, terrified by the scene, urinates. The dog wee mixes with the bleach and baking soda and causes a small explosion which kicks the machine into its spin cycle, which whirls the man at 70 mph (112 km/h) and kills him. As Adam and Jamie investigate the myth, it turns out that none – NONE – of its elements could be replicated. A washing machine of any domestic size cannot take 50 pounds of clothes. The washing machine's cut-off switch prevents the drum from turning when the lid is open. No washing machine on Earth could spin a person at 70 mph and dog wee does not make baking soda and bleach explode.

ADAM – That's actually a first for us. There's not one fact about this myth that's true … Myth decimated.

Kilogram

The kilogram is really a chunk of platinum/iridium alloy sitting inside three bell jars at the Bureau International des Poids et Mesures. We're more than 200 years on from when the gram was first decreed by the French to be the equivalent mass of one cubic centimetre of water, and yet we've not improved upon the way of standardising weight at all. Or mass. This grey area might be coloured in by

experiments with giant silicone crystals, but we're not holding our breath. Until then we might as well drill holes in a cannonball.

ADAM – Hey hey! How about that! Exactly a kilo.

See also: ***weight, mass, pounds, ounces, SI***

Kilojoule

This is in fact just 1000 joules – see 'joule' for the real story (apologies if you got here from 'calories')

See also: ***calories, joule***

Myths: ***Cardboard Cereal***

Kinetic Energy

As Einstein's famous equation suggests, mass is energy. However, a mass can pick up extra energy when it moves, and this energy is called kinetic energy, for the very good reason that the Greek word 'kineo' means 'to move'. We also get the word for cinema – aka 'movies' – from here. The Mythbusters are always calculating the energy of moving objects, whether they're bullets in *Shooting Hat* or tissue boxes in *Killer Tissue Box*.

Knots

The unit of speed you should refer to when that speed is being propagated on the water (or through the air) is the knot. Knots originally referred to the knots in a length of line paid out by a chip log on a vessel at sea, and is the equivalent of one nautical mile per hour (1.8 km/h). You'll hear Adam and Jamie referring to knots every so often when they're measuring the speed of a boat, a plane or a whirlpool.

JAMIE – Well as near as I can tell, that was around fourteen knots. That's close to the record speed that's ever been recorded in an oceanic whirlpool.

See also: ***nautical miles, chip log***

Myths: ***Alcatraz Escape, Killer Whirlpool, Air Cylinder Rocket***

Kurtis Dickey

Livermore-Pleasanton Fire Station knows what it's like to see a Christmas ruined by fire – and the display of destruction they put on with Adam and Jamie for the myth of *Christmas Lights* should have us all presenting Santa with a less-than-twinkly scene.

See also: **Josh Gaskin**

CAPTAIN DICKEY – We go to Christmas tree fires every year. We had a house burn up in December 26 of 1997 where a child turned the lights onto the Christmas tree and the tree immediately ignited and burned up the house and caused a lot of damage.

LabPro

These Sunnyvale, San Francisco distributors of laboratory necessities like beakers and test tubes do a roaring trade to the scientific community – and the occasional Mythbuster.

Myths: Octopus Pregnancy

ADAM – I love this stuff. One of everything. Oh. I've never seen continuous pipe cleaner before. I didn't even know it existed … Do you think we need to get some beard covers here? What you have isn't really quite a beard through.

JAMIE – I'm not sure what it is.

ADAM – It's like an accessory tuft.

LAD

At the heart of the Seven Up Vending Machine is Jamie's prototype electric engine, which he calls the Life and Death machine (or LAD). The LAD came to the rescue of the *Elevator of Death* by lifting the elevator up the 92 feet (28 metres) of shaft … so the lads could drop it again.

See also: Seven-Up Vending Machine

JAMIE – I've built a multipurpose platform that has the electric motors, the gear reduction for them, speed controllers and electronics and batteries all compacted into as tight a unit as I could come up with. And then we put these treads on it.

Lard

We wish there was more to it, something technical or chemical, something to do with molecules or hydrocarbons … but the plain and simple fact is that lard is pig fat. Once you're comfortable with 'lard is pig fat' then there's all sorts of qualities and grades and recipes and history we could tell you about, but just remember, it's pig fat baby! The Mythbusters tend to use it in more utilitarian ways as a lubricant, rather than to produce some classic tamales or a glorious zsírosdeszka. Adam or Jamie will pull out the lard to ensure the rails of the *Air Cylinder Rocket* rig are slippery enough to help the cylinder punch a neat hole in their cinder block wall, or to grease up a mould, or make sure the pogo stick springs in *Elevator of Death* is operating with as little friction as possible, or insert a probe.

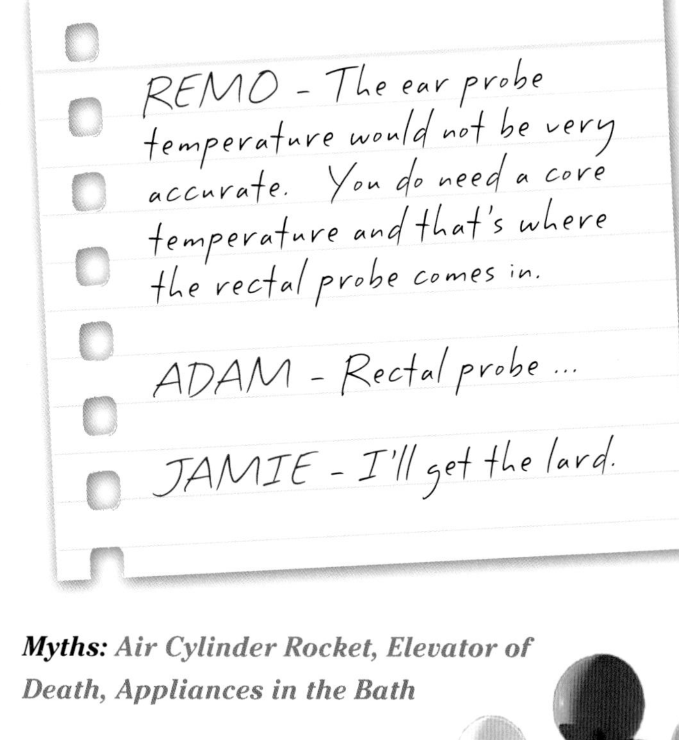

Myths: ***Air Cylinder Rocket, Elevator of Death, Appliances in the Bath***

Larry Walters

In 1982 Larry took to the air in a deck chair attached to a few dozen helium-filled weather balloons. Would he do it again?

Myths: ***Lawn Chair***

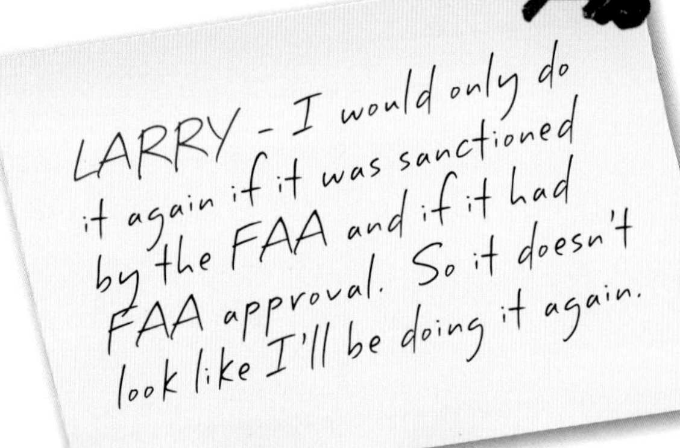

Laser

Light amplification by the stimulated emission of radiation has been foreshadowed by Einstein, but it's been just 50 years since the coolest acronym ever has graced public stage. Lasers are super-useful for measuring all the little bumps and hollows on a CD or for lining something up just right – like a little bag of semen.

SCOTTIE – Do you think the laser's jiggling when we fire it?

JIM – Could be the recoil, yeah.

TORY – Ah, come to your left, half inch there.

JIM – Perfect..

Latex

There are as many versions of this rubber-based material (or polymerised rubber substitute material) as there are uses for it. Body-hugging, neck-entry bondage suits spring to mind, along with face grabbing prosthetic makeup and home-made blood vessels for *Fan of Death*.

***See also:* blood**

***Myths:* Who Gets Wetter?, Fan of Death**

TORY – In the artery, when that blade comes flying through there, blood is going to spray all over the room. Kind of reminds me of alien, when the thing pops out of the guy's stomach and shoots across the table.

SCOTTIE – Oh yeah. It's alive.

KARI – This is so bizarre. This is so bizarre.

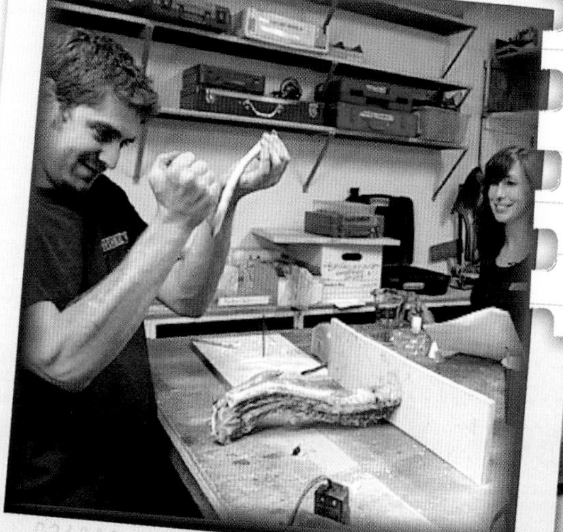

Latitude

If you were to travel all the way from the North Pole to the South Pole (or visa versa) you would experience all the joys that different points of latitude offer. Each degree of latitude is divided in sixty minutes, and each of those minutes is equal to one nautical mile. Neat huh?

***See also:* longitude, knots, nautical miles, meridian**

Lathe

In Jamie's workshop this tool holds a pride of place for its ability to spin stuff so it can be shaped by human hand (with a tool in it). The idea of spinning stuff in this way has been around for 3000+ years, so it's no wonder that modern lathes are precision instruments that weigh lots and cost plenty. Not cleaning up Jamie's lathe (or indeed any of his tools at the M5 workshop) is tantamount to sticking a pin in his eye.

***See also:* M5, tools**

***Myths:* Steam Cannon**

Lawn Chair

Another one for the 'it's crazy but it happened' file. In 1982 an unemployed truck driver called Larry Walters found himself with 40-odd weather balloons and a few industrial cylinders of helium to hand and decided to take a little trip. Up. Really? Did he? Adam and Jamie were determined to find out, and after combing the Bay area and beyond for helium weather balloons (and finding some duds) they manage to get sufficient buoyancy to hoist Adam 75 feet (22 metres) into that air. The thing was, what to do then?

***See also:* Larry Walters, helium, buoyancy**

JAMIE - It's been nice knowing you.

ADAM - I love you all.

JAMIE - Thanks for all your help ...

Laws of Motion

If there's one thing that Adam and Jamie love to do it's tangle with Sir Isaac Newton's Laws of Motion. They turn up in the most surprising places – when kicking a *Helium Football* for instance, or when you pick up a firearm to do a little *Hat Shooting* or rig up a weapon to fire off a grappling hook in *Superhero Myths*.

TORY – Whoa, dude.

KARI – We forgot the Newton's laws!

TORY ... You know, we've done a lot of experiments on the show, things have gone wrong, but that's the first time that I've ever felt that much danger.

Newton's Laws of Motion suggest (well, they do more than that, hence the word 'law') that firstly, a 'body' (say, a football) will remain in motion – or at rest – unless acted upon by an outside force. That force

An equal and opposite reaction

might be with foot of the kicker, or all the mass of the air the ball has to fight its way through, or the ground it eventually hits. Secondly, the rate of change in the momentum of that football (or body) is in direct proportion to the force acting upon it, and in the direction of that force. Finally (and this is the real crowd pleaser) that for every reaction there is an equal and opposite reaction. That was the one Kari and Tory forgot when they fired off their grappling hook cannon without first securing it to something at least as massive as the force it was going to exert.

See also:* *Sir Isaac Newton, gravity

Myths:* *Blown Away, Helium Football

Law of Universal Gravitation

Despite the fact that we don't really know what makes mass mass (unless CERN discovers the Higgs Boson – or makes a black hole – before this volume is published,

Gravity likes big butts – wherever they are

and either way you'll know about it) Sir Isaac Newton did ascertain back in the 17th century that mass LIKES mass. Mass is attracted to itself, and the more massive the more attractive. The Law of Universal Gravitation is kind of a 17th century boffin's way of saying 'I like big butts and I cannot lie'. OK, not really, but what Newton was getting at is the reason you're currently able to sit around on the sofa rather than float off into outer space. In a very profound way, your feeble collection of atoms are attracted to the largest local collection of atoms, and that happens to be the Earth. The Earth is similarly attracted to the Sun, the moon to the Earth, and also you to the sofa (but in a way much less important to astrophysics, but nevertheless makes for a great excuse when it comes time to wash up). However, when the Mythbusters took on *Anti-Gravity* there was the briefest moment when all the science seemed to have been turned on its head – but in the end sanity prevailed.

GRANT – OK, the lifter, very cool piece of technology. It works great but in the end it's not antigravity. It's all thrust.

KARI – So antigravity is busted.

GRANT – Yeah. It's busted.

TORY – Well I don't know if we can bust antigravity. I mean, we can bust our devices.

KARI – Alright, revised. Antigravity busted ... for now.

***See also:* gravity, Sir Isaac Newton, mass**
***Myths:* Anti-Gravity**

Leonardo Da Vinci

The penner of backwards Italian scribbles has not gone unnoticed by the Mythbusters. He was cited in *Steam Cannon* as the originator of a one-page drawing of the unlikely weapon, the concept for which he attributed to Archimedes.

***Myths:* Steam Cannon**

Lester Appel

Les knows his up from his down. Is it ironic that his elevator company is named for a fruit famous for falling? Or is it just … a misspelling? Either way, Les knows what to do if the cable snaps…

LESTER – I believe if I had the presence of mind, I would probably try to lay myself down on the floor, assuming I could get there, just to minimise the injury to my body.

Lexan™

First developed by chemical giants General Electric and Bayer, Lexan™ is the trademark of a particular kind of plastic polycarbonate favoured by the lads for their blast chamber and screens, because of its impact and temperature resistance.

***See also:* polycarbonate, blast chamber**

Leyden Jar

The first way to store electrical energy was invented by a Dutchman called Pieter van Musschenbroek (say it with feeling) when he coated the inside and outside surfaces of a glass jar (an insulator) with metal foil (a conductor), connected the inner one via a chain to an electrode at the top of the jar, and charged it up with an electrostatic generator. Adam used a Leyden Jar to store up a spark in *Cell Phone Gas Station* and also came across the concept when he painted up a bit of PCV pipe with metallic paint in *Static Cannon*.

***See also:* capacitor, insulator, conductor**

***Myths:* Static Cannon, Cell Phone Gas Station**

ADAM – So this is called a Leyden jar and it's actually just Tupperware with foil on the inside and foil on the outside. And it's an early capacitor, which is basically an energy storage device.

Lighter Rig (aka Automatic Match)

As used in *Cell Phone Gas Station* this temperamental little device was fixed with a pneumatic actuator to set off the *Racoon Rocket* –

ADAM – It works. Excellent. So: it is the worlds most complicated lighter.

Lightning

The greatest zap on Earth, lightning rents the sky in twain with bolts measuring 30,000°C comprising 100 million volts at 100,000 amps - and that's NOTHING to the lightning you'll find on Saturn, which is estimated to be a million times as powerful. So how does lightning work? Great question, and scientists aren't 100 per cent on top of it yet. It seems to work best when clouds start acting as capacitors, storing up massive charges on their top and bottom, before they let it all go at once – and this happens about 6000 times every day. The lads have tackled lightning several times – firstly to see if a tongue stud would attract it in *Lightning Strikes Tongue Piercing*, then whether it was safe to do regular household things when lightning is in the vicinity, in *Phone in a Thunderstorm*, and they also turned over the sods on Benjamin Franklin to see what the deal was with that kite in the thunderstorm in *Franklin's Kite*.

***See also:* capacitor, volts, amps**

***Myths:* Phone in a Thunderstorm, Lightning Strikes Tongue Piercing, Franklin's Kite**

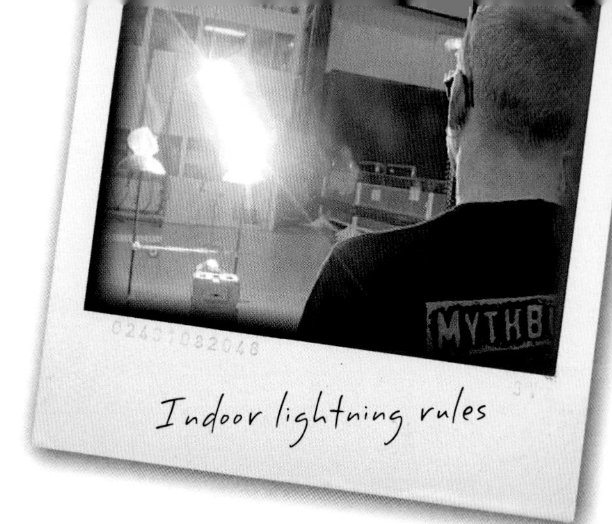

Indoor lightning rules

JAMIE – We could have done this a thousand times and still not gotten that same result. You know, lightning is just really unpredictable.

Lightning Larry Hamby

Larry is an expert in the classic craft of the quickdraw – pulling a pistol from your holster and firing so quick that the best way to appreciate his work is via the high speed camera. But that's not why they call him 'Lightning'…

LARRY - Well, they don't call me Lightning because I'm so fast, but like lightning, my bullets never hit twice in the same spot.

...which we should point out is a bit of a myth in itself. The Empire State Building has been struck about 7000 times.

***Myths:* Gunslinger Myths**

Lightning Strikes Tongue Stud

So, you're out hiking the treeless hills of Red Cone, Colorado, the stainless steel pride and joy in your tongue clicking against your teeth. The storm clouds seem close by, but – what the hell – whoever gets struck by lightning? ....zppcRKKKKZzz! And suddenly you're lying on the ground with your shoes blown off, wondering: where did my tongue stud get to? This reportedly happened to a hiker called Matt Thomsen in 2003, and before you could say 'holy tongue', the Mythbusters were on the case. First stop was the first-hand experience of having your tongue studded; Adam fronts up to a local piercing boutique and gets some tongue jewellery. Then the lads collect some fast ballistics gel heads, a few woks and set off to the local centre of high voltage to test whether lightning sized zaps would be attracted to a tongue studded gel head over an unstudded one. They weren't, but the lads kept adding jewellery and eventually discovered that lightning was attracted to a copper door know stuck in the cheek. The lesson is: when you're experimenting with body art, don't over-do it.

***See also:* Matt Thomsen, wok**

ADAM ... we do know that metal does have an effect. Depending on how much of it there is and where it is on the body. And we did get a strike right to the doorknob. Come on, who wears a doorknob?

Lightship Weight

If you picked up a ship and shook it until all the bits and pieces fell out (crew, cargo, fuel and so on) then put it back on some scales,

you could measure its lightship weight. This is the hull, engines, anchors, steering wheel and so on – the stuff that makes it a ship. The stuff you disposed of would have been known as deadweight (which is probably why you got rid of it). Taken together, lightship weight and deadweight is called displacement (thanks to Archimedes). Just because its called lightship weight doesn't make it light – the USS Nimitz weighs 68,000 long tons 'light' and would certainly bruise your foot if you dropped it.

***See also:* long tons, displacement, deadweight**

Lights On or Off

Is it true that turning your lights on and off when you enter and leave a room actually burns more electricity than just leaving them on? No. Turn them off! Just to prove it the Build Team lived up their name with a giant rig of all sorts of lights and switched them on and off and on and off and on and off and on and off…

GRANT – OK, so we've been running our longevity test with a two-minute on off cycle with over a month now, and the only bulb that has not burnt out is the LED.

KARI – So how does this test compare to say the average stress and usage that you put on a light bulb in a normal household?

TORY – Right, 'cause I mean, these lights have been turned on and off over 10,000 times in a month.

GRANT – Yeah, actually, that corresponds to over five years worth of stress turning on and off in a regular household.

KARI – And given that when you turn on an incandescent light bulb, it uses the same amount of power as point three six seconds of continuous use, and doesn't really take that much wear and tear. Jamie might be right. You're supposed to flip off the lights when you leave the room.

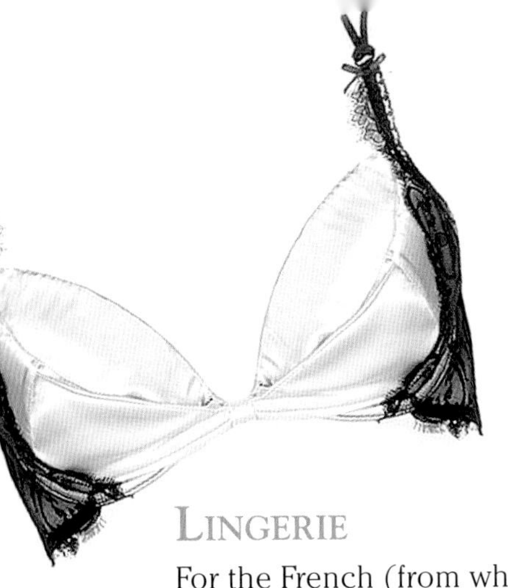

Lingerie

For the French (from whom we borrow the word) even a pair of white Y-fronts are lingerie, but for us English speakers (hello everyone out there) we know full well that lingerie suggests silk and lace and goodness me where is this entry going? The Mythbusters have dealt with lingerie as a material in different experimental set ups, including in *Cell Phone Gas Station* and *Killer Washing Machine* but for modesty's sake have not yet been faced with a myth ABOUT lingerie. Anyone know of one?

***Myths:* Cell Phone Gas Station, Killer Washing Machine**

JAMIE - We actually use a lot of lingerie on this show don't we?

ADAM - We have actually.

Liquefaction

The prime Mythbusters example of this phenomenon is quicksand, which occurs as a result of groundwater sneaking up to the surface where it reduces the friction between particles of sand or dirt to the point where they become suspended and are unable to bear weight. Essentially, they become a liquid. In the myth of *Quicksand*, Adam and Jamie get a nice mix going, but it doesn't seem to do the classic 'suck you down' thing. Liquefaction shouldn't be confused with liquefaction necrosis, which is also to do with stuff crossing over the threshold from solid to liquid but we're talking bodies here. This was the fate suffered by the poor pigs in *Stinky Car* and involves bacteria eating your cells until the entire architecture of your flesh is compromised. Nasty.

***See also:* putrefaction**

***Myths:* Quicksand, Stinky Car**

On the way to a litre of something

LIZ MASTERSON

'The Singbird of the Sage' is a professional yodeller who lent her talents to the show when Adam and Jamie wanted to know if a good, hard yodel could really set off an avalanche in *Avalanche Adventures*.

LIZ - When I get a certain pitch and a certain volume, I can feel my crown in my tooth sort of rattle. It's quite a sensation.

LITRE

Although the SI unit of volume is actually the cubic metre, this is not a very useful measure when dealing in domestic quantities of milk, water or petrol. So the litre is used, and qualifies as almost SI because it is equal to one 1000th of a cubic metre (that is there are 1000 litres in a cubic metre).

LITTLE MICKEY

A fictional character from the world of advertising who was the taste-test dummy for the original Pop Rocks. The actor who played Little Mickey in the ad never returned their calls, so we're sure not going to give him a naming plug here.

LOGARITHM

In order to describe the pressure created in your ear caused by the barely audible rustling leaves (about 10 dB) and the pressure on your body caused by the shockwave of a nuclear warhead landing in your back garden (over 200 dB) we use logarithms. Logarithms are a handy way of expressing numbers that would otherwise get very unwieldy as something more reader-friendly – decibels are just one example, the Richter scale for measuring the power of earthquakes is another (in fact, just another way of using the decibel scale).

See also: decibel

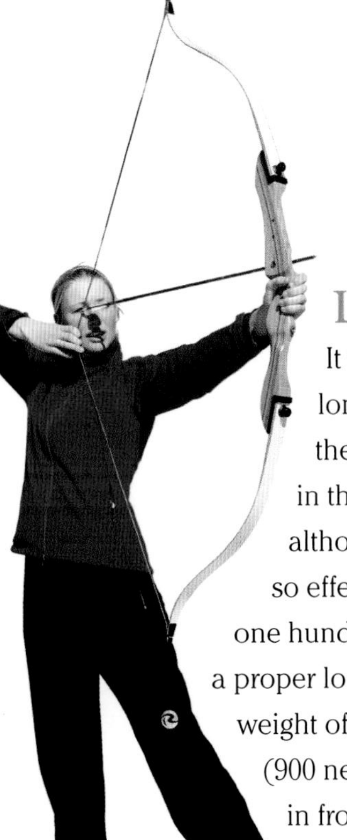

Longbow

It was the innovation of the longbow that made the English the force to be reckoned with in the Hundred Years War – although you have to ask, if it was so effective how did the war take one hundred years? Never mind that, a proper longbow of yew has a draw weight of as much as 200 pounds (900 newtons) so don't go standing in front of one. All this and more in the myth of *Splitting Arrow.*

Longitude

If you get your kicks by travelling right around the equator, or the Tropics of Cancer or Capricorn, or any of the other circles of larger or greater size that ring the belly of the Earth, then you are a very eccentric person who's probably the host of quirky BBC travel documentaries. You would definitely know all about longitude – which is the word used to describe those smaller or greater circles. Ships had a devil of a job finding out their longitude until the invention of the portable chronometer – a narrative beautifully told by Dava Sobel. And the Mythbusters? Well, they like longitude too. We just can't prove it with a quote.

See also: latitude, knots, nautical miles, meridian

Low Explosive

If high explosives exist, then you can bet your last rupee on the existence of low explosives – the sort of explosives easily tucked under a teacher's chair at school. 'Low explosive' is kind of a misnomer, especially when they're what make artillery shells and bullets fire, but nevertheless there is a reason to subdivide explosives into low and high. An explosion of classic 'low' explosive gunpowder (or black powder) deflagrates – or burns – rather than detonates. Never mind – it's still perfect for creating the kind of expanding gases that all guns need.

See also: explosives, high explosive, black powder

Lungs

They're about the size of a couple of footballs (whatever code, doesn't matter) and their job is to introduce oxygen to your body, and remove carbon dioxide.

Crack
MOMENT OF IMPACT
Newton/sq.meter
7401/
V = VELOC
T = TIME
Mmmmm!

Machinery & Equipment Company

Sixty years of dealing in pre-loved machinery (& equipment) has resulted in a large inventory of large machinery (& equipment) at the Machinery & Equipment Company of San Francisco. Jamie and Adam made there way here to find the perfect pressure tank for their *Chicken Gun*. In fact the final tank came from elsewhere, but it's a useful place to check out if ever you're in the same boat, or if you ever want to start a terrific argument about safety (& equipment) to be broadcast on international television.

"ADAM ... your INTUITION is that it's NOT like a bomb.

JAMIE – Yeah.

ADAM – But if it IS we're all dead and &^%$#."

Magnetism

From credit cards to speakers, magnets are a key part of so many technologies they should be given some kind of prize – although magnets are so intrinsically cool that they'd never turn up to the ceremony. The phenomenon of magnetism is of course a factor of electromagnetism, which describes the attraction between fundamental particles that make the universe the way it is. Thus in a way everything is magnetic, but the magnetism that makes some things stick to the fridge and not others is a narrower band of magnetism – those materials which can produce a viable magnetic field. The Mythbusters revel in a bit of magnetism and will pull out a neodymium magnet as soon as look at you, as they did in *Needle in a Haystack* and *Crimes and MythDemeanours*.

Mailbag Special – Archimedes Death Ray

Also known in some circles as the 'Death Ray Burnoff', this sequel to the myth *Ancient Death Ray* saw the Mythbusters call for those who challenged their original results (that is – busted) to put their rigs where their emails were. The best entrants included Jess Nelson, later to become a Mythbusters mythtern, a team of MIT ultra-boffins, a rocket scientist from Arizona, and students from the top colleges in the land – all vying to make real the myth that the ancient Greeks had harnessed the power of the sun to turn an enemy warship to ashes. And what happens? The students get focused on a small scale experiment that creates smoke, but no fire. The rocket scientist trucks in his big rig only to find that the big rig doing the trucking has smashed it to pieces (how many years bad luck is THAT?). The rest of the team get to work on a replica rig based on the MIT design that had already shown itself to be able to successfully flame-out an oak boat in a parking lot, using modern silvered mirrors. But will it be able to repeat the feat with ancient bronze? No… but not for want of trying.

ADAM – The large-scale rig that we built with MIT was stunning in terms of giving us so much more knowledge about whether or not this thing was possible. I was amazed at the efficiency of the thermal conductivity of the bronze, and I think it really can ignite dry timber at a distance.

JAMIE – I'm sorry, I don't agree. We had a stationary boat, we had a distance of less than a bowshot, we didn't have get open flame created from bronze mirrors. I think it's busted.

***See also:* Jess Nelson, Mike Bushroe, ballista, David Wallace**
***Myths:* Ancient Death Ray**

Manila Rope

Manila rope is woven from fibres of a species of banana plant called abacà that is grown in the Philippines (hence Manila – which is the capital of that country). The fibres are remarkably strong and hard-wearing, and Adam and Jamie will pick up a coil of Manila in preference to all other kinds of banana-based ropes (and did so in myths such as *Barrel of Bricks*).

***Myths:* Barrel of Bricks**

Mannlicher-Carcano

The rifle that Lee Harvey Oswald allegedly used to kill President John F Kennedy.
Myths:* *Ice Bullet

Mano-a-mano

The original Spanish translation would be 'hand to hand' and referred to bullfighting (although bulls don't have hands). Used in English it means competition and plenty of it. The Mythbusters go mano-a-mano whenever they get the chance, classics including *Levitation Machine*, *Needle in a Haystack* and of course *Ultimate Mythbuster*.

Put up your dukes bull...

Mare Island

Housing shipyards since 1854, Mare Island and its giant Whirley crane was the location for the testing of *Bridge Drop*.

Marin Headlands

If you were escaping from Alcatraz Island (when it was a prison, not a tourist resort) you would probably spray falsehoods about your likely destination among a few fellow inmates. You might, for instance, suggest that under the cover of darkness, you were aiming to paddle your raincoat boat towards Angel Island, from which you'd do x, y and z and send everyone a postcard from Mexico. Angel Island has such a glamorous, vibrant appeal that it would be memorable in the way that the Marin Headlands isn't. All speculation of course, but as Adam and Jamie demonstrate in *Alcatraz Escape* it is the Marin Headlands that Frank Morris and the Anglin Brothers would have ended up, leaving when they did. However, Alan West (the inmate who was left behind) was told Angel Island. Why? We may never know.
See also:* *Alcatraz, Angel Island, Frank Morris, Anglin Brothers, Alan West
Myths:* *Alcatraz Escape

Mark Pondelick

Mark is an engineer whose focus is on the comfort and safety of aeroplane passengers in a very specific way.

Myths: ***Vacuum Toilet***

MARK – In the aircraft market we have approximately 13,000 vacuum toilets in operation on a daily basis.

Mark Wolocatiuk

Mark must go to bed every night feeling lucky, and wake up every morning terrified. He's a driving instructor for a racing school, and he took time out from his schedule of near-death experiences to test Adam and Kari's driving when on a cell phone, and when drunk.

Myths: ***Cell Phone v Drunk Driving***

MARK – We did go past the stop sign here, right off the bat, by about four or five feet, so we ended up in the crosswalk.

Maselli and Sons

When you look up Maselli and Sons on the net and their page says they have a large inventory and too many items to mention, you just know that this is the God's honest truth (and that the seven acres of Petaluma devoted to this collection is seven acres Petaluma is never getting back). Adam swung by for a 200PSI pressure tank to use for their *Chicken Gun* and relieve the pressure of a large argument that he'd started with Jamie.

See also: ***Machinery & Equipment Company***

Myths: ***Chicken Gun***

Mass

If you're one of the many who think 'mass' is just another way to say 'weight' so it fits into the four squares allotted to 23 down, then you'd be wrong. 'Weight' is the ghastly number that blinks at you on the scales when you're squashing them into the planet Earth at more or less standard atmospheric pressure. However, dive into a swimming pool and suddenly those scales don't read so badly (if indeed they read at all). Hop about on the moon and it's a different story again, and never mind outer space – you will 'weigh' nothing at all. Mass is another

story and not so easy to shift without frequent trips to the gym and scrupulous dieting. Mass is that curious property of all things (except photons) that makes it *have* weight in a gravitational field. Strangely, the physicists who love to identify the basic elements of nature still haven't quite identified just where that 'massive' property is – no matter how small they dice the atomic pie into quarks, leptons and bosons. They've got a hunch that mass is squirreled away inside the Higgs Boson, but as no-one's ever spotted one of these, the possibility exists that mass (and hence weight) is just a figment of your imagination.

***See also:* density, kilogram, pound, ounce**

Mass Spectrometer

Because different particles have different and unique masses (or mass-to-charge ratios for the picky) you can work out what they are by measuring their mass. Say you had a container of flatus for example, you could (very, very carefully) place a sample in a mass spectrometer and measure all the different particles that it contained.

***See also:* flatus**

Massive

In reference to the structure of rocks, those without an internal structure are described as massive. Such rocks, like granite, retain their properties of strength and toughness when quarried into smaller sizes.

***See also:* granite**

Matt Broad

The San Mateo County Sheriff's Office Canine Unit is blessed with some top talent – man and beast. Matt has the lucky job of working as handler with Morgan the bloodhound, and it's great work.

***See also:* Morgan, Bloodhound**

***Myths:* Dog Special**

MATT – Morgan did really well on the test overall. It looked like we had a little bit of a problem at the shed, but actually in reality the thing I liked about it, Morgan never gave up. You can see it on the tape. He's always looking for the scent. He's always searching for it, and the two trails that went in and went out were actually, I think from the way he worked, really close together. So he just kept working until he found the way out, and once he found the way out he nailed it.

Porky got ink!

Matt Heron

Special effects creator Matt was pulled into service when the myth *Blown Away* was … blown away. How do the studios do it?

MATT – You're going to pull and it's a timing thing. So you pull, he's going to go flying in the air and when he gets over the mats ease him in gently.

Matt Thomsen

In August 2003, Matt was struck by lightning and survived. Impressive, although while at least 1000 people are struck by lightning and die, many more are struck and survive. More impressive was the fact that the lightning seemed to have been attracted to Matt's tongue stud. Adam and Jamie were on to this in a flash – would a tongue stud make you more susceptible to a lightning strike?

***Myths:* Lightning Strikes Tongue Stud**

MATT – I got struck by lightning?

MAN – Yes.

MATT – How the hell did that happen?

Matty the Tattooist

When the Mythbusters went after the myth of *Exploding Tattoo,* Scottie drafted in her friend and tattoo artist Matty to ink up a nice leg of pork with some iron-rich Mythbuster-brand tattoo ink. But as to the idea of an MRI machine making a real tattoo explode, Matty was doubtful …

MATTY – I don't think that it's true … I've never heard anybody come into a tattoo parlour and say 'I went and got an MRI and my tattoo exploded.' I think that would be pretty big news.

***See also:* tattoo**

***Myths:* Exploding Tattoo**

Maya Collard

There's fashion and then there's retro fashion. And then there's Civil War retro fashion – such as they worn by the parties subject to the myth of *Son of a Gun*. If you were to be impregnated by the hot remnants of semen on a Minié Ball, what might you choose to wear?

> MAYA ... pantalettes, and a chemois. She'd wear her corset over the top of that, and then she would have four to five petticoats, and then she'd put her dress on.

Measurement

The point about measurement is that everyone in the world can understand and agree with the findings you make, and thus celebrate them in the very next issue of the *Smart Boffin's Weekly*. If you go around measuring things in some obscure and out-dated regional syntax then you'll fail to hit Mars with your rocket and be laughed at from Ancud to Zhob – and quite rightly. Adam and Jamie do sometimes revert to their old school, dyed in the wool, zimmer-frame past and speak in pounds and ounces (and only occasionally cubits, spans and shaftments) and then sometimes become bright, sparkling internationalists who revel in centimetres, grams and litres. There are a thousand grams in a kilogram, as the word suggests, and only 20 ounces (or something) in a pound, as the name most certainly does not suggest. So let's all get on the same page – are you with us?

***See also:* kilograms, pounds, ounces, mass, Zhob**

Mechanical Advantage

The curious world of mechanical advantage is one in which many scratch their heads, whilst many more forgo head-scratching for wise nods, backed only by screaming ignorance. Never fear – explanation is here. A mechanical advantage is realized by a mechanical system when it is able to multiply the force enacted upon it. A classic example is the block and tackle, where multiple pulleys located on an object to be lifted as well as anchored to another point are able to multiply the pulling force – making the weight appear lighter to lift, although a correspondingly longer amount of rope needs to be pulled as well. Think of going up a hill on your 10-speed pushbike and you'll get the idea. Adam and Jamie take advantage of mechanical advantage in *Barrel of Bricks* and any other time they're relying on pulleys and rope.

***See also:* block and tackle, pulley, rope**

***Myths:* Barrel of Bricks**

Medical Team

Whether it's Paul, Sanjay or any of the other highly experienced and generous medical personnel who've helped out by making sure the team stay vertical (even when horizontal – we're thinking *Chinese Water Torture* and *Buried Alive* for instance) we love them all. Thanks for keeping the Mythbusters alive through more than 100 episodes!

Medieval

Usually descriptive of something beyond archaic, intimating senseless violence or mindless ignorance, the Medieval period (aka the Middle Ages) extended from the end of the ancient world (around the 5th Century) to the start of modern times (around the 16th Century).

***Myths:* Tree Cannon**

Medieval Gunpowder

So, you like gunpowder – but you're a bit of a medieval buff so what you'd REALLY like to pack into your *Tree Cannon* is some of the old fashioned stuff. What's different about old gunpowder to the newfangled gunpowder formula? Not much really, it's all about the purity of those same basic ingredients; saltpetre, sulphur and charcoal.

***See also:* gunpowder, saltpetre, sulphur, carbon**

***Myths:* Tree Cannon**

Memory Test

Ever had the dream where you were quizzed about your own life? Sometimes it comes true – especially if you happen to be a Mythbuster. To sort out once and for all who was the *Ultimate Mythbuster* Adam and Jamie quizzed each other on myths of the past, delving into details of what, where, how many, and how much black powder to blow it all up. The winner by a half point? Jamie Hyneman.

See also: ***tortilla throw, fear test, guess your weight, egg drop, pain test***

Myths: ***Ultimate Mythbusters Special***

Meridian

An arc of meridian is an imaginary straight line that travels all the way from the North Pole to the South Pole without even stopping for lunch. All the points along a meridian are different latitudes, while points on different meridian lines are different longitudes. All arcs of meridian are equivalent in length, which makes them a great excuse for a unit of measurement.

See also: ***longitude, latitude, nautical mile***

METHANOL

Yet another hydrocarbon, this one turns up inside formaldehyde, plastic, fuel, antifreeze and animal feed.

See also: ***hydrocarbons, formaldehyde***

MEYER SOUND

With all the brains of Dr Roger Schwenkee behind them, how can Meyer Sound go wrong? Building top of the line concert speakers isn't a job for the faint of heart (someone's got to test them to 11) and this team of sound engineering professionals put the highest technology in the hands of the best craftspeople to turn out the kind of speakers that let even Adam sing a glass to pieces.

See also: ***Roger Schwenkee***

Myths: ***Breaking Glass, Duck Quack Echo, Brown Note***

ADAM – I did it! Wow!

JAMIE – Well there you go.

ADAM – That was great.

JAMIE – You have graduated. You're now a full vocalist.

M5

Properly M5 Industries (or M5I) this is the company founded by Jamie to create special effects gadgets for motion pictures, television and just for fun. The name was Adam's idea, and was meant to reference James Bond's gadget making team – Q Branch. But as you can see, Adam's brain misfired, mistaking Q Branch with MI5, and thus a misnomer was born. M5 is based in the San Francisco Bay Area, and the facility consists of many 'departments' that include the machine shop, the modelshop, the woodshop, mouldmaking, painting, electronics, fabrication, robotics and welding. All exciting dangerous stuff, especially as while the regular M5 employees are making all kinds of fab stuff, a global television phenomenon is being shot wherever they are not.

See also: ***everything***

Myths: ***all of them***

Michael Martin

Dr Martin is a polygraphist (say it right or go to Utah) with 15 years and 8000 lie detection tests to his credit – and on cases as diverse as the Columbine school massacres and a Mike Tyson paternity suit. Adam and Jamie (who understandably impressed with Dr M's moustache) brought him in to discover which members of the build team were involved in a scandalous petty theft for *Nothing But the Truth*.

MICHAEL – In your particular case, it was your skin glands that were the most telling. You just couldn't suppress it.

Microwaves

Microwaves are one of the most popular brands of electromagnetic radiation, along with infrared, ultraviolet, radio and of course the waves of the visual light spectrum. While we don't see them, what we know as a microwave is a wave of electromagnetic radiation that is anywhere from 1 mm to 30 cm long. We use them for communicating and – of course – cooking small dogs. No, not really, but this was one mythette referred to in the *Microwave Madness* trio.

***See also:* electromagnetic radiation**

Microwave Ovens

Powered by what is essentially a radio transmitter (hold up a radio to a microwave if you don't believe me) called a magnetron, which funnels and directs the flow of electromagnetic radiation into your bowl of soup or, if you're particularly sick, a small dog called Jazzie.

Microwave Madness

Three myths for the price of one! A fundamental misunderstanding of the humble microwave is at the heart of all these myths – from the tanning bed that doesn't even use microwaves (but rather ultraviolet light), to the fact that microwaves cook from the inside out (they cook from the outside in). More interesting was the investigation into metal in microwaves – while it won't make a microwave explode, the right shape of metal (say a fork, or a scrunched up piece of aluminium foil) will act as an antenna for all that electromagnetic energy, and the sparks will fly. The myth that turned out to be true was that water can become superheated in a microwave.

ADAM – Hey. Spectacular.

JAMIE – That would suffice.

ADAM – That was exploding water.

JAMIE – It erupted. It left the container.

ADAM – Yep.

JAMIE – Quite a bit of it.

Mike Barrett

Mike's hay farm is just outside of Sacramento produces more than two million bales a year, and had plenty of product to offer the lads when they came shopping for the myth *Needle in a Haystack*.

JAMIE – Have you ever found a needle in the hay?

MIKE – No, I can't say I have. I've never found one.

Mike Bushroe

Monday to Friday Mike was controlling cameras on a spaceship bound for Saturn (really, he was) but for many weeks after viewing the original *Ancient Death Ray* episode Mike's weekends were devoted to building his own backyard death ray. But the trip from Arizona to California for the Mailbag Special was obviously paved with speed bumps…

MIKE - I worked really hard to get a chance to be here and show my stuff off to Adam and Jamie, and now I don't see how I can possibly do it, because it's so trashed, it's not going to showcase what I was able to do before it left. It's ruined.

Myths: ***Mailbag Special***

Mike Fournier

Mike knows his guns, and he especially adept with rare or unusual models. Thus he was able to furnish Adam and Jamie with a special weapon for the *Firearms Folklore* myth.

Myths: ***Firearms Folklore***

MIKE - This is the actual one hundred percent true copy of a Vietnam sniper rifle.

JAMIE - So is that a good rifle?

MIKE - Oh, man. You could hit a fly at five hundred yards with this if you're a good sniper.

Mike McLaughlin

Guard dog training wouldn't be everyone's cup of dog food, but for Mike, working with the German Shepherds like Eewan at Witmer Tyson Kennels is a calling and a joy. The Build Team tried a range of tactics to sneak past Eewan, and with a bite packing upwards of 550 pounds of force, any sneaking might have consequences…

MIKE - Anybody want to try it?

GRANT - Yeah - Tory volunteers.

See also: ***Eewan, German Shepherd***
Myths: ***Dog Special***

Miguel Ochoa

If it classifies as 'white goods' (a quaint old term) then Rancho Grande Appliances sells it, and Miguel can sort the sheep from the goats on your behalf. Which one would Miguel suggest for holding 50 pounds of clothes to test the myth of the *Killer Washing Machine*?

MIGUEL - The large one.

Myths: ***Killer Washing Machine***

Mind Control Chips

OK, so there are those out there in the broad diaspora of humanity who are just a little bit ... paranoid. Sometimes these people get certain ... ideas .... after presenting at a local hospital for a minor ailment, and sometimes this idea might be something like, 'the hospital staff have just planted a mind control chip inside me'. Of course, in these circumstances you reach for the nearest stud finder to affirm your suspicions. Adam and Jamie begin testing this myth by giving blood themselves at a local American Red Cross station, then Jamie sets Adam the task of using a stud finder to find hidden items behind a wall, including electrical wiring, studs and microchips. Although the first two were all easily findable with the stud finding technology to hand, Adam didn't find a microchip (or the wiring twisted to say 'Adam is a Spasm'). But could a stud finder spot a microchip buried in your flesh? Adam's ballistics gel experiment suggests so, but a lot of false positives at the same time. A dog test showed that flesh and blood was no problem for the stud finder. But the reality? When Adam and Jamie gave blood, not a skerrick of microchip action was found.

***See also:* Becky O'Connor, stud finder, Jeff Proulx**

Ming Dynasty

Although famous as the age of the intricately painted porcelain vase so frequently broken for comedic purposes, the Ming Dynasty of China saw a revival of agricultural systems, increased trade and activity with the West (all those vases...) that lasted from the 14th to the 17th century. As well the period gave rise to a burgeoning bureaucracy and the sophistication of many technologies, among them that of rocketry. Ahhh, now we're in Mythbusters territory. The Chinese had invented gunpowder of course, and were by now looking at innovative things to do with it, including making mines, exploding ordinance along with winged and multi-stage rockets. Government official, inventor and astrologer of the period Wan Hu, however, was not a success story, as the myth *Ming Dynasty Astronaut* made abundantly clear, and brought a whole new meaning to the word die-nasty.

***See also:* gunpowder, rockets, Wan Hu**

***Myths:* Ming Dynasty Astronaut... oh look, its right there.**

ADAM – Buster, aka Chinese astrologer, was completely obliterated. I mean the amount of heat was just unfathomable.

JAMIE – I really think that's one of the sillier myths that we could have run across.

Ming Dynasty Astronaut

When 15th century chinaman and rocketry enthusiast Wan Hu strapped himself into a throne with 47 top-shelf Ming Dynasty fireworks around him (and 47 attendants to light them) what was he thinking? Was he thinking 'Ah, now I will experience the low air-pressures and diminished gravitational pull of the extremes of the Earth's atmosphere'? Or was he thinking 'Damn, this was a stupid idea'? The results of the *Ming Dynasty Astronaut* tests seemed to suggest the latter, but Adam and Jamie took it all super seriously, finding bamboo casings for their period rockets, trying to mix their own Ming-era gunpowder (it didn't work, but …) and making a couple of repro Ming Dynasty thrones. By the time the experts in rocketry were called in, all they needed do is load the M5 truck and high-tail it to a quiet (and extremely hot) corner of the Mojave Desert. There they pack their 47 bamboo rockets with Morocco-blend gunpowder, attach them to the chair, add Buster, and stand well back. The result matched reports of the original myth reasonably closely – a great explosion, lots of smoke – but whereas Wan Hu had supposedly disappeared (into outer space) Buster was a smouldering wreck. Take two, with 47 top-shelf modern rocket engines, each with 50 pounds of thrust, and Buster managed a brief lift off – before flipping over and completing the burn from the 'prone' or 'death' position.

See also: Jack Morocco, Wan Hu, Ming Dynasty, E & D Gates, thrust, rockets

ADAM – And even if you got all of that to work perfectly there's NO WAY that this chair with these rockets is getting to 17,800 miles an hour … 28,646 km/h… and into orbit.

JAMIE – No, myth busted.

ADAM – Myth busted.

CHRISTINE – Completely.

ADAM – Let's go home. I need to get into a pool.

Minié Ball

It wasn't really a ball, more of a cylindro-conoid with another cylindro-conoid space in its rear. If all this isn't making sense, let's step back. We're talking about a bullet – in fact, the bullet de jour for those involved in a little action called the US Civil war. Its innovation over previous bullets was that when you poured your gunpowder down your muzzle, dropped in your Minié, rammed it down with the ramrod then you fired the rifle, the gunpowder inside the cylindro-conoid space in the rear of the Minié forced it to expand. This made the Minié grip the edges of the barrel, which imparted a goodly amount of spin, even enough to impart accuracy and power across 1000 yards; suffice, enough to kill a man. The Minié ball suffers from being frequently mispronounced (full marks plus a wink from the French teacher for *MIN-ee-AY*). Oh, and 'cylindro-conoid' just means bullet-shaped).

***See also:* US Civil War**

***Myths:* Son of a Gun, Firearms Folklore**

Mirror Neurons

Yawn. The reason advertising, mob violence and Nazi Germany might have happened is because of these mirror neurons, which are special kinds of brain cells. Sounds nasty – why not get rid of them then? Because they might also be at the root of language, empathetic emotion and the root essence of humanity and civilization. Probably worth hanging on to until the final studies are in then…

***See also:* yawning.**

Mission Dolores

The oldest church in San Francisco is also the oldest building, circa 1776. Don't confuse it with the larger church beside it – it's the little building that has the pedigree. Adam and Jamie paid a visit when researching *Buried Alive* and spoke to Brother Guire Cleary.

***See also:* Brother Guire Cleary**

***Myths:* Buried Alive**

Mixture

As opposed to an element or a compound, a mixture does not involve anything more than a bit of mechanical mixing. This means it can be unmixed – that is, no reactions have occurred between the ingredients that would make an unmixing impossible. Seawater is a mixture, as is milk and dynamite (no prizes for guessing what would *actually* be easier to unmix). Of course, that's all science talk – if you're a kid with a few eggs, some curry powder and a bottle of chocolate sauce then a mixture is whatever mess you can make and feed to your dog.

See also: ***compound, element, dynamite, seawater***

Mobile Phones

In something less than 20 years the mobile phone has already squirmed its way firmly into our urban mythology. Is it its ubiquity? Its mystery? One thing is certain – if we actually knew how they worked, we'd probably make up fewer myths about them (from whether they can blow up a gas station, to whether driving with them is as bad as driving drunk). The mobile phone is called a 'cell phone' in the USA for a very good reason – they were designed around the idea that 'cells', or areas of wireless coverage which would cross over and communicate in such a way that you could make a phone call that might start from one cell, and as your limo/scooter/feet carried you through the urban jungle, the cells would relay the phone call from one to another. Mobile phones do not call direct one to another, nor do they give off sparks – but they are MOST DEFINITELY a danger on the public highways. Brain cancer? We'll let you know.

Myths: ***Cell Phone Gas Station, Cell Phone Aeroplane, Mobile/Cell Phone v Drink Driving***

Moffett Field

Not so much a field as a Federal Air Facility that just happens to have air hangars large enough to be handy for testing myths free of wind and weather interference. Adam and Jamie have set up rigs here to test *Helium Football*, as well as *Concrete Glider* and *Seven Paper Fold*.

Mojave Desert

A big chunk of California is devoted to something called the Mojave Desert, as well as large parts of other states nearby like Nevada, Utah and Arizona. The name comes from a tribe indigenous to the area, and this is a giant, magical, mystical place full of extraordinary life and beauty. Oh, and things the Mythbusters are just as interested in such as airplane graveyards and big stretches of nothing in particular where no-one will complain if you blow up a crash test dummy attached to a Ming Dynasty throne. Adam is probably less fond of the desert than Jamie, and sometimes when the temperature soars, the redhead can only muster up one word:

***Myths:* Explosive Decompression, Ming Dynast Astronaut**

Mojito

After a long, hot day busting myths, Adam Savage likes nothing better than to repair to a favourite bar (address withheld) and summon up his favourite after-work beverage. The Mojito is a cocktail that originated in Cuba and contains six ingredients, including lime juice, mint leaves and sugar cane juice, which are muddled (a technical term) with a wooden stick before adding crushed ice, carbonated water and, finally, white rum. A few sips leave the fortunate drinker with a profound sense that the tensions, stresses and conflicts the rest of the world are currently enjoying can be ignored for the immediate future

Molecules

They're small, they're cheeky and they're everywhere. Molecules are the building blocks of everything. 'What about atoms?!', we hear you cry. Atoms are only cool if they've turned themselves into a molecule.

Molecules rule, and if you could understand them completely then an understanding of all the universe would be yours. But more about molecules – how big are they? Well, as big as a couple of atoms jammed together – that is, not very big at all. Nevertheless, contemporary nano-engineering is dealing on a molecular scale, and so eventually there will be myths relating to whether molecules can really do this or that. But so far, molecules and Mythbusters are only touching on the level of smell – for it is the molecules of a 'whatever' that waft up your nose (or that of a Bloodhound called Morgan) that tell your brain what that 'whatever' is. Think about that next time you're cleaning a *Stinky Car*.

***See also:* smell, Morgan**

***Myths:* Flatulence Myths, Stinky Car, Dog Myths**

Monterey Bay Aquarium

Pumping 2000 gallons (7570 litres) a minute through their facility (the fish tanks rather than the administrative offices) Monterey Bay Aquarium know about the life of the sea, so it was the logical place for Adam and Jamie to go to ask about the myth of *Octopus Pregnancy*.

***Myths:* Octopus Pregnancy**

Morgan

In the *Dog Myths* special this two and a half year old bloodhound was a sight to behold. Nothing escapee Adam did would put Morgan off his scent – and Adam had the full list of supposed ways to foil him. But zig-zags, showers, changes of clothes and coffee would not put off a trained Bloodhound when he has a sniff of his prey. But the prey had a good time:

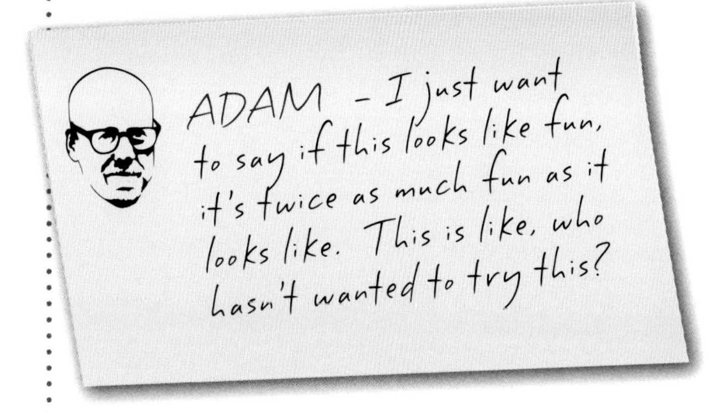

***See also:* Matt Broad, Bloodhound**

***Myths:* Dog Special**

Mould

A mould is a vessel carved, drilled or otherwise shaped to make another object. The Mythbusters use moulds to make everything from replicas of Adam's head to ice bullets.

Mpemba Effect

The curious phenomenon where hot water can freeze faster than cold water was the discovery of a high school student from Tanzania in the 1960s. Scientists have all sorts of explanations – which is pretty definitive proof that they're not 100 per cent sure why it should happen. Is it a myth waiting to happen? Or will this volume be beaten to the scoop by the process of publication?

See also: ***water, water vapour, steam***

Moustache

Sometimes called 'moustaches' by those seeking facial hair credibility, this covering of the upper lip and beyond has been a staple of homo erectus ever since hair began its slow retreat from the rest of the face. A moustache defines a visual follicular presence between mouth and nose, and Jamie's moustache is on its way to becoming the most famous moustache in the history of television, already edging out Hulk Hogan, Borat, Frank Zappa and is only a hair's breadth from Magnum PI. Jamie's moustache style would be described as Pancho Villa meets Friedrich Nietzsche, as in fact, could the man himself. Adam Savage also has a moustache, but it is often confused with a goatee.

See also: ***goatee, Jamie Impersonation***

MP5 Submachine gun

Used by the military and law enforcement agencies in 60 or more countries the MP5 submachine gun has many friends, including the Mountain Village Police Department where it was the submachine gun of choice when Adam and Jamie let a few rounds do the talking in *Avalanche Adventures*. They wanted to start an avalanche with a firearm – not so much as a flake was disturbed.

See also: ***firearms***

Myths: ***Avalanche Adventures***

Mr Bean

British actor and writer Rowan Atkinson developed the character Mr Bean when he was supposed to be studying electrical engineering at university. The physical comedy of Mr Bean has been explored several times by the Mythbusters, specifically in *Carried Away* and *Painting with Explosives*. Frankly it is about time Mr Bean did an episode with the Mythbusters set in M5 – Jamie would be a perfect foil.

MRIs

If you agree that there's very few things as exciting as big, powerful magnets used for the greater good of humanity, then you will join with us in celebrating the wonder that is the magnetic resonance imaging (MRI) machine. If you'd invented it then you'd be sipping champagne right now, still glowing from picking up the Nobel Prize for your efforts (or gnashing your teeth over the injustice of being overlooked for your contribution – depending on who specifically you are in this little fantasy world of yours…). Magnetic resonance imaging devices use a magnetic field about 100,000 times as strong as the Earth's to make all the protons inside the hydrogen atoms in a chunk of your body line up like they were the so many iron filings on so many sheets of card in a school science class. Just when the protons think all is fine, the MRI hits them with a brief burst of radio waves which flip the protons around, and when the protons flip back they send out a teeny burst of radio waves of their very own. These waves represent the particular kind of tissue of which they are a part – be that muscle, organ or sebaceous cyst – and this is all captured as an image for you and your doctor to look at and marvel at the wonder that is the MRI. The Mythbusters sent Scotty to get an MRI to test whether the iron oxide based ink many tattoos are created in would … you know, explode and stuff. They didn't.

***Myths:* Exploding Tattoo**

Multi-Meter

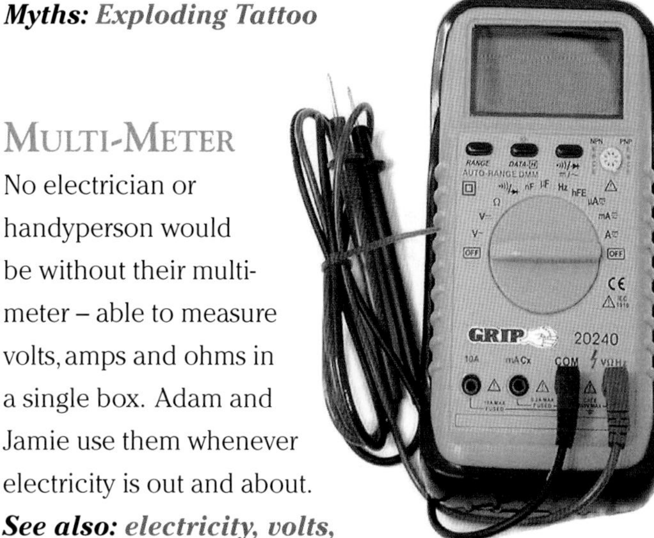

No electrician or handyperson would be without their multi-meter – able to measure volts, amps and ohms in a single box. Adam and Jamie use them whenever electricity is out and about.

***See also:* electricity, volts, amps, ohms**

***Myths:* Appliances in the Bath**

Mute

A mute is an item deliberately added to a musical instrument in order to affect the sound that it makes. While a vast array of noisemakers can be muted, the classic mutes are found on brass instruments, and the Mythbusters went to town on mutes when they took on the myth of the *Exploding Trombone*. They filled them with explosives to see if they could create a rocket, and certainly created a lot of mess and broken instruments. The myth was, however, busted. Mute can also mean a person unable to speak, in which sense it has rarely, if ever, been applied to Adam.

See also:* *trombone, slide
Myths:* *Exploding Trombone

Mythbusters

Mythbusters is a television program produced since 2003 by Beyond Productions for the Discovery Channel, SBS television and sundry other broadcasters. It uses the methods of science to reveal the truth behind everyday urban myths for an audience of millions all over the world. The series was conceived by Peter Rees, a television producer with a particular interest in bringing science and entertainment together for all to enjoy. The name 'Mythbusters' was plucked from the ether as it seemed appropriate for a show that would bust urban mythologies, but this didn't stop a previous user of the name from making a big fuss and hiring all kinds of lawyers in an attempt to make a few bucks. Mythbusters prevailed, and will continue to do so as long as human beings make stuff up rather than think.

See also:* *Beyond Productions, Discovery Channel, Peter Rees, John Luscombe, Adam Savage, Jamie Hyneman... and everyone else!

Mythopedia

You're reading it right now.

Myths Revisited

Going by various names (Myths Redux, Myths Reopened) this is a concept of startling boldness and simplicity wherein the Mythbusters will take on criticism from fans and others and actually go back to myths to retest them. In fact, the idea of taking on criticism is at the very heart of the scientific methods that Mythbusting reflects and recommends.

Mythtanic

This nine-ton (8164 kg) tug boat was minding its own business at Embarcadero Cove, when it became the star of a rather gruesome and painful (if you're a boat) myth. *Sinking Titanic* predicted that a boat on its way to the bottom of the ocean would drag down with it anyone who happened to be floating in the water nearby. Mythtanic was prepared with re-pluggable holes that would allow the poor old tug to be sunk any number of times with a lovely cable harness they had built especially. The boat was retrieved from the ocean floor and glimpsed ever so briefly in *Pingpong Rescue* before being identified as just too darn heavy, leading to the search for Mythtanic II.

***See also:* Mythtanic II**

***Myths:* Pingpong Rescue, Sinking Titanic**

JAMIE – It's a nice little solid hunk of steel. I think it ought to go down like a rock.

Mythtanic II

Because the original Mythtanic would have required 400,000 to 600,000 ping pong balls to refloat from beneath the waves, a much smaller vessel was sought. The sea-lion infested, fibreglass-hulled Jalapeño was offered up by the marina and was perfect for the job.

***Myths:* Pingpong Rescue**

ADAM – I think it's perfect. We just have to figure out where to drill the right holes. The Jalapeno makes the perfect boat for the ping pong salvage myth. Number one, its dirt cheap. Number two it's a piece of crap so no one will mind us sinking it. Number three, its fibreglass and has actually a whole bunch of compartments which we can fill each with ping pong balls and then seal off and move on to the next. That's more ideal than we could have hoped for.

Mythtern

A portmanteau of 'Mythbuster' and 'Intern', but more specifically meaning Christine Chaimberlain or Jess Nelson.

See also:* *Christine Chaimberlain, Jess Nelson

Mythwoofer

This was one of the great builds – the Mythwoofer is (as far as can be ascertained) the largest car speaker ever designed and built by human hand. Built into a Mercedes-Benz W126 300SD Turbo and powered direct from the engine via a crankshaft and pushrod, this beast measured 51 inches (129.5 centimetres) and was made from 12 steel trapezoids welded together into a dodecagonal pyramid, stuck to a tractor tyre inner tube which acted as a diaphragm. It was then built into a housing and the diaphragm attached so that it would push some air …

JAMIE … it better work. My shirt's all dirty.

ADAM – Holy Christ, it is. Look at that.

… and push air it certainly did, to a pressure of 161.3dB at a low, low frequency of 16Hz, all controlled remotely with string. Although the lads were hoping for some more significant destruction, the Mythwoofer sent the car sunroof up through its own tracks and thus the pressure was dissipated … milliseconds before the rig failed catastrophically. But oh boy, is this ever due for the Myth Evolution treatment … perhaps in a '73 Cadillac Eldorado, possibly the widest production car ever made?

See also:* *crankshaft, Wayne Harris

Myths:* *Shattering Subwoofer

The car never stood a chance

Naghol

Occasionally spelled 'Gkol', this is the much-feted practice of the inhabitants of Pentecost Island wherein vines are tied around a person's legs who then jumps from a considerable height towards the ground, only to have the vines snap them back at the last second. The reason why apparently harks back to an occasion where a husband was chasing his wife for some misdeed, the canny woman ran up a tree and tied some vines around her ankles. As her husband climbed up after her, she jumped, and he did too … but without the vines. To this day, the men of Pentecost Island retain the tradition 'just in case'.

***See also:* Pentecost Island**

NASA

For the benefit of all, the National Aeronautics and Space Agency has reached for the skies since 1958, and with nearly $US17 billion a year it is frankly the most exciting place on this planet to work in the entire history of everything – that is, if you're crazy about technology, giant rockets, very smart people and outer space.

Nautical miles

The nautical mile is a (non SI) unit of length used in marine and aviation circles, equivalent to the distance on the surface of the Earth from one minute of latitude to the next. The minutes of latitude all exist along a meridian, and as the meridians are equal, you end up with a useful unit of measure that can confuse almost anyone not trained in open water or air navigation. Use it with pride (or … are you confused?) The cheat is that one nautical mile is worth 1852 metres or 6076 feet.

***See also:* latitude, meridian**

Neila the Cowgirl

Expert cowgirl on John Growney's ranch, Neila had the enviable task of riding Pistol the psychic horse, dragging Tory along the ground behind in the hope that his jeans would catch on fire. Where's the downside in that?

NEILA – Wow, this rope's a lot shorter than I thought it was going to be.

Neal Smither

Crime Scene Cleaners do important but nasty work. If you die horribly or just messily, then Neal Smither and his team are the ones called in to clean you up. Neal acted as a consultant when Adam and Jamie took on the myth of the *Stinky Car*. Very enthusiastic about the world of extreme cleaning (he even believed that the stinky car could be cleaned) Neal had lots of knowledge to impart – none of it nice.

NEAL – And that smell, you can taste it. You just can't even describe it, it's such a unique flavour. Um, but you know instantly what it is.

Needlefinder 2000

The extraordinary water-born cunning of Adam's Needlefinder 2000 put the previous 1999 versions of the machine to shame. It was messy though:

Needle in a Haystack

This was just 100 per cent pure fun – take two haystacks, a couple of different kinds of needles and then set Adam and Jamie the challenge, mano-a-mano. Who can build a machine (or as it turned out, a series of machines) that could turn up the needles the fastest? First they would need some hay, next some needles – different materials would mean different methodologies for their finding. It just so happens that for generations (up till recently) bone was the material of choice for the canny seamstress (or indeed seamster). This was going to make it tricky – magnets would easily find a metal needle, but … bone? Do they get hold of a dog? No … Jamie decides instead for a rotating, slotted PVC tube with a neodymium magnet at one end and a leaf blower at the other. From here hay will be funnelled into a furnace and burnt. Adam's Needlefinder 2000 relied on the floatation of hay and the sink-ation of needles encouraged by large paddlewheels – and with 10 bales of hay each to sort through the needlework was on! Jamie's team found the first metal needle, and Adam decided to re-jig his rig with a few magnets of his own. The pace was fast, furious, hot and noisy, but with the light fading, tempers fraying and fingernails pricked to pieces, in the end the Needlefinder 200(1) did the job, and took the prize – never having to find a needle in a haystack every again.

***See also:* mano-a-mano, Mike Barrett, Cathe Ray**

ADAM … My back is killing me, I'm soaked to the bone, I don't even want to think about the brown wash that comes off me in the shower tonight, it was a total nightmare to find a needle in a haystack.

Kari works the Needlefinder

Neil Sutherland

Composer ala Mythbusters, Neil wrote not only the titles music that just screams 'crazy pop science', but also (with occasional assistance) all the stings that keep the show moving from link to link. If you don't think they're important, just count the number of stings in a single episode – and it's OK to stop when you reach 100. Neil, you rock (quite literally).

***See also:* Peter Rees, John Luscombe, Dan Tapster, Beyond Productions, Bob Brozman**

Neodymium

Although this element turns up as a colouring agent in glass and enamel, and is also part of a useful system for dating the ages of meteorites, neodymium is most and justly famous for producing the best, most powerful magnets on the face of the earth. The Mythbusters drag them out as often as they can, although there are dangers involved in carrying them around. You'll see neodymium magnets being used in myths like *Needle in a Haystack* and *Crimes and MythDemeanours*.

***See also:* magnetism**

***Myths:* Needle in a Haystack**

Newton

Imagine a litre of water on a little trolley that weighs nothing whatsoever. Now imagine the force it would take to push that litre of water one metre – not much huh? Now imagine that the force continues over further seconds so that each second the speed of that little weightless trolley and its load of water increases by another metre per second. What you have is a newton – the SI unit of force, which is otherwise defined (quite seriously) as the force the Earth's gravity exerts on a standard 102g (3.5 oz) apple (even though standard apple is not a SI unit of measure). Mostly the Mythbusters relate newtons in other ways, but when someone with a bit of modern scientific training like Grant is about, you've got a chance of hearing newtons talked up. He snuck mention of newtons into the myth of *Bulletproof Teeth* and into *Christmas Special 2* when they were calculating the damage a falling turkey could cause. But even if it's not mentioned, it's always there when the team are discussing anything to do with force.

GRANT – So you can see here the initial hit is 1901 Newtons.

***See also:* force, watts, Isaac Newton, joule, torque, SI**

***Myths:* Bulletproof Teeth, Christmas Special 2**

Nikola Tesla

Credited as 'the man who invented the 20th century' due to his contributions to electricity, robotics, ballistics and the understanding of magnetism, Nikola Tesla died alone and poor aged 86. Why? He was a financial duffer. He might have bested Thomas Edison in the 'battle of the currents'

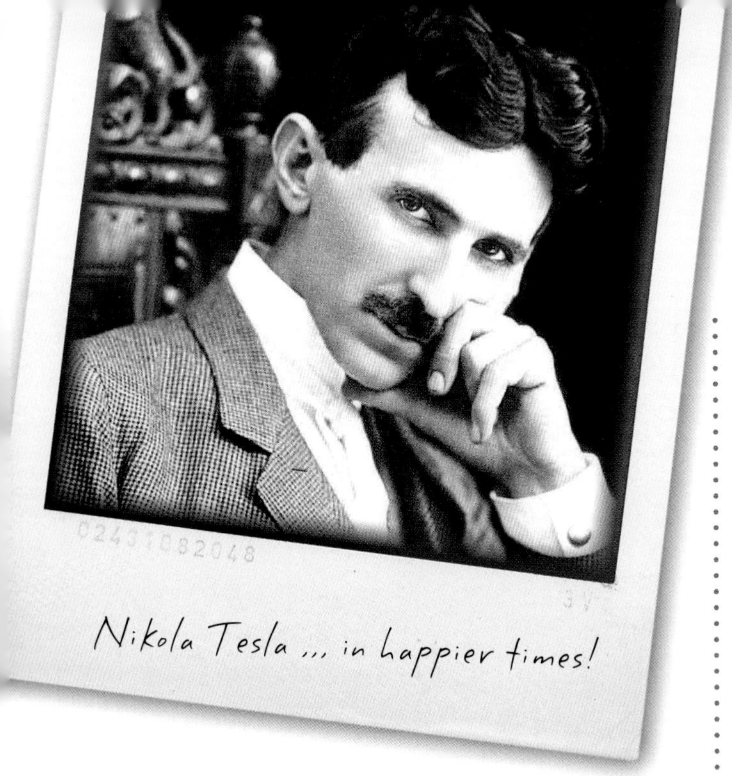

Nikola Tesla ... in happier times!

inventing AC in the process, and invented an *Earthquake Machine* (arguable) but putting one dollar away after another was not his strong suit. Ironically he's since been the face on banknotes in his homeland(s) of Yugoslavia and Serbia.

Nitrogen

At sea level and anything above -195°c nitrogen is a gas and is the major component of the air we breathe. But below -195° Celsius nitrogen is a liquid and is used in many industries (including the Mythbusting industry) to keep things cold or make things freeze very fast as they did when preparing the *Ice Bullet* or *Cooling a Sixpack*. By using pressurised nitrogen Grant was able to build a 3000 PSI cannon to fire a grappling hook in *Superhero Myths*.

Nitro-Glycerine

Once called 'blasting oil' this is indeed oily stuff, and nasty to boot. If it wasn't for the fact that it's very happy to explode we'd probably have nothing to do with it. The chief problem with nitro-glycerine (apart from it's explosive qualities, which many see as a boon) is that it'll explode at the drop of a hat – literally. Toss a Stetson on a bottle of nitro and you've got yourself a hole in the floor (not to mention any legs that happen to be standing around). Nitro-glycerine is made by mixing up one or other kind of sulphuric acid with this or that kind of nitric acid, to which glycerine is added BUT VERY SLOWLY. It almost goes without saying that you don't do this at home.

***See also:* explosives**

Nitrous Oxide

When Joseph Priestley discovered nitrous oxide in 1775 he was surprised and delighted to have found '...an air five or six times as good as common air...'. What became quickly know as 'laughing gas' was more than a bit of a giggle for doctors and their patients, who used it as the first anaesthetic. The Mythbusters found that it's oxygen side made it a perfect way to burn their paraffin fuel for the *Confederate Rocket*.

***See also:* paraffin**
***Myths:* Confederate Rocket**

Nock

The uncool end of an arrow is called the nock – the bit that you fit into the bowstring. Traditional nocks are made with a bit of goat horn in the crevice, and the only reason we tell you this is that archery-mad Mythbusters' fans insisted on complete historical accuracy for the revisit of the myth *Splitting an Arrow*.

***See also:* longbow, yew**

Nothing But the Truth

Are the Mythbusters just a bunch of liars? Taking on the polygraph would test the fibbing prowess of the Build Team once and for all. Tempted by offers of a 1st class flight, and terrified by the prospect of washing every crew member's car, Tory, Grant and Kari strap on the best polygraph-beating tricks money can buy. Will pinpoint pain cover your tracks? Will a focused mind? Let's just say not a dirty car was on the lot before the Build Team returned to the scene of the crime to test the MRI brain-mapping, lie detection technique. With $1000 or a bus ride home from South Carolina on offer, only Grant was smiling at the end of the day.

***See also:* Frank Kozel, Roy Varney, polygraph, MRI**

TORY – Holy crap!
3077 miles!

Nylon

At some point you've probably all slept through a dull presentation on the history of nylon and how it was instrumental to the war effort (depending on who you backed) and yadda yadda yadda. But nylon was not the first artificial textile (that was probably rayon) and the fact that it took three years to just NAME nylon says nothing about the chemical industry at the time, other than the fact the inventor killed himself before the name was coined. Nylon is indeed the first completely artificial textile, and is made from coal, air and water. The word 'polymer' should be used about now, before some list of the amazing properties of strength, durability and economy (one a certain scale of production is developed) that nylon can claim. The fact that more than 70 per cent of the textiles we produce today has a lot to do with the commercial success of nylon – which the Mythbusters will use in applications that require strength, durability and economy (did we say that already?). An example was the rig they built for *Killer Tissue Box* which looked like being a remarkable failure until they saved it by strapping nylon around it to hold it together, adding several tens of thousand of pounds of braking force instantly and immediately.

Oats

Those which some people feed to their livestock we prefer to heat gently with water in the microwave and eat ourselves, perhaps with a little coconut and brown sugar.
***See also:* microwave, Samuel Johnson**

Octopus

These eight-armed sea creatures of the cephalopod family are so smart they can open jars, break out of an enclosure, board a chip and steal food, or recognise a soul partner in Adam.

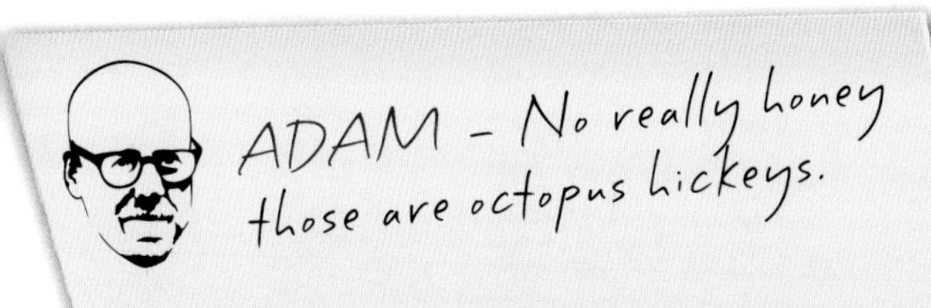

Octopi are truly amazing and if you're a student of biology or zoology looking for a PhD project, look no further. Adam and Jamie did their own research into octopus when they busted the myth of *Octopus Pregnancy*.
***Myths:* Octopus Pregnancy**

Octopus Pregnancy

An oldie, but a silly. Imagine the surprise of the mythical human female with an interest in diving who finds herself with a stomach ache, takes herself to the doctor and finds that inside her tummy there is a live octopus that's grown from a tiny egg she's swallowed. A variation on the absurd parental 'don't go swimming with boys' warning, this myth is equally crackers. Using different beakers to represent the different conditions found

inside the human stomach (temperature, salinity, acidity) the lads used octopus stand-ins (frog eggs and tadpoles) to see what is survivable. Well, salinity isn't a problem for tadpoles – 98.6° f (37.0° Celsius) and an acidity of 2 pH killed them in 15 minutes, meaning you will never have to chat casually with octopus relations at Christmas.

ADAM – Well Jamie, I think we've done everything we can to show that octopus pregnancy is absolutely ridiculous. We've busted it wide open.

JAMIE – And the octopus really liked your hand.

ADAM – I think I'm actually in love.

See also: ***octopus, parasite, pH, salinity, stomach***

Ohm

Signified by Ω, the ohm is the SI unit of electrical resistance. If that's not enough for you, then know this: Georg Ohm was a high school teacher and his experiments with electricity not only saw him discover the relationship between current, voltage and resistance. That's Ohm's Law (his lesser known laws all had to do with the amount of talk in his classroom and the speed of the chalk he'd throw at the loudest point in the room – important, but less celebrated).

See also: ***resistance, electricity***

Myths: ***Octopus Pregnancy***

Old Sow

With a speed of 14 knots and a maximum recorded diameter around 200 feet (60 metres) the Old Sow is the biggest regularly ocurring whirlpool on the planet.

See also: ***Whirlpool of Death***

One Way Valve

The name is a good hint (better than its other name which is 'check valve') because a one way valve is a special kind of valve that will only let whatever is passing through the valve (water, air, tomato sauce) through in one direction. They come in very handy when you're trying to push air into an escape raft

made of raincoats, as Adam and Jamie were in *Alcatraz Escape*, and if you're ever in this situation, you can make one from a ping pong ball ... somehow. You'll have to ask Jamie.
***See also:* valve**
***Myths:* Alcatraz Escape**

Oscillation

A primary element of a frequency is the oscillation, or the vibration, between the maximum and minimum points. Think of the swing of a pendulum, or a spring bearing a weight against gravity, these are all oscillating systems – but they occur almost everywhere in all kinds of media. If you can get your oscillation just right ... wacky stuff happens.
***Myths:* Avalanche Adventures, Breaking Glass, 360º Swing etc, Earthquake Machine, Breakstep Bridge**

ADAM – It's about tuning the amount of vibrations per second precisely to what the bar needs. It's that every time the bar flexes, when it comes back up that you're hitting it, boop, at the top of that arc. Then it goes back down and back up and bang, you're hitting it right at the top of that arc. That timing is absolutely critical to this and we saw, that once you get that timing right and you eliminate the ability of the bar to move and bounce and lose its energy, the deflection was just diabolical.

Breakstep Bridge

Ostension

An excellent example of ostension is an excellent example of ostension. For example, Adam and Jamie attempt to test the myth *Jet Car* by building an example of a jet car, replete with rocket engines. Ostension describes something demonstrated by example, say, suggesting a drink by gesturing with your hand miming a cup, or asking for the time by tapping where your wristwatch would be. In the world of folklore studies, ostension describes an urban myth that becomes accepted to the point where people actually change their behaviour. An excellent (and ostensive) example of this is the myth *Pop Rocks and Cola* where the myth that your stomach would explode if you drank too much soda with too many pop rocks made sales of the candy fall

through the floor, and 50,000 letters to high school principals and 45 pages of media advertisements could not assuage the converted. You probably accommodate many examples of ostension in your daily life – stepped on any cracks recently?
***Myths:* Pop Rocks and Soda**

Ounces

Cryptically known by its abbreviation 'oz' a single ounce is the equivalent of 28.3495231 grams. A lyrical, lilting casualness comes with talk of ounces, sadly disrupted by that fact, true of all imperial measurements, that they mean completely different things depending on where you are on the planet. Go to China, or Holland, or Ethiopia and you'll see what we mean. Oh, and the 'oz' comes from an old Italian word for ounce (onza) which has even changed spelling to 'oncia' these days. Old fashioned? Just a bit.

Oxygen

The third most abundant element in the universe and the MOST abundant in our bit of the Earth isn't all about fun times. The word 'oxygen' comes from the Greek for 'born of acid', which is surprising because we think of oxygen as vital to the prolongation of life and health, and we think of acid as a rather unpleasant, burn-y liquid stuff that eats through the floors of spaceships. In fact oxygen does turn up in rather a lot of acids ... and a lot of everything else as well. In fact it will team up with almost any other element – which is why there are so many compounds that end in 'oxide'. On Earth the prevalence of oxygen in the atmosphere is chiefly due to the work of bacteria. Once it arrived it changed the face of the planet, because oxygen is highly reactive – don't go lighting matches in a pure oxygen environment or you'll regret it. Breathing oxygen at higher than normal atmospheric pressure can lead to hyperoxia, which is nasty too. Oxygen toxicity does nasty things to your cells, and there's a good reason the beauty industry is all on about antioxidants – oxygen ain't all good! In the myth *Confederate Rocket* they find that there was no way liquid oxygen could have been used to fuel a rocket, as the technology simply didn't exist to liquidise the stuff.
***See also:* bacteria, rust**

Pacific Gas and Electric

When you need volts and plenty of them, do what Adam and Jamie do in *Phone in a Thunderstorm* and go to a place that makes their own – and has the big weird round transformers. However it's not a patch on the real thing …

ROBERT – This would be called man's feeble attempt to generate lightning. We can't even come close to generate what Mother Nature can generate.

Pain Test

There is always an opportunity to get hurt when you're busting myths – and normally strict measures are enforced to make sure this doesn't happen. However, with the title of *Ultimate Mythbuster* on the line, sometimes you need to drop the rules and prepare to get hurt. The Pain Test saw Adam and Jamie line up 'old West' style with a paintball gun apiece. The method was simple; shoot your man, take a step, take a hit…and try not to cry. The winner?

JAMIE – It's only the pain part that I like.

***See also:* tortilla throw, fear test, guess your weight, egg drop, memory test**

***Myths:* Ultimate Mythbuster Special**

Pachish

A mediaeval Hungarian tribe who became famous for blowing themselves to smithereens with a *Tree Cannon* they'd made only the night before. One of the few survivors, the chief, calmed his people by telling them that if THEY suffered such devastating mortality, how many left of the enemy could there be?

ADAM – That's the earliest known record of spin, I think.

***Myth:* Tree Cannon**

Pacifica Archery

Daly City, California is about a 5 mile (8km) trip from San Francisco, and if you like your sport pointy with feathers on the tail, then it's a trip worth taking. This was the place where the build team came to take aim at the myth of the *Splitting an Arrow*.

Painting with Explosives

Ah, Mr Bean: comedy institution and man of courage, resource and industry. When faced with a task like painting a room, Bean won't take the easy way out and reach for a brush – oh no! A stick of dynamite is all that is required, although the neighbour who walks into the room at the wrong moment would argue otherwise. Adam and Jamie set about this myth quite sensibly – they build a transportable room and take it out to the local Alameda County Bomb Disposal Range, pop some high explosive in a big bucket of paint and … blow the room to smithereens. The phrase 'back to the drawing board' beckons, and at a smaller scale the Mythbusters try and get black powder to blow paint onto a small scale room. It's not as easy as Mr Bean's scriptwriter had assumed, but eventually the lads each have a plan, and back to the range they go. Adam hopes that tubes of paint and long charges of explosives will do the job, while Jamie opts for multiple pots. Neither gets anywhere near total coverage.

***See also:* Tom Stein, Joe Konefal, Frank Doyle**

ADAM – Yeah. I think the best that can be said about what we achieved was that you found a stunning way to make instant modern art.

Palindrome

If it spells the same backwards as forwards, then it's a palindrome.

Pants on Fire

It's just another day on the prairie, just you and your trusty horse, an open horizon, until suddenly a rarely sighted Colombian Sharp-Tailed Grouse startles you both. Your steed rears, throws you to the ground, and gallops away, but as luck you have it your foot is caught in the stirrup and you are dragged behind. But that's not the worst of it – somewhere in the back of your mind you recall tell of a cowboy's jeans catching fire under just these circumstances! Could it be true?

KARI – How can you tell the sex of a chromosome?

TORY – How?

KARI – You pull down its jeans!

The panty static generator in mid ... generate?

The answer, after a combination of real horse dragging and the application of a belt sander, is no.

***See also:* belt sander, Neila the Cowgirl, ham hock, denim, cotton, Pistol the Psychic Horse, John Growney**

Panty Static Generator

A device created by Adam Savage that relied on the Triboelectric Effect to generate static electricity with: a pair of panties, a PVC pipe and a car seat covered in some fake leopard fur. A remote controlled hydraulic actuator rubs the panty-covered PVC pipe on the leopard fur-covered seat. Electrons leap from the panties to the PVC then to a

Leyden Jar, where they were stored for later explosive use. The whole experiment was conducted inside a blast chamber filled with vaporised petrol - hence the remote control. The panty static generator was used in *Cell Phone Gas Station* to establish if people getting into and out of their cars when filling up at the gas station were responsible for starting explosions.

***See also:* PVC, actuator, Leyden Jar, static**

***Myths:* Cell Phone Gas Station**

Paper

It is entirely possible that paper might have been invented elsewhere if had not been already by Chinese courtier, bureaucrat and eunuch Ts'ai-Lun (sometimes spelled Cai-Lun) but you never know. It took Europeans more than 1000 years to get up to speed on papermaking after the Chinese had already perfected it, and even then the round-eyes cheated by looking at what Arabs were doing. Today, the process is more technologically refined, but the basics have not changed. It is directly because of paper that human beings have been able to create more efficient education, financial and administrative systems than the Dark Ages, and that is a very good thing indeed. We also have paper aeroplanes, for which we should be grateful as well. The Mythbusters push paper constantly, but have turned to it in myths infrequently – the notable example being the *Paper Crossbow.*

Paper Crossbow

Can you make a lethal weapon out of paper? We know that paper cuts can be nasty, but ... lethal? Surely not! Adam and Jamie go mano-a-mano in this battle of the bureaucrats (eh?) to turn out the most lethal paper weapon. All this is based on prison reports that sharpened chunks of plastic food tray, underwear elastic and paper had been combined into an instrument of death. After messing around in prison cells, at underwear stores and with different kinds of glue, Adam and Jamie build their own weapons and fire them. Jamie's achieves a maximum speed of 60 feet per second (18.2 m/s) but Adam's crossbow, which he dubs 'Dreamcatcher' reaches 91 feet per second (27.7 m/s) and hits the ballistics gel Imahara guard in the jugular to boot!

***See also:* paper**

ADAM - Alright, Grant. Going for the neck. In three, two, one.

JAMIE - Yeah! Good shot!!

Not your general, friendly, garden-variety worms

Parasite

A living organism that feeds of another without contributing anything by way of food, rent or washing up is a parasite. You may know one yourself, or you may have one living on, in or with, you. Classic parasites like tape worms and fleas actually do some harm to their host, and are best avoided. Adam and Jamie got close to some thankfully dead parasites when they looked into the myth of *Octopus Pregnancy*.

***See also:* tapeworm, Jim McKerrow**

***Myths:* Octopus Pregnancy**

Parabolic Mirror

A parabola is a two-dimensional shape well known from its starring role in maths textbooks and with very occasional cameos in the real world thanks to the skilful addition of a third dimension. Such parabolic mirrors or dishes are top notch tools you'd find in car headlights, telescopes, a satellite dish or at the bottom of your can of soft drink – as the Build Team discovered in their quest to become the *Fire Starter*. The *Ancient Death Ray* was another example of a parabolic dish, designed apparently by the ancient inventor Archimedes in his quest to bend light to his will.

***See also:* Archimedes**

***Myths:* Firestarter, Ancient Death Ray**

Pathology

The study of pathology enriches humanity because it is the study of the diseases of which large numbers of us might otherwise be dying. The Mythbusters have rubbed shoulders with at least one professor of pathology (and you want to be careful about that) during their investigations into the *Octopus Pregnancy* myth. This professor's name was Jim and he had white hair, a little goatee and a very cool attitude.

***See also:* parasite, Jim McKerrow**

***Myths:* Octopus Pregnancy**

JIM – The acid in your stomach is there to dissolve meat and other food materials. And any type of living organism that doesn't have a way to protect itself against that is going to just wind up as digested food.

Pat Quinn

A structural engineer with experience in high-rise construction, Pat could fill the lads in on why a *Leaping Lawyer* might have smashed through the thick glass of a skyscraper.

PAT – Probably a thousand times nothing will happen, but you're dealing with a very brittle material and it doesn't give you any warning. It doesn't bend like steel, it doesn't bow like wood, it just goes 'ka-pump' and then you're out on the street.

See also: stack effect
Myth: Falling Lawyer

Paul Turek MD

A specialist in the male reproductive system at USCF, Dr P knew all about certain 'claims' that cola might act as a spermicide. We're talking *Cola Myths* here, not just a bit of light dinner party conversation.

Penetrating Trauma

Essentially we're talking about gunshot wounds, although, yes, anything that penetrates the body in a bad way is a penetrating trauma. They're defined in opposition to blunt trauma, and tend to involve a lot more bleeding outside the body. Any kind of bleeding is bad, so the best thing if on the receiving end of a penetrating trauma is to rush yourself to hospital rather than look it up in your recently acquired *Mythopedia* … thanks for thinking of us, but hurry! For the Mythbusters, penetrating trauma (or its possibility) is the focus of a couple of myths – namely *Frog Giggin'* which demonstrated that being shot in the groin could come as a direct result of injuring frogs, and *Bulletproof Water* which demonstrated that diving underwater is an excellent way to avoid penetrating trauma. Avoiding penetrating trauma is advised in all instances.

See also: blunt trauma, death
Myths: Frog Giggin, Bulletproof Water

PAUL – I think it's a great myth. To summarise, I think the experiment kind of shows what I thought would happen, which is cola will dilute the sperm but it won't be necessarily toxic to it. And a spermicide is different. A spermicide actually stays in there so it doesn't really dilute anything. It just kills the sperm on contact.

Penny

A small coin, both in actual size and in economic terms, but nevertheless a fundamental part of urban mythology. Can a penny inflict a mortal wound when it is dropped from the Empire State Building? No, as Adam and Jamie discovered in *Penny Drop*. Pennies just can't build up that kind of speed; they're not aerodynamically designed to achieve the kind of MACH3+ speeds that it would take to drive such a small mass (like, 2.5 grams) into a tough material like your brain box. Having said that, you'd be a moron to try it yourself. Oh, and cola will clean on pennies, as demonstrated in *Cola Myths*.

***Myths:* Penny Drop, Cola Myths**

Penny Drop

One of the most basic myths of all, one which every primary school kid knows, is that if you drop a penny from a REALLY tall building it will kill someone walking on the pavement below. Sounds sensible, but really it's completely crazy. A penny weighs so little that Adam and Jamie are able to shoot each other in the hand (well, Jamie shoots Adam) without lasting injury. Having previously tested the terminal velocity of a penny by jumping out of an aeroplane with a handful of them, he then builds a wind tunnel and calculates their speed to make doubly sure – it turns out they have a velocity of just 65 mph (104.6 km/h). Adam is excited – Jamie isn't.

ADAM - This matches the math, the complex equations that we have showing the velocity. I think we should go for a worse case scenario like 65 miles an hour.

JAMIE - OK. Works for me.

ADAM - This is excited Jamie.

JAMIE - Yeah.

ADAM - We've got a world first. It's going out on television that we did the experiment that showed exactly how fast a penny goes. No map, no ideas, no timing off a building. We've got it right here in the lab.

JAMIE - It's great. Good job.

ADAM - Totally %$#^&! We finally get a reasonable experiment here and he's like 'well that's great'. You know, it's like, what are you gonna do? How are you gonna please the guy?

JAMIE - I don't consider it an enormous feat to be able to you know, elevate a penny in a wind chamber.

See also: ***terminal velocity***

When in Rome... or on Pentecost Island...

Pentecost Island

One of the many islands that make up the Pacific nation of Vanuatu, Pentecost is exactly the kind of idyllic island of rainforests, rivers and mountains that you'll dream about but never actually live on. In some ways this may be a good thing, because as a fan of Mythbusters you'll be no doubt tempted to try the local tradition of land diving, locally known as naghol. This will not be good for you.

See also: ***naghol***

PermaGel™

A brand of ballistics gel, finally mentioned by name in *Jeans Death Shrinkage*.

See also: ***ballistics gel***

Myths: ***Jeans Death Shrinkage***

Peter Rees – Originator and Former Executive Producer

Peter was gainfully employed at Beyond Productions making television with a science bent when, in between all those lasers, animal attacks and miracle cures, an idea struck him: why not make a television program that would put science to work on urban myths that would otherwise become accepted wisdom? Then Peter recalled a high-functioning San Francisco special effects maestro called Jamie Hyneman with whom he'd filmed a story about his killer robot called 'Blendo'. Rees approached Hyneman about being the host of a series that would require broad technical and scientific skills. Hyneman joined forces with Adam Savage and production of the first series of one-hour programs commenced. Rees found himself in the director's chair for the following 70 episodes.

See also: ***Dan Tapster, Beyond Productions, Discovery Channel ... all of it really***

Petrarch

If Francesco Petrarca (known as Petrarch) did half the stuff he is supposed to have done, he was way cool. Living in 14th century Italy, he shrugged off the career in law that his father had ordained for him, saying 'I couldn't face making a merchandise of my mind [dude]'. Instead he traveled around Europe as the first tourist, then became the first mountaineer, the first to spot the fact that civilisation had just gone through the dark ages, the first to discover hidden works by several great ancient writers, and is best remembered for his own writing, for which he was honoured as the first ever poet laureat. It was in this capacity that he came to the notice of Adam and Jamie, who quoted his 'Remedies for fortune, fair and foul.' In the *Steam Cannon* episode.

ADAM – We have, 'what used to be thrust forth by the clouds of heaven is now being thrust forth by a machine conceived in hell.'

The reference is broad to say the least, but if only valuable as an introduction to the work of the first humanist, then Mythbusters, we are grateful.

***See also:* humanism**

***Myths:* Steam Cannon**

pH

The yin and yang of chemistry is acidity and alkalinity, measured in terms of a scale called pH (pronounced pH). Although pH is essentially a logarithmic system for measuring the presence or otherwise of hydrogen ions, the term 'pH' was coined by a cheeky Scandinavian chemist called Søren Sørensen, and stands for 'potential hydrogen'. Purists will argue that it really means exactly the same thing, with the same initials, but in Latin. The pH scale runs (logarithmically) from zero to 14. Bang in the middle is pure water with a pH of seven. Acids are down towards the zero end (even in the negatives for the very strong stuff like the superacid Fluoroantimonic acid) and bases are up towards the 14 end. Adam and Jamie are known to mess around (in a safety conscious manner) with both ends of the pH spectrum when the mood takes them, or to do a little light Mythbusting.

***Myths:* Octopus Pregnancy, Salsa Escape, Pop Rocks and Soda, Exploding Pants**

Phase Transition

Simply put, a phase transition is a transition from one phase to another. Aha, but what are these phases? All materials have at least three phases – the most common being solid, liquid and gas. Taking water as an example, the solid phase is ice, the liquid phase is water, and the gas phase is water vapour. Ice melts into water, then vaporises into water vapour. In the other direction, water vapour condenses into water, then freezes into ice. Materials don't have to go from solid through liquid – they can move straight to gas (or vice versa) as does carbon dioxide when it sublimates into a gas from a solid, and deposes into a solid form being a gas. The arbiter of all these changes is temperature, the lower the temperature the more materials change into solids, and the hotter the temperature the more they become gases (or even plasmas – but we won't go there).

***See also:* sublimation, carbon dioxide, steam**

Pheromones

Pheromones are simply chemicals made special in that they are exuded by a species with the purpose of changing the behaviour of another member of that species. In the *Dog Special* Eewan the German Shepherd was able to be tempted from duty by the scent of a female dog on heat.

***Myths:* Dog Special**

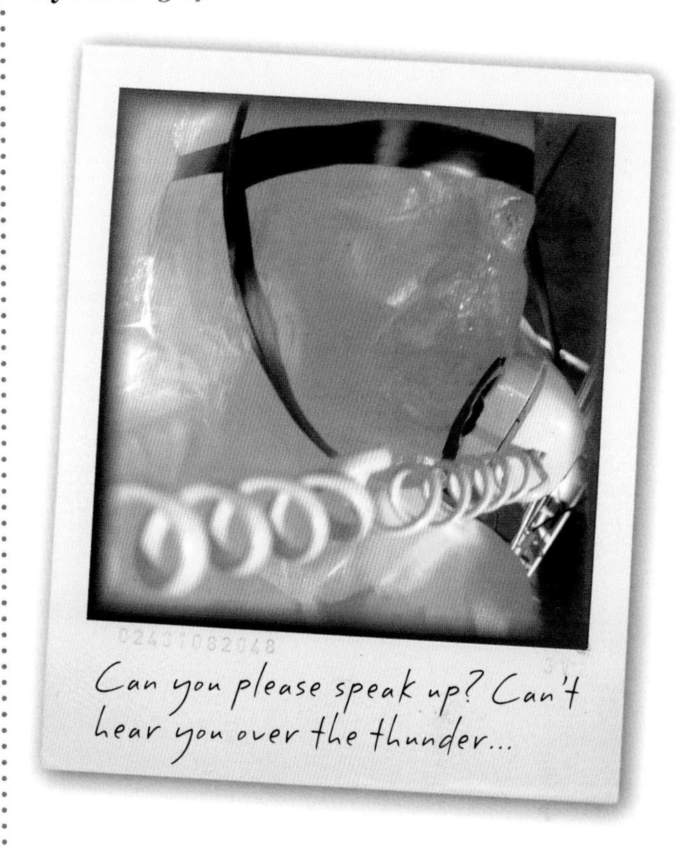

Can you please speak up? Can't hear you over the thunder...

Phone in a Thunderstorm

Ever picked up the phone and got a million volts in your ear? No, and that's why you're here today to read this exciting and informative book. But would it really happen? If lightning struck your house when you were on the phone, would you

get fried? How about in the shower? Adam and Jamie love a bit of high tension, and so after building a chunk of house and getting it wired 'to code' they set out in search of the big zaps. However Chip (the ballistics gel dummy) has escaped unscathed. Seems this 'building code' and its ground wires has some purpose after all! A few modest alterations by Adam (that is, cutting that darn ground wire) and Chip is fried – and the electromagnetic pulse from the zap is so strong it throws their cameras out of focus! They proceed to the shower, and with Chip's foot on the (grounded) plug hole, generate a baby bolt of lightning which is enough to start a fire, but the test on Chip's voltmeter is inconclusive. Again, the ground wire might have saved him … but, would you take the chance? Adam has the take-home advice…

ADAM – Stay away from things that can conduct lightning to you. Appliances can do it, water can do it, your plumbing can do it. Stay away from those things. I think we're done.

See also: **conductivity, building code, ground wire**

Phrenology

If phrenology was true then Adam Savage should be right now gainfully employed as an assistant canal lock operator, and Jamie as a rat catcher. This is not the case. Phrenology is the (ahem) 'science' of reading the bumps and divots in the human skull, and has long been a source of quality laughs among thinking people from Kansas to Kalimantan. A pity really – if only SOMEONE still believed in it then Adam and Jamie could set about busting it …

Phosphoric Acid

The active (and tasty) ingredient in everybody's favourite cola (or top two) is an excellent way to clean up rust, or lower the density of your bones, or fix the pH in your face cream, and gives your glass of black refreshment that certain tangy something as well. Adam and Jamie tangled with phosphoric acid H_3PO_4 in *Cola Myths*.

See also: **cola**

Pick-up Truck

Called a ute in Australia and New Zealand, a backie in South Africa, a kangaroo-chaser by Henry Ford and goodness knows what elsewhere in the world, these much-loved metal workhorses have been taken to the hearts of honest working folk everywhere. They combine the comfort of a passenger vehicle with the utility (hence 'ute') of a truck. With a tray in the back, you could take your pigs to the market on a Friday, and then your family to church on a Sunday (or vice versa). Adam and Jamie love their pick-up truck, and they've found a couple of myths that needed a-bustin' that relate – namely *Tailgate Up or Down?* However, the pick-up is a background presence in countless other myths, just toting gear or materials from place to place, never fussing, never arguing, just doin' the job it was born to do (and loving it).

***See also:* anthropomorphism, vortex**

***Myths:* Tailgate Up or Down? and Chicken Gun**

Pigs

This is not in any way a reference to individuals employed in the law enforcement industry, who are very generous in their support and encouragement of Mythbusting. The pigs we're talking about are real swine; that's right – flat-nosed, curly-tailed beasties much loved by Adam and Jamie for being those 'go to' pals when they need a subject on which to test something that is more real, internal or … stinky than Buster can get. The truth is that pigs mirror human beings in many ways – physiologically and (some argue) emotionally. With organs and internal architecture are not so different from our own, you'll have spotted them in myths like *Pop Rocks and Soda* and *Stinky Car.* Pigs are intelligent, omnivorous mammals given to foraging and frequent mud baths but when washed down, grilled and served with a little apple

sauce, taste fantastic (although under those circumstances the physiological mirroring doesn't bear too much thinking about). A dead pig or two can come in very handy, but have to get the right bits – and as the lads have discovered, this can be tricky.

ADAM (on phone) – Does it have like the oesophagus and the intestines attached at all? I need all the tubes attached to it. Would it be possible to get it with as much of the attachments to it as possible?

Only 59,950 to go...

The good news is that sometimes you just want a bit of a pig, a stomach say, with all the working bits. Or a spine, as was used in *Fan of Death*. Whatever you get hold of you can count on Kari the vegetarian to want out.

KARI – I can't believe they got spine with meat on it. This is disgusting.

***Myths:* Pop Rocks and Soda, Stinky Car, Bullets Fired Up, Snow Special, Blown Away, Fan of Death**

Ping Pong Rescue

At first glance this myth seems absurd – how could ping pong balls float a sunken ship? There are so many impossibilities – how do you get them down into the boat? How many would you need? How would you keep them in the boat? However, these and more imponderables were all answered clearly and clinically as Adam and Jamie and 60,000 ping pong balls made the Mythtanic II rise from the deep. And who could possibly forget the image of Jamie doing his sea-lion impression? And who could also forget the GIANT argument about the test rig?

ADAM – I mean if you want to go without caution and put all our eggs in a single basket, we can but I'm just advocating caution cos I'm not sure. I'm happy to do a myth where we go out and have no caution, and get up and have you eat it.

JAMIE – Ah you big baby. Stop whining.

ADAM – You're such a %$#^ing pain in the ass about it.

JAMIE – You're always whining about something, you always want to waste time on all sorts of crap.

ADAM – %$#^ off!

In the end the rig works perfectly, the sea lions are safe and Jamie gets to spend all day reliving his past as a salvage diver.

Ping Pong Ball

If you drop it from 30 cm and it bounces to 23 cm, then chances are it's a ping pong ball. Adam and Jamie have probably seen enough of ping pong balls since the myth of *Ping Pong Rescue* required some 60,000 of them. However, they did come in handy when Jamie needed a one-way valve for the *Alcatraz Escape* raincoat boat.

***See also:* one-way valve**

***Myths:* Pingpong Rescue, Alcatraz Escape**

Pint

Whether it's a Scottish pint, a US dry pint or any other local variation on 'pint' you can be sure that this archaic measure will be slightly different to what you expect. Go with the litre – you know it makes SI sense.

***See also:* litre, SI**

Pipe Dope

A material used to make a pressure-tight seal between two pieces of pipe. Spread onto the threads of pipes to be sealed together, pipe dope fills any gaps that would let water or air (or whatever the pipes are being made to

carry) out. Anytime you see Adam or Jamie with a pipe in their hand, the dope will be close at hand.

See also: ***X-Pando™, sealant***

Myths: ***Steam Cannon, and anything with pipes***

Pistol the Psychic Horse

Although he knew that Tory was in for a dangerous ride, even Pistol the Psychic Horse (who was, after all, about to do the pulling!) couldn't tell whether Tory's jeans would catch fire in the myth *Pants on Fire*.

GRANT – Are the jeans going to catch fire? Yes? No? Not sure? OK.

Piston

When placed inside a cylinder and sealed gas-tight, a piston takes the brunt of an explosive or expanding force of gas, and translates that force along a piston rod towards a crankshaft whereupon that motion is translated from the up-and-down to the round-and-round. 'What possible point could there be to that?' you say, in your supreme

ignorance, just before you step out onto the street and are run down by an internal combustion-type automobile.

See also: ***stroke, 2-stroke, 4-stroke***

Pitch

There's the sporty kind that has to do with throwing a ball referred to in the *Baseball Special*, the sound kind that has to do with frequency referred to in *Breaking Glass*, and then there is the black, gunky, hydrocarbon kind that is used as a sealant on ships and roads.

See also: ***sealant***

Myths: ***Ancient Death Ray***

Placebo

The fascinating phenomenon of the placebo has been only lightly touched by the Mythbusters to date – the idea that the mind can be tricked into healing itself when offered a 'placebo' pill which has no medicinal effect on the condition was amply demonstrated by Grant in *Seasickness – Kill or Cure?*

Myths:* *Seasickness – Kill or Cure?

JAMIE – What's the result with you on this one, Grant?

GRANT – Ah, I think it works.

JAMIE – You think it works?

GRANT – I'm thinking like it was trying to do something, but you know, it was just staying down there.

JAMIE – I apologise for this. It ... it wasn't my idea. But what you just took was B12. It was a placebo.

Plangent

Loud, stirring, bold – a word that perfectly captures both the music of Pyotr Ilyich Tchaikovsky and the attitude to science, life and urban mythology of the Mythbusters.

***See also:* Exploding Trombone**

Plasma Cutter

It's exciting to be able to use the phrases 'high-energy' and 'precision cutting' in the same sentence, to apply to the same tool. A plasma cutter is a tool that turns gas into the even higher-temperature phase of plasma in order to cut all kinds of things with great precision.

***See also:* tools**

Plumbing

From the Latin 'plumbum' we get both plumbing, and the scientific symbol for the element lead (Pb) which the Romans used for all their plumbing. Ahhh, plumbing – seldom do we see Jamie get quite so excited as when he's on a mission at the plumbing supply store. In fact both Mythbusters love plumbing with the sort of passion more usually reserved for sports finals or annual fashion sales. To Adam and Jamie, a few pipes, sealants and tools can be turned into a rocket in a couple of days, as they did in the myth of the *Confederate Rocket*. Throw in few different bits and pieces and you have yourself a *Chicken Gun*, or a *Steam Cannon*. When it comes down to it, plumbing is behind almost every contemporary convenience – from toilets to automobiles and aeroplanes. Bless plumbing, and all who sail in her.

See also: *X-Pando™*

***Myths:* Confederate Rocket, Chicken Gun, Steam Cannon**

Plywood

Say you lived in a land not known for its endless forests, such as ancient Egypt, where wood is a commodity of particular value. You and your Egyptian wood-turning cronies might be tempted to use every last scrap of it that was around, even if that meant sticking thin offcuts together with glue to make new bits, cunningly putting nice bits on the outsides and scrappy bits in the middle where you wouldn't see them. You might also discover that laying the bits of wood with their grains in different directions would add to the strength of what was probably by now being called plywood. It's a useful material – cheap, supple, attractive and strong enough for a range of applications, but wings for human powered flight is not one of them.

take an ordinary piece of piping... and suddenly it's a chicken gun!

Plywood Builder

Also called *Plywood Parachute*, this myth postulates what would happen if you were a builder a few storeys up on a scaffold and carrying a big piece of plywood when a gust of wind blows you off. Could you use that piece of plywood as a wing or chute, and gently 'Mary Poppins' yourself to the ground? No, sorry bub, it's not going to happen, but Adam and Jamie gave it a red hot go. Or rather, Buster gave it a red hot go, and the plywood slows his fall by about a quarter – not nearly enough to stop you getting a substantial dose of death, as the freshly- made accelerometers demonstrate. Adam and Jamie go into a build-off – who can use plywood to best effect a gentle fall? Neither Adam's plywood chute nor Jamie's wing design save any of the blood-filled lightbulbs. It all seemed very simple, but what about updraft? The wind rushing up the side of a building can reach 90 mph (144 km/h), so why couldn't that be enough to save the builder? Because, as the build team demonstrated, you can't hang on to a giant piece of plywood in any kind of strong wind at any kind of useful angle … so take the stairs.

***See also:* accelerometer**

Pneumatic

When you use compressed air to perform a mechanical function – say, driving an actuator or controlling movement with a strut, then you're using all the power and glory of pneumatics! So many things can be driven by air that in the future your car may be one of them.

Point Blank Range

You all know what point blank range is – or do you? The popular police drama phrase actually stems from the early days of artillery. Back then the greatest range for a cannon was discovered to be made by elevating the barrel to 45°. At the other end of the scale was the 0° (or horizontal) angle you would use to aim the cannon at something so close the projectile would not fall under the influence of gravity. The popular meaning of point blank range just means 'darn close'. Closer still is a 'contact shot', which means exactly what you think it means. Ouch.

See also: ***firearm, gun, barrel, projectile, horizontal, gravity***

Myths: ***Killer Butts, Splitting Arrow, Ice Bullet (and more)***

Polycarbonate

A polycarbonate is a particular kind of plastic (also called a thermoplastic polymer – but don't look that up in this 'opedia, this is as far as we go) with interesting properties in areas like impact and temperature resistance, due to their long chains of molecules. They can also be made transparent, which is nice for looking through, if you are building a blast chamber or screen. However, you might also find them in spectacles, DVDs and your computer.

Polygraph

A lie detector by any other name, the polygraph works by measuring the physiological changes your body that are associated with stress. If you've been a bad boy or girl, then you can rest assured that a modern polygraphist will be able to measure the stress you're experiencing under some probing questions.

See also: ***Michael Martin, galvanic skin response***

Myths: ***Nothing but the Truth***

Poplar

A tree common to the Northern Hemisphere that is popular with butterflies, ornamental gardeners, paper manufacturers and Mythbusters. Why Mythbusters? Seems that a spar of poplar has the same load bearing capacity as human bone, at equivalent thickness. This is how Buster is rebuilt – he's the most poplar Mythbuster of them all.

Pop Rocks

Invented in 1956, the pop rock was based on the idea that an instant carbonated soda was exactly what the public was looking for. However, eating the results meant that this carbonated reaction happened inside your mouth, and a candy sensation was born. The Mythbusters wanted to delve deeper; could pop rocks combined with soda create so much gas that it would make your stomach explode? *Pop Rocks and Soda* was busted – and so all that remains is for us to offer you Adam and Jamie's taste test.

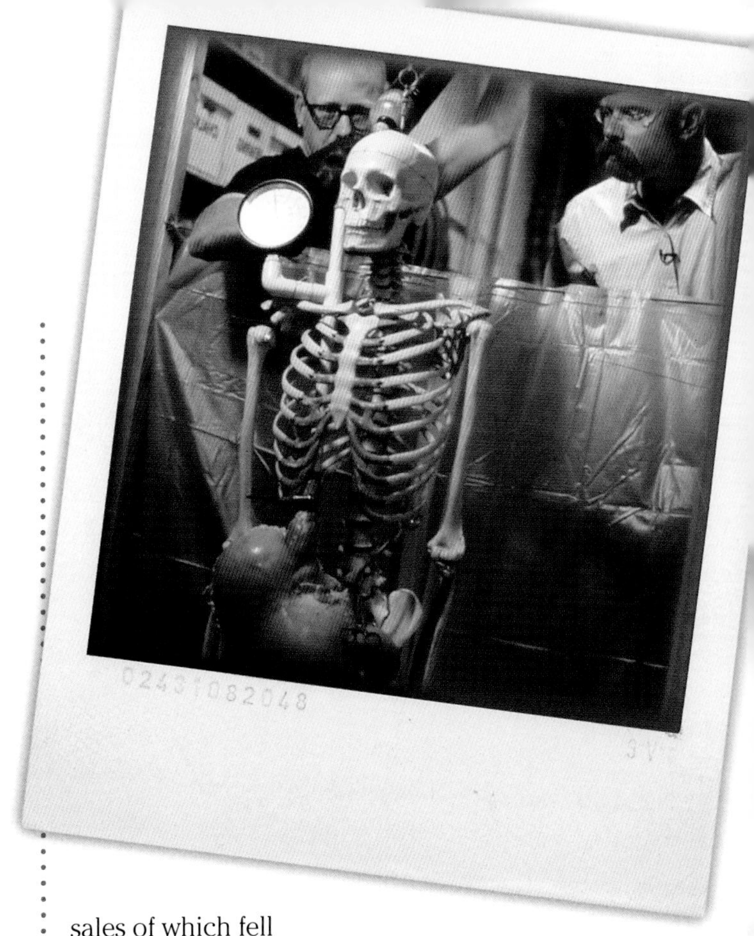

ADAM – Ah hmm.

JAMIE – Hmm.

ADAM – It's kind of gross.

Pop Rocks and Soda

Could it be true that a teenager could actually die from a speedy consumption of six packets of pop rocks, followed by a six pack of soda beverage? Sounds absurd, but it was a devastating myth for the candy, sales of which fell through the floor. Adam and Jamie were determined to find out the truth, and for that they would need a strong stomach – an actual strong stomach, ideally from something that wouldn't see them serving 15-20 years in a padded cell. A pig would be an ideal candidate, and although it wasn't the easiest procurement, the stomach when it arrived was a marvel of evolutionary engineering. But how much pressure could it withstand? And how would they get the pop rocks in without them sticking to the walls of the oesophagus? Trial and error, friends, and with a pig's stomach nestled gently inside a skeleton's rib cage, the testing commenced. Six packets of candy and six cans of soda

later, the stomach grew – but not enough to even read on the pressure meter. To actually blow a hole in the stomach they turned to everyone's acid stomach friend, baking soda, and what do you know? Soda and bicarb don't mix so well – they busted the gut with a reading of 3 PSI! But the pop rocks myth was busted too, and Fernando Arguis of Pop Rocks Inc was terribly grateful.

JAMIE – Somebody that's just … you know, eating candy or something, I don't see it happening.

See also: ***stomach, pigs, Fernando Arguis, PSI, pop rocks***

Port

You probably don't want to know about port wine, the popular alcoholic beverage that is made from wine fortified with brandy, which is itself wine, distilled into a spirit, making port wine mixed with more wine. Tasty enough, but not really Mythbusters territory. No, you'd like to know why the word 'port' in naval-speak means both 'the left side of a boat' and 'the facility where a boat can unload'. If you're thinking that the term 'port' (meaning left) probably came into service because that was the side of the ship closest to the port (meaning place where the boat can stop to unload) you would be 100 per cent correct. Nice when you get a win isn't it?

See also: ***starboard***

Portmanteau

If you've pushed two words together to make a new, exciting and spunky word, then a portmanteau is what you've created. The classic Mythbusters example is 'mythtern', but with any luck 'Mythopedia' will also catch on.

See also: ***mythtern***

Pounds

What is a pound? And why is it abbreviated 'lb'? The abbreviation is thanks to the Romans, who used 'libra' (scales) to weigh things. As to the pound itself, well, a pound can be anything from 454 grams to 500 grams, depending on where and when you are, and is thus another example of the value of the SI.

See also: ***kilogram, SI***

Pressure

If you've ever been sat on by an older sibling or large friend, then you'll be perfectly aware of what pressure is. Literally pressure is the force enacted along the perpendicular upon a certain two-dimensional space – often measured as so much weight per so much area. Although the SI unit of pressure is the pascal (named for Blaise Pascal, a tangential figure in contemporary Mythbusting circles, but central to them in 17th century France) pressure is also measured in psi (pounds force per square inch) bars (and millibars, you might recall from weather forecasters) and in atmospheres. The force enacted by a certain amount of pressure varies dramatically depending on the surface area it works with: you might stand upon a patch of parkland and cause no bother, but the same or less pressure from your feet upon the much smaller surface area of a spade would easily push it into the ground and dig a hole. Bad for the public park, but good for your scientific understanding of pressure.

***See also:* atmospheric pressure, sound**
***Myths:* Silicone Breasts, Breaking Glass**

Pressure Gauge

When measuring pressure we're usually talking about water or air (among other liquids and gases to be sure) rather than stress-induced human tension, for which there is sadly no calibrated gauge. There are almost as many ways to measure pressure as there are reasons why you'd want to; all to do with the different places (and pressures) in which you'd like to measure pressure – a few thousand metres under the surface of an ocean, inside a car tyre, at a gas main and so on. The Mythbusters mostly use pressure gauges when they're pushing lots of air about the place, often into vessels designed to cope with pressures up to a certain level. Think about the nifty little dials screwed into rigs like the *Steam Cannon* or *Chicken Gun* and you'll be on the money.

Projectile

If you've ever sent something flying through the air, then you'll know what a projectile is. Usually used as a noun to describe something launched or fired through the air (or into space).

***See also:* bullets, Minié Ball, rocket**

Proof of Concept

Such a cool phrase to be caught using correctly, it refers to a stage in a research and development venture that aims to demonstrate the correctness of a key element of the overall idea. Say you were Adam and Jamie and your task was to demonstrate whether a cannon could be built that would fire a projectile using steam as a propellant. Although the science tells you that water expands 1600 times when it becomes steam, before bashing out cold, hard readies on a Howitzer-sized barrel and Civil War era cannonball, you would (and they did) build scaled-down versions of such a cannon to test whether all that potential could in fact be used to fire something smaller, like a tennis ball. And you'd build them and test them and build them and test them until the concept had been proven, or substantively disproven, even if it took days and days and days and days.

ADAM – Look, we've got a proof of concept. I want to move on.

JAMIE – Yeah, I'm tired of these little things.

Propellant

Put simply, a propellant is a substance that propels something. Often a propellant is a chemical substance like gasoline in your car engine, or gunpowder in your trusty muzzle-loading rifle, but it could be something simpler, like the pressure that sprays water in a trigger bottle, or a good push and a hint of gravity that sends your soapbox or billycart down the hill.

See also: ***aerosol, gasoline, gravity, gunpowder***

Prototype

Literally this is the first example of something, but in practice any new invention goes through a process of prototyping, that sees any number of prototypes created before it is either finished, abandoned or explodes.

Pulley

A subtle variation of our mechanical friend, the wheel, a pulley is often built into a more complex and useful system called a block (or 'roofer's block' as was used in *Barrel of Bricks*) as part of a 'block and tackle' system – the tackle being rope. The ancient Greek Mythbuster Archimedes is claimed to have invented the first block and tackle, which

has changed little over time but for the materials used and the power source on the pulling end. A block is a combination of a number of pulleys, or grooved wheels, that can be made to work together to deliver a mechanical advantage to the puller, making a load lighter to lift by distributing the weight across a number of points – although the distance the 'tackle' must be pulled is correspondingly increased.
***See also:* roofer's block, block and tackle, Archimedes, mechanical advantage**
***Myths:* Barrel of Bricks**

Pulmonary Embolism

When a little clump of something gets stuck in your pulmonary artery and blocks it enough to cause anything from noticeable pain to an advanced case of sudden death, you have a pulmonary embolism and you should shout it out loudly with what might be your last breath. If you had another breath, you might choose to say 'curses to these skin tight jeans in which I sat in a warm bath to make even tighter' but you'd never get there.
***See also:* Edward Kersh, deep vein thrombosis**
***Myths:* Jeans Death Shrinkage**

Your classic push start

Push Start

An internal combustion engine likes to start in the regular way by turning the key in the ignition, which makes the battery start the electric starter motor, which drives the pistons and gets the engine itself moving. However, if your battery doesn't have the juice to kick over the starter motor, or if the starter motor is cactus, or if any one of a frillion other things go wrong, then you can try a push start. The push start – called a hand start if it's on a propeller aircraft (such as was the focus of the *Shredded Aeroplane* myth) – assumes the gearbox is in neutral, the ignition to 'ON' and you are on a slight hill, or have some burly mates on hand. You get the car moving at a fast walking pace, then jump in to the car (or, more sensibly, are already IN the car), engage the clutch,

throw the car into second and let the wheels turn the gears in the gearbox, which in turn get the motor ticking over. A push-start is essentially using the power of the wheels turning to do the same as the power in the starter engine to get the fickle beast that is an internal combustion engine going. Naturally problems arise – as they do in *Shredded Aeroplane* – when the aeroplane gets into gear itself and takes off without you. But it's something to practise just in case…

***Myths:* Shredded Aeroplane**

Putrefaction

Hmm, bacteria. Amazing creatures in so many ways, and you don't want to mess with them when they're dealing with something recently dead – especially if that something is sealed off from the rest of the world in an air-tight container, like the *Stinky Car*. These are the sort of circumstances that anaerobic bacteria just love, and what they do with organic material under those conditions must be smelled to be believed.

***See also:* airtight, anaerobic, bacteria, liquefaction**

***Myths:* Stinky Car**

ADAM – If my baby's poo smelt like that I'd take him to the hospital immediately.

Pyrex®

If you're working in a lab, then Pyrex® will likely be your brand of choice for all your glassware. Of course, it's not the only thing that's ever been made of borosilicate glass, but surely it is the most significant. Mythbusters recommend borosilicate glass for all their laboratory needs.

***See also:* borosilicate glass**

***Myths:* Octopus Pregnancy**

Quack, Damn You

A delightful t-shirt of a phrase which first appeared in the myth *Duck Quack Echo* but entered the Mythbusters lexicon almost immediately afterward.

Quart

A great way to describe a measure of liquid equal to two pints, which is not very useful to those of us living in the land of SI standardised decimal. It's almost, but not quite, equal to a litre (precisely 946 ml), but only in the USA. In the United Kingdom a quart is just a little more than a litre (precisely 1.136 litres). Why the hell is a quart different in the UK and USA? Why is a pound half a dozen different things? Or a horsepower? ***See also:*** ***litre, pint, horsepower, pound, SI***

Quick Release

The Mythbusters are always dropping things – not in a forgetful or clumsy way, but in a timely, mechanically precise and endlessly repeatable way. Often the things being dropped are heavy, and the heights from which they are dropped very high indeed. Danger is ever present, and it's no place for a human agency – but handily there exist some gadgets that take much of the danger out of such situations. These are quick releases – and there are many kinds, but their aim and principle are the same. They are mechanical devices that look a bit like a hook or a latch, and can be triggered remotely by wireless or pull cord. A large quick release can bear the weight of an elevator, as it did in *Elevator of Death*, and a smaller sample was perfect for the timely release of the *Barrel of Bricks*. In almost every case of the Mythbusters dropping something, a quick release has been successfully deployed.

Quicksand

Is there really such a thing as quicksand – that classic concoction of sand and water that would suck you down as soon as you stepped into it? In theory yes it exists, and the process by which it is created is called 'liquefaction' and involves water bubbling towards the surface where it starts to mess around with the solidity of what you would otherwise call the ground. To test just what a 'quicksand' might do, Adam and Jamie get hold of some very fine sand and perform some scaled down bucket tests before choosing a type of sand and preparing for a VERY large scale build – involving chunky pumps, 20,000 pounds (9071 kg) of sand and enough water to, with any luck, sink a Mythbuster. After a few arguments about how best to fill the tank with water, a brief and scary discussion with quicksand-expert geologist, the sudden introduction of a large piece of earth moving rescue equipment and a pith helmet, they're all set.

ADAM – The pith helmet is always a good technique for finding someone who has drowned in quicksand 'cause it'll be floating on the surface there.

But sucked down and drowned Adam is not – just like the hydrometer, Adam and then Jamie find themselves buoyed up by the density of the quicksand. After some initial fears that they could be forever stuck in their own creation, they find the whole experience rather thrilling. Now, it (almost) goes without saying that real quicksand might not be so forgiving, and it's an interesting sideline that recent research (post-myth) suggests that salt has a key in the creation of an authentic quicksand. Time for a revisit? Your email could count!

See also:* *liquefaction, hydrometer, Thomas Holzer, buoyancy, density

Quorum

The legislated minimum number of persons on a decision-making body who must be at a meeting in order to decide what decisions will be made. It is safe to say that no quorum-related myths have ever been brought onto the show – so why refer to it here? It's a great word, and it's just demonstrating that our knowledge extends (just a little) beyond the bounds of Mythbusting. And now, so does yours.

Rachel Saunders

The Monterey Bay Marine Sanctuary takes its role of protecting the local wildlife very seriously. So how did Rachel feel about bringing 60,000 ping pong balls into the sanctuary to attempt a *Ping Pong Rescue?*

RACHEL – Well we would want to make sure that no marine animals swallowed them, for example, and hurt them in any way. So that would be the primary concern. If they swallowed it, it might get lodged in the throat and they could choke, they might pass it through, but you don't know.

ADAM – You know I think Jamie here actually possesses a certification in Otter CPR.

RACHEL – Well, hopefully that won't happen and we won't have to learn how that would work.

Racoon

Distinguished by their funky face fur, the racoon is an omnivorous mammal common to North America and increasingly Europe as well, ever since they were released by the Nazis into their own German forests so that they'd have something to shoot at before they invaded Poland. Contemporary populations in the old country suggest they missed plenty. The fun in Mythbusters terms began when a good ol' boys myth was uncovered and before long Adam and Jamie were intent on building their own *Racoon Rocket*.

***See also:* good ol' boys**
***Myths:* Racoon Rocket**

Racoon Rocket

It just so happened that one lazy early evening a couple of good ol' boys were sitting on their porch in Carbon County, Pennsylvania sharing a few yarns over a few beers, when a racoon happened along. The good ol' boys reach for their guns naturally and let fire, but the varmint high tails down a nearby drain pipe. One among them has the bright idea of pouring a few gallons of petrol down this pipe, the aim being to blow the racoon out. The petrol fails to ignite, so in he crawls to do the job properly. You can see where this is going yes? And you'd be right – he blows himself and the racoon across the yard with no considerable damage done. Of course, this is impossible, and Adam and Jamie knew it from the moment they walked onto the pipe-sellers lot. Ain't no way a person can build up enough pressure in a 3 ft (1 metre) pipe to get some compression working, unless they're a cake-scoffing shut-in (in which case they're not going to be scurrying down pipes after racoons). However, they get a pipe, fill it with a racoon, Buster and plenty of petrol and their remote lighter rig. Action? Not much, and it was mythbusted – but the lads want to see Buster launch! So they build a sabot and turn to explosives for help. Jamie was so confident that he put Buster's wheelchair out for him to land in – and was only off by a few metres!

ADAM – Oh my God.

JAMIE – I almost made the chair.

ADAM – You almost made the chair.

***See also:* sabot, ligher rig, racoon, Buster**

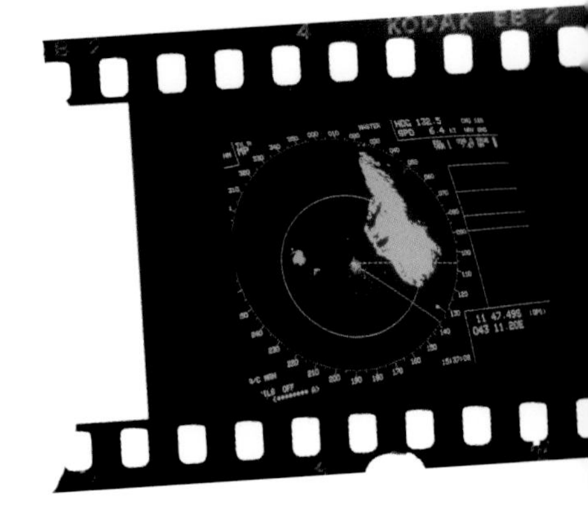

Radar

When you want to see something that you can't see, you can either fumble around for your spectacles (if you're Adam) or reach for your nearest radar system. Radar is a terribly useful way that we use what would otherwise just be pointless electromagnetic radiation from the 'radio' spectrum to do very, very useful stuff, like 'see' things that you can't see. Radar stands for Radio Detection and Ranging, and so even though it isn't quite one, it does make an appearance in the top five Mythbusters acronyms. What's more useful to know is that just like that other useful bit of the electromagnetic spectrum, light, radio waves live to bounce off things – like aeroplanes that are hiding behind clouds. By sending out a blast of radio waves, and then catching the echo they make when they bounce off something, you can tell where and how far it is away – do it a couple of times and you can tell near as dammit how fast it's going too, and thus when it's likely to drop a whole bunch of bombs on you. Of course a whole lot of terribly complicated calculations are important in between the not knowing and the knowing, but that's what computers are for. Smart computers now allow radar to be used by police people who have the very important job of catching people driving their cars faster than they are allowed, and also by people who want to know if Jimmy Hoffa is buried in a patch of dirt.

Radio Control

Radio is a wonderful thing, and the ability to control something with electromagnetic waves in the radio frequency is even better. The Mythbusters have some top notch radio control kit that they're always prepared to rig into a vehicle if the myth required – but it does have a downside...

***See also:* Jet Taxi**

Radio Tooth Fillings

Lucille Ball was a remarkable woman whose comedy gifts charmed generations – yet as fate would have it, her teeth brought her to the attention of the Mythbusters. Seems that after having some fillings changed, she began to pick up local radio stations IN HER HEAD. Not only that, but she also claimed that her peculiar gift lead to her busting a Japanese radio spy network during WW2. Crazy? Kooky? Wacky? Most certainly. But … possible? The lads borrow Adam's dad's skull (no, not his actual skull) and drill holes for some fillings, their theory being that a reaction between the saliva and all that metal in her mouth was giving Lucy the impression that she was hearing Morse Code. All attempts to replicate the myth came to zip …

ADAM – I think definitively we've shown that two different types of fillings do not act as a rudimentary radio crystal. And that there is some potential voltage or battery action occurring if you've eaten a lot of acidic food and you do have different types of metals in your mouth.

JAMIE – It's busted.

…but an interesting sideline is that there have been cases of people with metal in their heads ACTUALLY picking up radio waves so they can hear them! You'd want to be tuned into something decent…

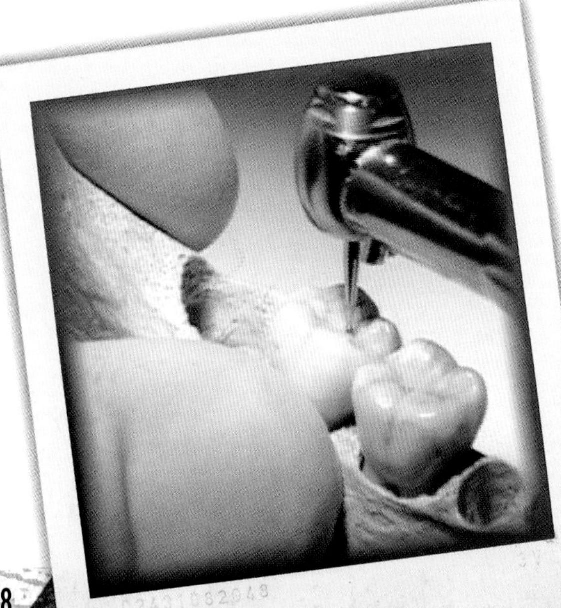

Ragwort

This little green nasty will grow just about anywhere, and when it hit New Zealand it caused a rush on certain brands of chemical herbicides. Problem was the herbicides were just a tad explosive, as the Build Team discover in *Exploding Pants*.

KARI – I think this might be my new favourite myth. We actually had exploding pants.

Railroad Ties

Perhaps better known as railway sleepers (or just big ol' hunks of wood) these guys have the unenviable task of keeping the railway tracks pointed in the right direction. As they tend to come in the same size, railway sleepers can also be a useful material if you're planning a big quick build – say, an old West-style jail in *Western Jail Break* or reinforcement for a massive water vortex tank in *Killer Whirlpool*.

***Myths:* Western Jail Break**

Raw Meat

M5 contains a billion tubs, boxes and drawers, each clearly labelled with the contents to be found within. Viewers have noted that one box is labelled 'Raw Meat'. No raw meat is stored in this box.

Red Converse Sneakers

This is no product placement – Jamie Hyneman buys each and every pair of red Converse sneakers that he's ever worn. The company that began as the Converse Rubber Shoe Company in Boston has now traded for 100 years, and the best of luck for another hundred.

***See also:* beret**

Regan Kuja

Regan was an animal-handling professional with enough skunk experience to make him of great value to the Mythbusters when they took on *Skunk Cleaning*. Their problem was actually getting a skunk to spray them – Regan couldn't believe it was that hard.

REGAN – I'll tell you I have not found it difficult. All you've got to do is expose that thing. Right now it's covered and when you take that off it's gonna feel threatened.

JAMIE – So you think we're gonna get sprayed.

REGAN – Yeah, absolutely. I'd be shocked if you didn't.

He was then suitably shocked when the skunk held its fire. Funny thing, life ...

***Myths:* Skunk Cleaning**

Remo Morelli

Dr Morelli helped monitor Adam's health when they retested the myth of *Goldfinger.* Believing that Jamie's own blood pressure might have been responsible in the original myth, he's pleased to note that Adam is fine in the revisit.

REMO – Blood pressure is being still within normal limits. The heart rate is being also within normal limits. The temperature went down. Definitely nothing abnormal.

Remote Rig

A remote rig is any experimental apparatus that can or must be operated from a distance, chiefly for safety reasons, but also to stop the controlled conditions of an experiment being compromised. The rig might be as simple as a piece of string tied around the trigger of a rifle so it can be pulled from behind a wall, as in *Ice Bullet*, or as complex as the Faraday Cage that was built for *Cell Phones on Planes.*

***See also:* Faraday Cage, controlled conditions, rig**

***Myths:* Ice Bullet, Cell Phones on Planes**

Replica

Whether for good or ill, a replica is a copy, and a fairly precise one at that. The best replicas not only look like the original, but are made with the same materials and tools and with the same tolerances as would have originally been used. On Mythbusters they aim for the best … but time and budget constraints, as well as making the thing actually work, often get them in the end from creating a perfect replica. The best attempt at an historically accurate replica was the *Tree Cannon* which was made with historically correct materials (except for the electric igniter), and even with some input from original tools including a spoon drill. Then they blew it to smithereens. Other historical replicas included the *Steam Cannon, Archimedes Death Ray* and *Steam Machine Gun.*

***Myths:* Tree Cannon, Steam Cannon, Archimedes Death Ray, Steam Machine Gun**

Replication

When the Mythbusters are faced with a new myth they have two tasks – the first of these is to replicate the myth. Whether that means building a medieval *Tree Cannon* or sinking a 8164-tonne tugboat, their aim is to see if

the myth can be confirmed by recreating the events and actions that supposedly happened. The second is to duplicate the myth. Duplication is always more fun, because nine times out of 10 it involves an explosion.
***See also:* duplication**

Rescue Randy

Buster's understudy is dragged in whenever the man himself is on *Letterman* or writing his memoirs in his trailer.

Randy chills out while waiting for a call up

Resistance

Different materials react to electricity in different ways. Some have lots of time (and more importantly, free electrons) for an electric current and let it zip along with minimal loss of energy. Other materials put up a fight, say 'no' to resistance and are generally placard-carrying naysayers to all things electron-like. Materials like wood have a high resistance, and things like copper a low resistance. By knowing the resistance of a material you can work out what will happen when you attach some jumper leads to it. Oh, and it's measured in ohms.

Adam and Jamie know that something like distilled water (which remarkably has a very high resistance) can be made less resistant by adding 'salts' (you can go ahead and read 'urine' here) as they did in the myth of *Appliances in the Bath*.
***See also:* Ω (aha! We mean ohms of course. Got you!)**

Resonance

Give them dynamite, gunpowder, cell phones or human excretions, given the choice the Mythbusters will always plump for a new myth about resonance. Why? Take a look at the following list – Breaking Glass, Brown Note, 360° Swing, Avalanche Adventures,

Earthquake Machine … are you excited yet? Resonance (and more specifically mechanical resonance) is a phenomenon of all mechanical systems (that is, everything) which suggests that the system in question will oscillate (or wriggle) at a maximum value at a certain frequency. Thus, sing at a wine glass just right and it will break. Tap a bridge in just the right way and it will fall down. Do you see what we're getting at here? Resonance is the key to destroying just about anything, and although it's not always possible, it's always worth a try.
Myths: ***Avalanche Adventures, Breaking Glass, 360º Swing etc.***

JAMIE – Hold the phone. Oh my God. It feels like a big semitrailer truck is rolling by us right now.

ADAM – And that's only six pounds of weight moving 25 times per second.

JAMIE – It actually makes me a little concerned, believe it or not.

ADAM – I'm totally startled to come out here and find this thing vibrating at the correct frequency to be felt hundreds of feet away from the source. That is totally amazing. Did not expect that.

RFID TAG

Standing for 'Radio Frequency Identification' these nifty little devices are turning up just about everywhere, from the toll-paying tag in your car to the tiny chip that the Blood Bank is certainly NOT injecting into your skin when you donate. They work by reflecting back information to an electronic reader, often using the energy in the initial transmission to power the return signal. The Mythbusters have tested whether an RFID tag inside a human being (one of those NOT placed there by the Blood Bank) would explode in an MRI machine – thankfully for Kari it didn't. They also looked into whether a stud finder could spot an RFID tag inside a dog – which it certainly could.
See also: ***stud finder***
Myths: ***Exploding Tattoo, Myth Evolution, Mind Control Chips***

RICHARD VANN, DR

Richard appeared in the myth *Silicone Breasts* as an expert in hyperbaric medicine, which involves doctors using oxygen at higher than atmospheric pressures to treat patients

with exiting but uncomfortable conditions like decompression sickness or Necrotising Fasciitis (that flesh eating disease).

RICHARD - Well I think they're worried about it because the supermarket tabloids have got their attention. It's another good story along with Big Foot and the Loch Ness Monster.

***See also:* hyperbaric chamber, oxygen, atmospheric pressure**
***Myths:* Silicone Breasts**

Ricin

Ricin is a rather nasty poison seventy times more deadly than cyanide, and made infamous by 1960s Bulgarian secret service agents in the pursuit of the aspirations of their nation. Ricin is extracted from beans – the beans of the castor plant to be exact. This should not be confused in any way with castor, an oily substance secreted by beaver's from a small gland in their groin. Nor should it be confused with castor oil, which is also extracted from the castor plant – but not the beans. There's also a star of the same name, but that's not going to confuse you now…you'll be confused already. Ricin acts to clump together red blood cells in a way that is deleterious to your ongoing verticality, and thus is not available in retail outlets. Ricin was referred to in the myth *Ice Bullet*.
***Myths:* Ice Bullet**

Rig

A classic Mythbusters term that describes an apparatus of any kind used to test a myth (the word 'build' is also sometimes used, in its gerund form). Some classic rigs include the 'stone roller' from *Rolling Stone*, the aeroplane section from *Killer Brace Position* and the needle-finding machines in *Needle in a Haystack*.

Rigging

One of the more dangerous jobs in the world, rigging is all about lifting heavy things, and usually involves working with scaffolding, cranes, ropes, block and tackle (and of course, very heavy things). The term rigging comes from ye olde days of sailing ships where 'rigging' was the ropes used to hoist sails, booms and so on. The Mythbusters have had several occasions to call on riggers; for *Barrel of Bricks* for example, they had to lift 1000 pounds of barrel and counterweight on a scaffold – classic rigger territory all round. Riggers are also found in the film and television industry where they … lift things. But riggers are also involved in the building of sets that are able to bear the weight needed to … lift … things.

***See also:* block and tackle, Whirley**

***Myths:* Barrel of Bricks**

Rimfire

Most firearm rounds are discharged when the firing pin makes contact with the primer – a fuse, if you will – that sits in the centre of the rear of the round. However, the centrefire round (as it is known) is not the only way firearms can be made. The whole rear end of the cartridge can be made a primer and a bullet thus fired when the firing pin strikes anywhere on the rim. Most rimfire rounds are smaller calibre rounds – just the sort of round that Adam was likely to mess around with while experimenting towards the myth *Ice Bullet*.

ADAM – You know I could have read the directions and it wouldn't have made any sense to me because I don't know what a rimfire bullet is. I would have been blissfully proceeding without thinking I was in danger.

JAMIE – I was raised up on a farm and them is varmint bullets.

Robert Flores

Professional salvage diver Robert knows the dangers of the deep, but even so he took the time to help the Mythbusters with *Ping Pong Rescue* – he even made some suggestions about the rig when it wasn't working.

ROBERT – I think this hose is still too long. If you can take another 10 or 12 feet off of this thing.

ADAM – Can take 10 feet off in five seconds.

Robert Lee

The voice of Mythbusters (in most territories) is a pro in the audio world. With more than 10 years and plenty of gigs behind him, he knows what it takes to bring tension to the screen simply by jiggling the ivories. Lee's narration has, as much as anything, contributed to making Mythbusters the intergalactic success it is.

Robert Malahowski

Robert knows likes his zaps big, and his work at Pacific Gas and Electric gives him plenty of chances to show them off – and the myth *Phone in a Thunderstorm* gave him every opportunity.

ROBERT – What we can generate here is up to seven hundred thousand volts at about half a million watts.

Roberto Valturio

This 15th century papal bureaucrat-turned engineer came to the notice of Adam and Jamie when they were researching the *Steam Cannon* episode. They had Valturio's 'On Matters Military' translated into English, viz:

JAMIE (quoting) – 'The cannon, or bombarda, as it's commonly called, is a contrivance made of metal, which through the agency of metal and a sulphurous, or perhaps one should say hellish, powder hurls bronze missiles.'

'On Matters Military' is notable for being illustrated with technical woodcuts of the weaponry described – but sadly nothing on Archimedes Steam Cannon itself!

***See also:* Petrarch, steam**

***Myths:* Steam Cannon**

Robert Slay

Doc Slay isn't a character from a violent Western, but is in fact a rather charming and whimsical medical doctor who has conducted his own Mythbusting experiments on fruit and exploding toilets. Adam and Jamie just had to bring him in on the myth of the *Exploding Toilet* because … how could you not?

ROBERT – By myself in Texas investigating this with a large watermelon … a full can of spray was only able to singe the bottom…

Rob Lobenstein

The superintendent of the New York Transit System was in no mood for easy relief when the lads consulted him on the myth of *The Third Rail*.

***Myths:* The Third Rail**

ROB – My first day on the job, they give you all the safety tips and the warnings, and that's the very first thing they tell you not to do.

Rocket

It is a curious fact about rocket science that it has somehow built up an awesome reputation for extreme difficulty and cleverness when in fact rocket science really boils down to filling containers with propellant and seeing what happens when you ignite them. We can feel the rockets being trained on our headquarters even as we write this, so let us continue by saying that the CONTROL of the power in those containers of propellant is what takes all the cleverness. Phew. Rockets filled with black powder were not uncommon in olde China, and the history of rocketry is as impressive as it is hilarious. The *Ming Dynasty Astronaut* is but one example of craziness; the Turks claim a 17th century rocketeer called Lagari Hasan Çelebi. Eyewitnesses stated he flew a seven-winged rocket into the Bosporus Sea, lived to tell the tale,

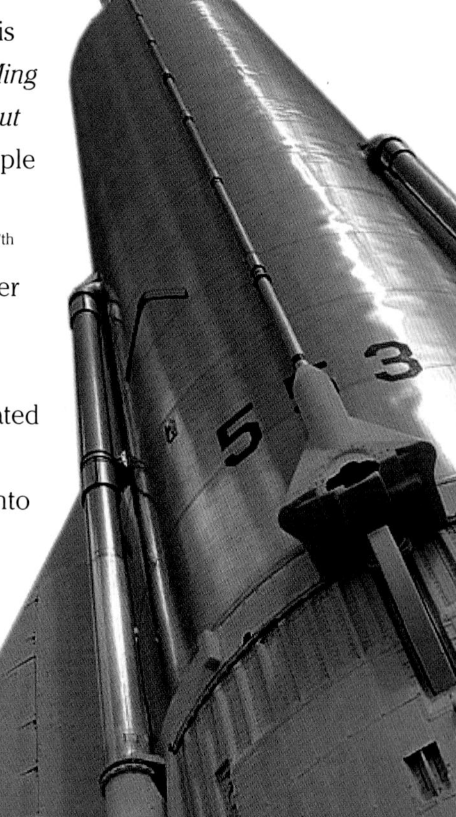

and was rewarded by being sent into the army. All this history is fine and dandy and doesn't actually tell us anything about how rockets actually work – which they certainly do. In fact it is the force of gases produced by a rocket's propellant that do the hard work, and by forcing them through a small opening in the base of the rocket, the gases actually produce force in all directions, including the upwards force we love to call thrust. While the presence of olde worlde rockets in the USA is underlined even by their National Anthem (you know the line, don't make us sing it) and covered in *Confederate Rocket*, some of the earliest serious rockets in contemporary US development were the JATOs. Adam and Jamie tried to replicate their power in *Jet Car*, but really these rockets were built in the 1950s to assist fat aeroplanes that couldn't otherwise get into the air. The Mythbusters have continued their fascination with rockets in gosh darn it SO MANY episodes that we feel obliged NOT to list them all for fear of leaving out a really obvious one. In fact, it has become de rigeur for the team to strap a few rockets to anything that won't work of its own volition – see *360° Swing Set* for proof.

***See also:* thrust, propellant, Gates Brothers Rocketry, hobby rockets**

***Myths:* read above**

Roger McCarthy

He made himself and his company a success out of failure – literally. Exponent studies why things, systems or anything in between, fail, and McCarthy has put up his hand up to help Adam and Jamie on a number of occasions; in the *Ice Bullet* myth he suggested other options such as a liquid-filled bullet, and in *Archimedes's Steam Cannon* he suggested increasing the brass surface area inside the cannon. Clever? Oh yes. He's across everything from Exxon Valdez to the assassination of JFK. So who killed him Roger?

ROGER – And the answer is we'll never know until the National Archives finds President Kennedy's brain, because President Kennedy's brain was not buried with his body. It was put in a specially-sealed container and given to the National Archives for safekeeping. They have subsequently lost the President's brain.

***Myths:* Ice Bullet, Archimedes's Steam Cannon**

Roger Schwenkee

What is an acoustician? Well, Roger Schwenkee is one, and so that means being an acoustician has a lot to do with growing beards, speaking softly and fiddling with knobs. In fact, Roger has given such sterling support to the Mythbusters he has been named an honorary Mythbuster, along with Roger McCarthy, Eric Gates and Frank Doyle. Roger knows so much about sound that he's actually a doctor of the stuff, and that means if you ask him a question he's likely to say something like:

ROGER – It's a series of exponentially decaying impulses, which looks almost exactly like room reverberation.

Myths: ***Duck Quack Echo***

Rolling Stone Gathers No Moss

This is an extraordinary example of Mythbusting at work. Profound dedication to a quality result was seen at all levels of this experiment, from the lateral concept to the final rig. The fact that the Nobel Prize for Science Television did not come the way of the Mythbusters can only be a demonstration that such an award does not exist.

Ronald Brancaccio

A New York dermatologist who was as surprised as anyone that the *Goldfinger* myth turned out to be strangely true.

RONALD – The only way I can explain this is again by the occlusion of the skin causing an increase in body temperature and then the body reacting in a fight or flight mechanism and increasing its blood pressure and heart rate.

Myths: ***Goldfinger***

Ron Hood

Not to be confused with his near namesake Robin, Ron nevertheless specialises in the craft of survival in the wild, tuned from years of military service and personal interest. He's the master of any number of skills, almost the least of them being how to start a fire without matches. But he was gracious enough to lend the Build Team a hand when they tried the classics out for themselves – like starting a fire from a battery.

RON – Here's the trick. Steel wool. What we want to do now is touch it across these contacts and see if we can make a contact that'll ignite some of the steel wool. Look there. Fire. OUCH – it's hot, too.

***Myths:* Firestarter**

Roofer's Block

A pulley system designed for lifting heavy things onto a roof, floor, or any other part of a building – no-one'll stop you (notice that roof and floor are almost palindromes – weird!). A key element in the kit of a rigger, a roofer's block hints at the more ancient term 'block and tackle', and can deliver a mechanical advantage to the puller, making loads lighter to lift because the weight is distributed across several points – although the puller must yank on a correspondingly greater amount of rope.

***See also:* pulley, block and tackle, mechanical advantage**

***Myths:* Barrel of Bricks**

Ro Sham Bo

Known elsewhere as rock-paper-scissors this is a classic children's game and decision-making tool. Two players face one another, fists raised horizontal to the plane of the playing surface. Eye to eye, they count 'one, two, three' (or Ro, Sham, Bo!) while simultaneously moving their fist up and down on the words. On the fourth beat each player makes a split second decision to 'throw' their hand into one of three shapes; rock (the original fist), paper (open palm, facing the playing surface) or scissors (two separated fingers pointing forwards). A winner is chosen based on the following formula – rock beats scissors (rock blunts scissors), scissors beats paper (scissors cut paper), paper beats rock (paper WRAPS rock – don't you know anything?). Players showing the same sign will repeat the game until a winner is found. Any signs 'thrown' beyond the vertical are a foul throw, and the thrower is either forced to take a rock throw, or dunked upside down in the nearest toilet bowl. The Mythbusters call on Ro Sham Bo to make difficult personnel decisions such as who will lick an ice cold flagpole in *Frozen Tongue*.

***See also:* mano-a-mano**

***Myths:* Driving on Ice**

Round

The ignorant call it a bullet, but the fact remains that the bullet is only one component of a gestalt. The round is the whole object you pop in the chamber and discharge hopefully without doing injury to yourself or others.

Roy Varney

Lieutenant Varney of the South San Francisco Police Department took Grant into his confidence when the Mythbusters sought to out-lie the fearsome polygraph machine in *Nothing But the Truth*. It wasn't going to be easy...

ROY – If you wanted an accurate test of this, you would need to commit a crime.

***See also:* polygraph**
***Myths:* Nothing But the Truth**

RPM

Revolutions Per Minute is a measure of how fast something is spinning. Scientists will insist that it is a unit for measuring frequency, and that's fine too. Essentially, if you could count the number of times you turned the handle of your pencil sharpener in 60 seconds, then you'd have a measurement in revolutions per minute (a revolution being the action of completing a circle). The Mythbusters are always measuring things in rpm – just one of the perks of the job. Key myths involving revolutions per minute include *Shattering CD ROM* where the lads were spinning CDs to destruction, and *Killer Deck* where they devised high-speed spinning machines for throwing cards.

***See also:* frequency**
***Myths:* Killer Deck, Shattering CD ROM**

Rubber

It's good because it's stretchy. Can you imagine a world without rubber? Even if you regularly wear a full-body step-in, you probably drive a car, wear sneakers or erase pencil marks. And yes, rubber was named for its ability to rub out pencil marks, but the uses don't stop there. Once Europeans had stopped connecting rubber with evil spirits, they vulcanised it and soon after turned it into tyres, waterproof clothing and footwear. Of course, the Mayans had done all this

centuries before (perhaps not the tyres) but Western industry still exploded in excitement and started growing rubber anywhere they could, and wrecking havoc in a few local societies into the bargain. So what is rubber? Natural rubber is the sap of the rubber tree, and if you're a chemistry type then you'd be interested to know that rubber is a polymer of hydrocarbon molecules, particularly isoprene.
***See also:* vulcanisation, hydrocarbon**

Rube would have been proud

Rube Goldberg

This much-beloved cartoonist of the first half of the 20th century tickled readers across the United States and the world with his absurd drawings of extraordinarily complex machines that performed the simplest of tasks. Rube was in fact a qualified engineer, but poking fun at the foolishness of politicians, society and technology at the end of his pencil was his stock-in-trade. Rube Goldberg Machines have become a popular way to celebrate technology and absurdity simultaneously, and the phrase has entered the lexicon to describe any pointlessly convoluted process that might better be performed in a simple, straightforward manner.
***Myths:* Rube Goldberg Machine**

Rube Goldberg Machine

A Rube Goldberg machine describes any system that is absurdly more complicated than it need to be to achieve the outcome it is designed to accomplish. Wits among you may spot some Rube Goldberg machines among the regular Mythbusting work of the team (we're thinking *Lights On or Off* for a start) and it may well be for this reason, as well as having a little fun, that Adam and Jamie have built the occasional devoted Rube Goldberg machine, such as the one for the *Mythbusters Holiday Special*. This wasn't a myth of course, unless that was whether the lads could build and shoot a Rube Goldberg machine in less than a week. The results were remarkable and although it's more of a visual gag, Adam does a tremendous job describing their creation ...

ADAM – Play close attention 'cause here's exactly what's going to happen. At the top of this cone are 10 bottles of cola. At a prescribed moment, Jamie will yank on this string, releasing a 'Mento' into each of those 10 bottles which will then spray cola down into this funnel, down into this tube, up to this pair of wires which will make an electrical contact which will release this motor, sending this bowling ball spinning, spinning, spinning, spinning, spinning, spinning, spinning, spinning down. It'll stop BUT the bowling ball will keep on spinning, release itself from the screw, fall down, hit all 10 Santa bowling pins which will yank on the string, send the skiers down. The skiers going down will yank on this magnet which will release this soda bottle sending the party favour going bu-bu-bu-bu-bup going like this, releasing this mento tikatikatikatikatika all the way down into the basket, releasing this mento ... tikatikatikatikatika ... all the way down into this basket. This ball will go down here, tunk tunk dunk, release the train, whoo whoo, all the way around, all the way around, into the present, boom! The present closes, releases a Mentos into this bottle of soda, sending this robot pushing the candle under the string. The candle will burn through the string, the string will release the hammer, hammer will 'smack' ... hit the stove. The stove, whi[ch] has a roast in it, will release its roast ont[o] the seesaw, onto the dinosaur platform, jiggling this thing, releasing the two littl[e] ... doodads here, which will send this sees[aw] going this way, releasing a ball into this robot, turning him on. This robot will fin[d] his way eventually to this hand which wi[ll] BOOM, turn this switch on, sending th[e] Jacob's ladder up eowwweowwweowww li[ke] Frankenstein's monster, that will set off this fuse, jcheowwwwwwwww BOOM, setting the cannon off. The cannon will release the pirate's hat, the pirate's hat will turn on the monkeys, the monkeys will go down the ramp, ahahh-hahhh, releasing the nut – hahhh – from this nutcracker's mouth, which I just did, releasing another Mento into this bottle of soda, sending thi[s] thing spinning, pulling a string out which lets this foot kick the broken clutch here, sending Buster crashing into the ground. And that's what's going to happen.

Rust

Oxygen is powerful stuff, let it loose in an atmosphere and it will start combustions happening all over the place. This is what rust is – a very slow form of combustions where iron reacts with oxygen creating iron oxide, and yes, even a little heat (a very little).

***See also:* corrosion, oxygen, bacteria**

Sabot

A wrapping or casing for a projectile that keeps it snug in the barrel of a weapon when the projectile itself is just a teeny bit small. Sabot is also the name of a small sailing dinghy about which no myths have yet arisen. With it being very unlikely in Mythbusterland that a projectile will ever fit snugly into one of their crazy weapons, Adam and Jamie find themselves making sabots pretty much any time they're firing a projectile – no matter what the shape.

Myths: ***Racoon Rocket, Chicken Gun, Knocking the Hide Off, Tortilla Throw and more…***

JAMIE – And I gotta say, this is a clever idea. You know, you've made a flat sabot.

ADAM – Yeah.

JAMIE – In this show, we've been very familiar with sabots, and I didn't even think of doing that, so that's a cool idea. Whether it actually works very well or not, it's a good idea.

Safety Valve

Also known as a release valve, a safety valve is a valve that releases from a system whatever it is that is likely to cause something to be unsafe before that situation arises. Look at your coffee percolator and you'll see what we're talking about.

ADAM – What I hope that people get out of this episode is when they see that pipe sticking out of the hot water heater that doesn't go anywhere, and it's dripping water, that they don't go, oh, maybe I should cap that.

Myths: ***Water Heater Rocket***

Salami

Three cheers for the salami, a tasty, air-cured sausage that won't go off and give

you food poisoning. There is a world of salami out there to be discovered, and a hundred lifetimes of experience go into their making, and what do the Mythbusters add to the world of salami? They use them as fuel in a hybrid rocket.
***See also:* curing**
***Myth:* Confederate Rocket**

Salami Rocket

See *Confederate Rocket*.

Saline

Saline is just water with salt in it (pretty much good old sodium chloride, although other bits and bobs sneak in as well, especially in sea water). You can add a little salt or a lot of salt and can tell how much salt is added by testing it with electricity – the more salty it is the more conductive of an electric current, which was the point in *Salsa Escape* as it made the bars on the window rust quite a bit faster than normal. It also turns up as a key component of your stomach, as the lads demonstrated when they tested the myth of *Octopus Pregnancy* with a bunch of little tadpoles (who did fine in the saline, thank you very much).
***See also:* sea water, conduction, tadpoles**
***Myths:* Octopus Pregnancy, Cola Myths, Salsa Escape**

Salsa

Whether you reach for the roja, the verde, the ranchero, the taquera or any of the other classic Mexican salsas (or sauces), as a Mythbuster what you really care about is their ability to corrode the bars of a prison cell. Acidity? Salinity? Read all about it downstairs…

Salsa Escape

Given a bowl of salsa, a barred prison window and six years (thanks to a stretch for crimes unknown) Mexican prisoner Juan Lopez effected the first known 'salsa escape' in 1996. The Mythbusters agree that six years is a little more than they can afford to run a repeat experiment, but nevertheless aim to make their own test rig a bastion of multi-faceted complexity. They will test five kinds of metal bars (galvanized, stainless, hot and cold roll steel … and wrought iron for flavour), six kinds of salsa and end up building a prison wall with six windows testing four possible

elements for a salsa-litic escape; salsa itself, its acidity and salinity, and the addition of electrolysis. The blueprint looks like a madman's scribblings, but not only that – Adam and Jamie also go mano-a-mano:

JAMIE … this is an opportunity for you and I to pit our minds and our salsa against this problem, and see who wins. We're going to see who can escape first.

ADAM – I don't know. I think you still have an advantage over me. I mean, you escaped from a Mexican prison and I didn't.

Be that as it may, Adam sets about the test with the verve and determination of a man prepared to cheat to win. Sadly, his electrolytic rig fails because it uses AC current (Jamie's cheat rig, using DC juice borrowed from a 'prison-issue radio', works fine), his vacuum-motored drill rig is just scary, and his Jackie Chan inspired urine-soaked silk shirt just a bit … warm. However, the control test using real salsa manages to eat 8/1000ths of an inch of the iron bar in ONLY 110 days, making the myth plausible (in 37 years). Perhaps Juan had that radio after all…

See also: electrolysis

Saltpetre

Also known as potassium nitrate (although it can also refer to sodium nitrate, another key ingredient of some explosive preparations), this is one of the key ingredients of gunpowder. Saltpetre is an old fashioned name, but so is gunpowder and we like them for that very reason. An unprepossessing white powder in its pure crystalline form, saltpetre is a naturally occurring substance and was once created in a time-consuming and fiddly process involving both manure AND urine. These days you are more likely to come across it as an ingredient in your grandpa's heart medicine. In gunpowder it introduces oxygen to the chemical reaction, allowing the other ingredients to do their stuff.

See also: gunpowder, urine, explosive, oxygen, sulphur

Samuel Johnson

A large and frequently-quoted inhabitant of the 18th century, Johnson's famous concept book, *The Dictionary,* was only 42,773 words long, and even so, many of them were

misspelled. His long-playing album of the same name never achieved for him the infamy which he sought, possibly because it was released before the long-playing record player. He was amply-played in *Blackadder* by Robbie Coltrane.

See also: **oats**

San Francisco

The home of the Mythbusters (except for Sydney) this is a place of innovation, art and trolley buses. It is to the credit of the Mythbusters that a trolleybus has never made an appearance.

San Francisco Bay Model

Meticulously constructed in the 1950s to test the environmental impact of development work in the Bay, this hydraulic model covers 1.5 acres (6070 m^2) and can replicate a whole day's tides on the San Francisco Bay and San Joaquin River Delta in just 15 minutes. Apart from it being extra especially cool and worth the visit anyway, Adam and Jamie had reason to use the model to test their theories in *Alcatraz Escape* of where Frank Morris and the Anglin brothers might have ended up after escaping Alcatraz prison. The results were … impressive.

ADAM – We're escaping Alcatraz at Mach 1.

JAMIE – No wonder they didn't find them. They're probably in Japan by now.

San Francisco Dry Dock

The port where the Mythtanic was sunk … twice.

San Francisco Water Quality Control Plant

This facility was used in *Crimes and MythDemeanours 2* to crack a safe, but it's regular business was regular business, if you know what we mean…

ADAM – In other words, it's a sewage plant, and on any other day, this trough I'm standing in would be filled with poo. But today, we get to blow a safe up in it.

Sarcophagus

A kind of a coffin that is traditionally made from some sort of stone – limestone was a popular choice in the way-back, when it was thought the stone actually assisted in decomposing the corpse. This is where the word sarcophagus comes from, the Greek for 'flesh-eating'. Nice. The Mythbuster have not resorted to a real stone sarcophagus for any myth, but have loosely applied to term to the metal shipping container they bring in to house the *Stinky Car.*

Saturation

Ever tried to dry yourself with a wet towel? There's only so much water a towel will suck in, and once it's full – or saturated – it won't take any more. The same condition is true of other stuff that try to squeeze into different things: vaporised fuel in air, vaporised water in air, water in soil and so on (doesn't have to be water, doesn't have to be air…). The lads fooled around with saturation in myths like *Quicksand* where they battled to get their quicksand mix just at the right balance (pre-saturation) of sand and water.

See also: ***water vapor, quicksand***
Myths: ***Quicksand***

Scaffold

Made of metal pipes, (although bamboo is popular in lands where it is widely available) endless clamps, ladders and wooden platforms, a scaffold is a temporary structure that is build around another structure in order to effect repairs or construction work – OR to rig multi-storey Mythbusting experiments. Scaffolding has been used most notably in *Barrel of Bricks* where a thousand pounds of bricks, ballast and Buster were hung from one.

Other myths have involved people falling from scaffolding, including *Plywood Builder* and *Hammer Bridge Drop*, but the myths were filmed without use of scaffolding.

***See also:* block and tackle, rigging**

***Myths:* Plywood Builder, Hammer Bridge Drop, Barrel of Bricks**

Scale Test

If it's been built small to replicate something big, then it's a scale test.

JAMIE – Well, you know with a big build like this, it's always best to start with a small scale. It ought to tell us something.

***See also:* rig, prototype, controlled conditions**

Science

Boy, this is a biggie. Look at it this way, there's science and there's the methods of science. When you're talking about science you can tend to think of 'science' as an endless world of facts: some extraordinary, some weird, some very, very arcane. All are represented in this volume. However, science is really a way of examining the world. It's a method by which you can come to understand anything better. You may have heard people bandy about the term 'scientific method'. What they're probably referring to is a more or less rigid set of procedures that for want of a bit of levity we will describe in this way: if you were to see something you don't quite get (a 'phenomenon'), then you should observe it closely and collect information – or data – about it. This observation isn't just watching, it's getting to grips with the phenomena in any safe way you can, and for as long as it takes to come up with an idea of what might be going on. You then have to test this idea in experiments that might or might not reveal more about your initial observations. Then you make up more ways to test your theories, which have doubtless changed. All the time, you're collecting more and more data, which can then be the subject of analysis by another scientist who might want to test what you're doing themselves. In this way knowledge can take on a life of its own, never lost at the death of a particularly smart or insightful person, and falsehoods, superstitions and mythologies can be cast aside forever.

Scissor Lift

A mobile lifting apparatus used to elevate a person, their tools and materials to a useful working height. The Mythbusters use the M5 scissor lift for other things as well – for example, turning it into the support for a large slingshot.

***Myths:* Border Slingshot**

Scottie

She of the tattoos, pigtails and welding mask, Scottie Chapman joined the show along with other members of the original Build team in the first *Mythbusters Revisited* episode. She brought a certain 'who cares?' cool to the Build team activities, which turned into actual 'who cares?' when she left after 20-something episodes. Celebrated for her metalwork, eating toast off the ground and her tattoos, she only ever got terrified when facing the possibility of losing an inked-in friend (see *Exploding Tattoo*).

SCOTTIE – It's my ghost dog!

Scott Thomas

Scott is a blacksmith and was consulted for the myth of *Exploding Hammers*, which supposed that hammers can actually explode in your face when using them. But … it couldn't be true, could it Scott?

SCOTT – It can be bad. Generally because the hammers are both made out of hardened steel, and when you strike two pieces of hardened steel together, something's going to give. And you're usually going to get chips or one might even break or fracture on you.

***Myths:* Exploding Hammers**

Scuba

Scuba ('self-contained underwater breathing apparatus') is without question one of the top five acronyms of all time.

***See also:* acronyms**

Sealant

If it seals a material (or two) from the ingress of a substance like air or water, then you've got yourself a sealant baby! Let's celebrate!
***See also:* pitch, X-Pando, Teflon tape, adhesive, butyl**

Sea Level

Just another of those simple everyday phrases that describe a phenomenon completely inaccurately. The sea is simply not level – and we're not just talking about waves and swells here (despite their key role in *Seasickness; Kill or Cure?*) but also the tidal pull of the moon that makes that part of the Earth's oceans and seas closest to the moon it slightly bulgier than the other parts. Then there is a suspicious inertial bulge due to the rather rapid speed at which the planet spins (1038 mph at the equator, or about 1600 km/h) that you can replicate by pushing that mug of coffee away from you so that the beverage slops out onto the table. Having said that, the whole sea level concept is with us now and does give us a short hand to describe certain things like atmospheric pressure, which at sea level is one atmosphere (or more usefully 14.7 psi). Imagine that! A tall column containing 14.7 pounds (6.6 kgs) of atmosphere (well, air) is pushing down on you all the time – and you don't even have to imagine it because it's happening to you right now (a little less if you're in Mexico City to be sure). It's a wonder you can get out of bed at all in the morning, and we're not even accounting for gravity. There are some who suggest that when the atmospheric pressure increases (say, a high pressure system floats across your home) that it is in fact easier to get out of bed because of the extra buoyancy this pressure gives you – just like your ability to float around a public pool but not a public library. While the sea may not be 'level' as such, if you were to reduce the entire planet to the size where it could sit on a billiard table, the entire thing would be smoother than the actual billiard balls it sat next to, with its oceans the barest smudges of mist. For all of that, the Mythbusters have never had the opportunity to put the boot into sea level because, for all its faults, it's a useful concept to have around the place – a bit like democracy really.
***See also:* atmospheric pressure, buoyancy**
***Myths:* Seasickness – Kill or Cure?, Killer Whirlpool, Sinking Titanic**

Seasick Chair

This rig was based on NASA's original, and is simply a chair on a platform that rotates at about seven revolutions per minute. The final touch is that the sit-ee has to move their head up and down and from side to side – and if you're prone to the condition, results are guaranteed.

***See also:* seasickness**

***Myths:* Seasickness – Kill or Cure?**

And you thought the dentist chair was bad!

Seasickness – Kill or Cure?

The myth of seasickness is all too real to many, but what about the supposed cures? Pressure points, herbal remedies, electrical stimulations, ginger? With pharmaceuticals set aside because of the drowsiness side effects they cause, the first step in this myth was to create a rig that would bring on seasickness in the shop. Fortunately, just such a rig was developed by NASA to test their astronauts, and the team have no trouble whipping up their own version – the Seasick Chair. Adam and Grant are soon identified as the test subjects by the nice shade of green that they turn within a few minutes on the rig, and so the team schedules a daily regimen of Seasick Chair time with the testee subjected to different supposed cures. First up, a homeopathic tongue tickler is sprayed into the mouth 'as often as required' to keep the breakfast at bay – but this turns out to be less than successful. Same for the wrist straps (as recommended by Barry Manilow) and their electrically-stimulating cousins. The ginger pills on the other hand work a treat – neither Grant nor Adam suffer the tiniest twinge.

ADAM – I mean, at this point I'm trying to think of things that are sickening, like when you throw up, and you can taste it in your nose, and you've got to blow it out of your nose. That kind of stuff. It's still not doing anything.

However, tests with a placebo demonstrated that at least with Grant, the mind has a lot of influence over the body – not much with Adam.

ADAM – Oh, stop, stop.

GRANT – OK.

ADAM – Oh %^$#♥. I hate this &^%#$♥♥ chair.

***See also:* seasick chair, seasickness, placebo, ginger**

Seasickness

Previously known as 'camel sickness', this arresting malady caused much grimacing and groaning when the time came to test the myth of *Seasickness – Kill or Cure*? Happily no-one on the team was in fact killed, and we can relate the facts about seasickness: when half your senses are telling you that you're on a steady footing, with solid hand rails to cling to and so on, but the other half are relating an up-and-down, side-to-side kind of experience of the world, then the brains of many stout yeomen experience seasickness. Nausea, vomiting, misery – we'll let Adam give you some details…

ADAM – The frequency that makes you the most ill … turns out to be about point two Hertz, about a pitch roll or yaw every five seconds, which is generally what you'd experience on a large boat … That's why surfers don't get sick and people on big boats do.

***See also:* nausea, vomit**
***Myths:* Seasickness – Kill or Cure?**

Seawater

Seawater? It's water from a sea or ocean! 1220 billion billion litres of it is floating about the place! True, true, but there's more. Seawater is really defined by what's in it rather than where it comes from: 96.5 per cent water and 3.5 per cent salts (mostly sodium chloride but other things creep in there as well, like magnesium, calcium, bromine, carbon and potassium). This is the more or less stable recipe for water, which makes us wonder where the salt comes from.

The most satisfactory answer reasons that salts come from the land, swept into the sea by rains and rivers. There's also a suggestion that it leached out of the land when the seas were first formed. In which case, why aren't the seas becoming more salty? This question plagued some scientists for years (others just ignored it) before the action of plate tectonics offered an explanation, that being the 'conveyor belt' action of the ocean floors suck in as much salt as is deposited from the surface. How convenient. Adam and Jamie (Jamie in particular) love the opportunity to cover themselves with seawater whenever a suitable myth is on hand – *Sinking Titanic, Pingpong Rescue* and *Shark Myths* to name but three.

***See also:* water, tectonic plates.**

***Myths:* Sinking Titanic, Pingpong Rescue, Shark Myths, Seasickness; Kill or Cure?**

Segway

Somewhere around the *Speed Camera* revisit, the Mythbusters got a Segway. From then on, Adam and Jamie (OK, just Adam) can be spotted doing PTCs (pieces to camera) on the ubiquitous, gyroscopic two-wheeler. Why? Well – why not? It can't be long before a myth related to Segways emerges that will give them the opportunity to blow one up.

Sensors

There's all sorts of fast-moving, microscopic, explosive and/or bone crunching things happening in the world all the time. Often human beings are too slow witted, lazy or combustible to spot them happening. And yet these things are frequently very exciting, or important, or dangerous, so we like to know that they're happening. To this end, clever people have invented all kinds of mechanical, electromagnetic, chemical and 'other' sensors that are calibrated to identify and react to that certain special something; perhaps the blood pressure of a walrus-moustached special effects expert lying in an hermetically-sealed coffin.

***Myths:* Buried Alive**

Servos

Servos automatically adjust the operation of another device by responding to some kind of feedback. A basic example of a servo is a thermostat, which adjusts the operation of a heating or cooling unit according to the temperature of the immediate environment. Servos can be much more complex, such as the servo motors used by the *Jet Car* which controlled its steering.

JAMIE – Servos are motors that are positionable so that we can precisely control the steering. We need to have something pretty good because if it's going that fast, you know we need to really be able to dial in on the aim or you know, it may go out of control.

***See also:* thermostat**
***Myths:* Jet Car, Shredded Aeroplane**

757 Grams

The exact control weight of the white overalls used in the myth *Who Gets Wetter?* After the first experiment they weighed in at 785 grams (when Jamie ran through the rain) and 781 grams (after Adam walked through the rain) … and I'm afraid that's just as much detail as we're going to give you.

Seven Up Vending Machine

Built by Jamie and his merry men for a commercial, the 7-Up Vending/Attack Machine still works a treat, and was rolled out as an example of how perfect compressed air can be as a propellant in *Chicken Gun* – which was to feature a weapon with similar characteristics. They also used it to power up their *Killer Washing Machine.*

***See also:* compressed air, propellant**
***Myths:* Chicken Gun, Killer Washing Machine**

SF Party

With more than 100 years in the party business in a party town, these guys should know how to tie a balloon or … several thousand. Well, they didn't tie all the balloons in *Carried Away* but Feliciano's lessons sure helped save some time …

FELICIANO – So you bring two balloons, same size, and you tie them into each other.

OK, it doesn't work without the visuals, but … you'll have to watch the episode. The columns look so pretty!

Shattering CD ROM

Can a high-speed CD ROM drive spin a CD so fast that the structural integrity of the CD is compromised? Will shards of aluminium-coated plastic exit the drive at a speed that could kill, blind or maim? This is what Adam and Jamie wanted to know – and they'd do anything to get a CD spinning at upwards of 30,000 rpm. After some tinkering with towers, high-speed drives, microwaves and woodworking equipment, they were finally able to send pieces of CD two inches into the ever-compliant Buster. Nevertheless, the Mythbusters were happy to say that such an event would be highly, highly unlikely in real life.

ADAM – I think we've done a good day's work here.

JAMIE – Any day we create that much shrapnel is a good day.

Shattering Sub Woofer

Another destructive sound record beckoned with this myth – having already demonstrated the shattering power of noise in *Breaking Glass* the aim now was to turn the power of pressurised vibrations in air on that symbol of freedom and independence – the automobile. In short, can a speaker break a car? But whereas *Breaking Glass* was all about tuning a human voice to the resonant frequency of the wine glass, what the Mythbusters are dealing with here is pure power and as much of it as they can squeeze into a Mercedes-Benz W126 300SD Turbo. Once they turned out pretty much everything else (seats and so on) it turned out to fit rather a lot of speaker – the 51-inch (or 129.5-centimetre) Mythwoofer. Not only that, the speaker was direct drive … powered directly from the engine itself! When finally installed and wired in, the giant woofer produced 161.3dB at an astonishingly low 16Hz. This was just below the level of human hearing, but not beyond busting the roof of the host vehicle. It's not enough to completely destroy the car, so the myth is busted, but how does it compare on the scale of loudness?

ADAM ... 140 decibels is plenty to severely damage your ears, no matter how short a time you're exposed to it.

JAMIE – And 165 decibels is what you get out of a jet airplane with 15,000 pounds of thrust.

ADAM – 198 to 201 decibels is enough to kill you from the shockwave alone.

JAMIE – Yeah, and I believe 248 decibels is what the atomic bombs that were dropped on Hiroshima and Nagasaki put out.

See also: ***crankshaft, decibels, Mythwoofer, Wayne Harris***

Shipping Container

When the humble shipping container was invented (yes, invented) it ushered in a massive change in the way stuff was shipped around the world. Previously cargo had been shipped in all sorts of sizes of box (or other container) but from the 1950s onwards, a push began to standardise the shipping container so that efficiencies could be found by bringing the same container from warehouse via truck to the dock, where it would be loaded onto a specially designed ship, sailed to another port, unloaded onto a train, then another truck, and unloaded at a warehouse. It took a while for this system to be constructed (imagine all the docks and ships they had to build) but today we benefit by lower costs for all our imported goods – meaning more of them get shipped (and we burn more fuel doing so). At least it means there is the occasional shipping container on hand when Adam and Jamie need something big, metal and boxy to do some terrifyingly dangerous experiment – such as a firing range for *Bulletproof Teeth*, the *Confederate Rocket* which needed a rocket-resistant bunker for the early experiments, and the *Stinky Car* where the lads needed somewhere to park their Corvette so they wouldn't hurl their guts every time they walked past it.

Myths: ***Confederate Rocket, Stinky Car, Bulletproof Teeth, Gunslinger Myths***

Shirley Eaton

Actress behind the role of Jill Masterson in *Goldfinger*, Shirley remembers the day of the notorious 'gold paint scene' as vividly as if it happened yesterday.

See also: ***skin***

Myths: ***Goldfinger***

SHIRLEY – That morning wasn't pleasant. I almost felt like I had flu. I suppose becoming hot made me feel and I suppose a little fear with everybody saying we must be careful with Shirley, we must be careful with Shirley.

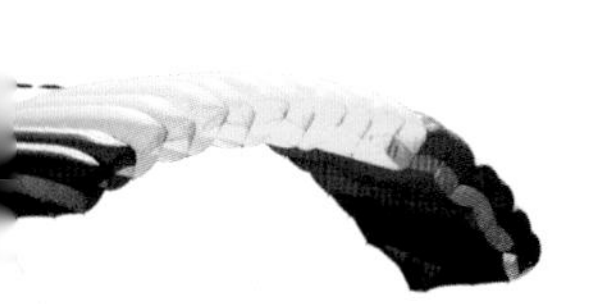

Shock Cord

Similar to bungee cord, the shock cord is made of stranded synthetic and natural rubber materials, and gets its name from absorbing the shock of a parachute's opening when supplies are dropped by air.

***See also:* bungee cord**

***Myths:* Border Slingshot**

Short Circuit

A short circuit occurs when an electric charge is allowed to flow along a different path to the one intended; perhaps from the wall outlet through the vacuum cleaner, then into that loose wire, from there through the case to your left hand, through your heart down to the big toe on your right foot (rather than from the outlet to the motor as the manufacturer intended). This is called electrocution, and sometimes it's the last thing you experience.

***See also:* circuit**

Short ton

Usually just called the ton to confuse people, this measure is equal to 2000 pounds, which sounds sensible until you realise that one pound is equal to 0.45359237 of that much more sensible and widely respected unit of mass, the kilogram. Of course there are types such as Adam and Jamie who cling to their tons and pounds, but at the end of the day we shall all bow to the masters of SI.

***See also:* SI, pounds, kilogram, tonne**

Shredded Aeroplane

God bless the internet and all who post on her – for without delightful images like that which started this myth, where would the Mythbusters find their kookier material? The kind of myths that take them out Alameda with 10,000 bags of sand and a 380 horsepower aeroplane engine to set up 200 feet (61 metres) of railway track leading to an old fuselage? It all started with an image that circulated on the ubiquitous internet of a neatly sliced up aeroplane – but with no explanation as to how it happened. Adam and Jamie just had to know how it happened, and although they were able to demonstrate that a jilted lover could indeed have taken a chainsaw to her wandering partner's pride and joy (it's the plane we're talking about) the demo cuts Jamie makes simply don't look like the ones in the picture. This is where the second theory comes in – that a runaway aeroplane took exception to a winged colleague and chopped into him with their propeller. How could this happen?

Did someone say shred?

Well, if say, the electric starter motor in your single-engined propeller aeroplane failed, it's conceivable that a pilot might hop out of the cockpit and try an old fashioned hand-start (that's where you push the propeller around yourself until the engine catches – like push starting a car). That cantankerous aeroplane could very well kick into a fast enough propeller rotation to roll away at around 30 mph (48 km/h). If another aeroplane was in the way …

JAMIE – Mayhem, destruction, the whole nine yards.

ADAM – Absolutely radical.

And indeed, with all the equipment, safety gear and remote starts working perfectly (it didn't happen first time by any means) they get the kind of result that makes even Adam grasping for words…

ADAM – That's EXACTLY the slice pattern we see in the picture. I mean, it's a little bit different, but we see that the airplane …

JAMIE – You're excited.

ADAM – I'm SO excited, man! It's exactly what we see in the picture! It's vertical slices from the blade. That's just … I'm … stunned.

***See also:* Alameda, fuselage, Josh Smith, push start, Brian Sullivan, Earl Hibler**

SI

Sneaking around only at night, swathed in ritual purple robes and leather underpants, the glorious masters of SI (Le Système International d'Unités, or the International System of Units) steal children from their beds at night and impale sheep on one-metre lengths of pure platinum. Thus is the legend of metric measurement told on ye olde United States of America (3,794,066 sq miles in area, highest point Mt McKinley Alaska, 20,300 ft above sea level, lowest point Death Valley, California, 282 ft below

sea level) despite the fact that the rest of the world came along on the 'one planet – one ruler' jaunt decades ago.

Simulaid Suzie

Weighing only 65 pounds (29.4 kilos) Suzie is the stock standard seven or eight year old kid – missing only the brain, heart, lungs, tantrums etc. Used by the Mythbusters for testing those kid-sized myths like *360° Swing* she hasn't seen a rocket yet she didn't love.

KARI ... how cool was that when she's going (sound effects) and ends up on the top of the swing set.

ADAM – I don't know. By 'cool' if you mean 'absolutely terrifying when it started spraying smoke and fire towards us only 15 feet away'?

KARI – Yeah, cool!

Sinking Titanic

A large ship – a very large ship ... in fact the very largest ship ever yadda yadda. We all know that, along with the fact that it was sunk tragically by a stray iceberg and most of the passengers drowned. Was it … terrible seamanship? Poor design? Bad luck? The spontaneous combustion coal fire that had been burning in the coal store since before the ship left? In fact that's not the question in front of the Mythbusters today. Rather it is this – will a sinking ship somehow drag you down with it if you're floating in the water too close by? There are three major theories that Adam and Jamie test:

JAMIE ... the first one is that air that mixes in with the water as it rushes up from boat. It makes the water less dense. And so it's like you're going to fall through the water quicker that way. The second theory is that the cavities in the ship will create an area for the water to rush in and that'll pull you into the ship. And then the third one is that the ship moving through the water rapidly towards the bottom will create a vortex above it.

And the results? The small scale tests didn't cut it, but the medium swimming pool scale tests worked a treat. So the lads went right out and bought themselves a nice nine-ton (8164 kg) tug boat. However, despite Adam's terror, the boat simply failed to suck him down.

ADAM – The speed of descent was just like 'whoosh'. I mean, my job I know was to stay with the boat and feel the suction. But I swear to God, standing on there my body just goes move that way, not that way. Survival kicked in at a critical moment.

See also: ***vortex, aerate, density***

Have you been working out Adam?

Silicone Breasts

Will your implants explode at altitude? Adam and Jamie had to know, so they build their own pressure chamber to find out. Yet no matter how hard they tried, the little silicone-filled bags were up to the task – from the high pressures of the deepest ocean to high in the atmosphere the implants were always at much greater risk of ridicule than rupture.

ADAM – You're more in danger of your canoli rupturing than your implants actually exploding.

JAMIE – Your canoli?

ADAM – Canoli, it's Italian pastry. It's cream-filled.

JAMIE – Oh, OK.

ADAM – It's not a euphemism.

Single-Action Revolver

A single-action revolver is so-called because the trigger performs only one action, that being to release the hammer to fall down on the chambered round igniting the firing cap and sending the bullet through the barrel and out into the world at large. You need to use your hand (classically the thumb of your firing hand, but the other hand can be used instead) to pull the hammer back to fire the next round, and the action of doing so revolves the cylinder to place a fresh round under the hammer. In double-action revolvers the trigger turns the cylinder and draws the hammer back before releasing the hammer and firing a round. The Build team wrestled with single-action revolvers in *Gunslinger Myths* when they tried to replicate the claim that the outlaw Kid Curry could fire his single-action revolver five times in the time it took a poker chip to fall from his hand.

***See also:* Kid Curry, firearms**
***Myths:* Gunslinger Myths**

Siphon

Liquids can be convinced to go up a hill if there's a nice big drop on the other side. This is the principle of the siphon as it is used in toilets and explains all the wacky bends you see in plumbing systems.

***See also:* toilet**

Skin

It's very easy to ignore how important your skin is. It's not just about keeping the rest of you in and the world at large out (a relatively important task) but your skin also helps you breathe and keeps your temperature under control, as Jamie discovered in *Goldfinger.* In fact, skin turns up all over the place in the Mythbusters, the fact that dead skin cells are constantly floating away from you gave Morgan the Bloodhound the edge over his human quarry in *Dog Myths* no matter how many showers Adam had. It also proved safe and stable for iron oxide heavy tattoo ink in *Exploding Tattoo* and even an RFID tag in *Myth Evolution.* They discovered that they could beat the supposedly unbeatable fingerprint scanner in *Crimes*

and MythDemeanours 2 despite its claim to measure galvanic skin response. They also found that whether or not a Daddy Long Legs spider was packing the most lethal poison in the world, it couldn't pierce Adam's skin to inject it. Then there's all the other kinds of skins they've dealt with; goat skin that needed shaving before it could be turned into a drum for *Chinese Invasion Alarm*, the parasitic tapeworms with a specially evolved skin that could have made them the starting point for the myth of *Octopus Pregnancy*, the Dragon Skin made especially for Buster 2.0 and the *Eel Skin Wallet* that was in fact made from the disgusting hag fish. All together, skin is as vitally important as it is cool.

Skunk Cleaning

The stink of the skunk is legendary for its pong as well as its staying power; the myth here was to do with what can get rid of it once it's on you. However, as Adam and Jamie found, skunks are not as prone to spraying as the cartoons would have you believe – even the professional critter handlers were amazed. But with Mythbusters dedication to the job, they eventually got a skunk to go to town on Adam's shoe: – and we're able to establish once and for all that neither beer nor commercial douche would clean a skunk spray, while you were in with a chance using commercial skunk smell remover, an mix of hydrogen peroxide, baking soda and hand wash, and even good old tomato sauce.

ADAM – Finally we smell foul. I'm totally psyched.

***See also:* Jeff Anderson, Regan Kuja**

Sledgehammer

This great Peter Gabriel song is also a fabulous way of transferring energy from a human being into something that is hopefully not a human being; a football say, or a pair of trousers into the infamous *Exploding Pants*.

***See also:* football, hammer, Deadblow**
***Myths:* Helium Football, Exploding Pants**

Slide

In a playground, a slide is a smooth and angled apparatus on which children (actual, and 'at heart') can experience safely the phenomenon of gravity. In a concert band, a slide is that part of the trombone which moves in and out of the rest of the instrument to lengthen the distance the sound must travel, which changes its pitch.

***See also:* Exploding Trombone**

Slime Eel

Also known as the hag fish.

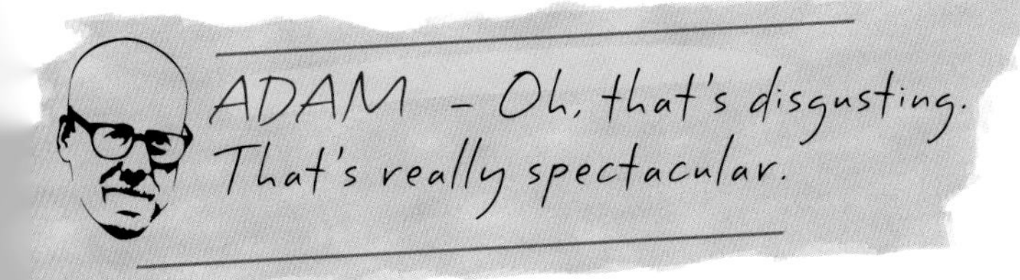

Sling

One of the most simple weapons you can make (not that we encourage you … in fact, on the basis of several fortified legal opinions, we expressly discourage you from ever making anything that will harm you or anyone like you) a sling cleverly extends the length of the human arm. This extra length translates to leverage and means that you can throw a projectile much farther. A sling is made of a piece of cord with a pouch in the middle and perhaps a loop at one end. You fire a sling (no, no, no you don't) by placing a projectile in the pouch, spinning it around your head and releasing one end of the cord (hence the loop BUT DON'T EVER DO THIS). There is a bit of a knack to it, but if you've done it right (not that you ever will) the projectile will be released in a straight line, hopefully not into your eye, but rather the temple of some fabled giant. A sling differs from a slingshot because of the use of rubber material in the latter, but not the former.

***See also:* rubber, slingshot trebuchet**

***Myths:* Border Slingshot**

Slingshot

A top notch slingshot can toss a steel ball bearing at more than 200 mph (322 km/h+) and even though the best Adam and Jamie could muster in their scale tests for *Border Slingshot* was 85 mph (137 km/h) that's still going to hurt. A slingshot differs from the ancient weapon, the sling, in one vital respect – rubber.

***See also:* rubber, ball bearing**

***Myths:* Border Slingshot**

Slisting the Wand

An archaic term for the act of splitting an arrow.

***Myth:* Splitting Arrow**

Smell

Molecules vapourised in the excitement of the moment are just the sort of thing that a smell is made of. Whether that's a roasting turkey or a dog poo, the airborne molecules of said article strikes your nose in ways not yet confidently confirmed by science. Best

guess is that your nose includes a 'lock and key' type system for individuating the molecular elements of a smell, information which is then passed onto your olfactory bulb for processing into consciousness (be that a 'phew' or a 'hmmmmm!'). And some smells can be toxic – check back over the myth of the *Stinky Car* for a reminder of how putrid smells can get. What makes it all the worse (or better, depending on the smell) is that your nose can register frillions of smells so specifically they can bring you to tears, leaving your tongue and its taste buds far behind.

***See also:* tongue,**

***Myths:* Stinky Car, Flatulence Myths**

Snarge

The remains of a bird that has struck an aeroplane in a bird strike.

Snow Plough

Can a snow plough generate so much air pressure that at high speed it could push a car off the road? Thinking thrifty, the build team get hold of a decommissioned snow plough which they soon find has more things wrong with it than there are hours in three days for them to fix, especially important things like, you know, the brakes. But when their snow plough is moving relatively smoothly it's another chance to get out the long cables and test for the truth. The specially- chosen 'light' car with high centre of gravity barely moves a whisker as the plough cannons past at 60 mph (96.5 km/h) … and then crashed spectacularly into the barricades. Whoops…

GRANT – I forgot to activate the brake.
KARI – You didn't activate the brakes?
GRANT – Well I activated it after crashing into the barrier.

***See also:* centre of gravity**

SNOW SPECIAL, THE

A special series of myths devoted to a fuller and franker understanding of snow and ice. Adam and Jamie attempted to yodel up an avalanche in *Avalanche Adventure*, while the build team licked cold poles to test the myth of the *Frozen Tongue* while simultaneously examining whether a car is safer in reverse while *Driving on Ice*.

Myths: ***Avalanche Adventure, Driving on Ice***

SODIUM CARBONATE

This industrial chemical was once known as soda ash, and is an important ingredient in glass and dynamite. It was once obtained from the ash of burnt plant material, but is more commonly derived from table salt today in a complex process we won't go into now.

SON OF A GUN

One of the all-time classic myths – is it really possible that a Civil War soldier could have impregnated a virtuous lady who just happened to be standing behind him when he was shot in the testicles? Could sperm travel so far, so fast, so hot and so effectively? Adam, Jamie and the build team just had to know, and if it meant putting their own bodily fluids to the test, so be it. Really this myth came down to two things – what was left on a Minié Ball after it blasted through a scrotum, and could that detritus result in conception. The answer to the first was 'not much' which left the second in the realm of the academic really. But the costumes, the olde worlde rifles, the insight into the male reproductive material all made this a myth in a million. Oh, and a GREAT explanation for a mid-war fling...

ADAM – Either they fell in love and got married or he felt some sense of cosmic obligation, and they had several children together, and as the doctor stated, none of them looked as much like the soldier as the first one.

In fact, there is no chance of anything sperm-like surviving the a trip on the hot surface of a musket ball – and in any case the whole thing turned out to be based on a gag in a 19th century medical journal. So be warned gag-writers! You may be taken seriously!

See also: ***John Nevis, Minié Ball, sperm***

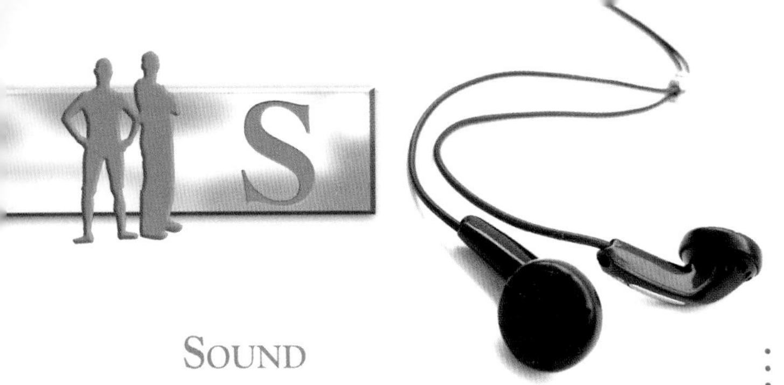

Sound

This curious phenomenon is about as insubstantial as they get – no matter how complex the timbre and tones of an 80-piece orchestra playing Stravinsky, the sound you hear is nothing more than vibrations pushing air around. Perhaps this very ethereality has brought about an opus of sonic myths with which Adam and Jamie have jammed with great joy. From the world first images of *Breaking Glass* to the waddle of *Duck Quack Echo*, the merest whiff of the *Brown Note* and the auto destruction of *Shattering Subwoofer* the world is all the better for a fuller and franker understanding of the sounds that fill most of our lives, between the frequencies of 20 and 200,000 hertz.

***See also:* supersonic, tie clip mike, sub sonic, hertz, frequency, decibels**

Specific Gravity

This is a ratio of how dense something is relative to water. This is expressed as a number where 1 is … pure water. Sea water with all those salts in it is a little denser than water and thus has a specific gravity of about 1.03 (if you've ever dived the cenotes of the Yucatan then you'll know what we're talking about). Beeswax and raw cane sugar are both a little less dense than water at 0.96 and would thus float in pure water. Twenty-four carat gold has a specific gravity of 19.29 and would not.

***See also:* density, buoyancy, cenote, sea water, pure water**

***Myths:* Sinking Titanic**

Speed

The rate of movement of an object, irrespective of its direction. Literally the distance travelled divided by the time taken to travel that distance.

***See also:* velocity, acceleration**

Speeding Ticket

Never, never assume that you can get away with speeding – if Jamie can get caught, how will you get away with it?

JAMIE – I rushed right down to the local hardware store and thankfully they had just what I needed. It's sort of a gate valve. There's no visible rubber seals or anything. It's rated for the pressures we need. It's metal to metal. I think it's going to work just fine. Unfortunately, since the water is heating and we're behind schedule now, I was rushing. I got a speeding ticket.

Sperm

The Mythbusters have dosed them with cola and fried them on a Minié ball, but the real job of sperm is to find an ovum and implant enough genetic material to kick start a new life.

***Myths:* Octopus Pregnancy, Son of a Gun, Cola Myths**

Splitting an Arrow

Robin Hood may or may not have existed, but Errol Flynn certainly did. In the classic film *The Adventures of Robin Hood* buffs might recall the scene where Robin (nee Errol) splits a competitor's arrow to win an archery contest. Modern archers with aluminium arrows call it 'telescoping', and claim it's a 1 in 3000 shot. But that's not the same as actually splitting an arrow from tail to tip, as the build team discovered. An enthusiastic archer himself, Tory led the way, but success was hard to hit – even with Grant's 'arrowbot' on the case. Not even creating a guide track for the arrow, fired point blank, could help. 'Busted' was the call, but the fans called a foul, and some even donated materials for a revisit (thanks George). It was back to the workshop for the build team, where they: made authentic medieval arrows from George's straight-grain cedar and steamed them free of any deviance; home-forged armour-piercing arrowheads; reinforced the nock with goat horn; even rebuilt the arrowbot from scratch to fire a traditional long bow. None of it worked – until they called in professional archer Jim Long who, after 60 shots, made a 10 inch (25cm) split in the authentic arrow. It turns out the special effects wizards in the Errol Flynn movie probably used a bamboo

arrow, and sure enough, the Jim could split one of them from nock to tip first time. But the myth? Busted.

TORY – I mean, we gave 'em what they asked for. We made our own arrows, we had a traditional longbow, we even brought in a skilled archer who hit it, and he couldn't split it.

KARI – After we were at the range and we saw how the bamboo split right down the centre, and we saw how we couldn't get in to the cedar arrows more than ten inches, I think the movie used bamboo.

GRANT – And as we know, anything's possible in the movies.

See also: ***fletching, nock, longbow, yew, Travis Fletcher, Jim Long***

Spoon Drill

Also known as a spoon-bit auger, this is was the mediaeval equivalent of a 15.6V cordless drill (they didn't have nickel-metal hydride batteries back then). Why a spoon? Well, it looks a bit like a spoon – a very sharp spoon which should never under any circumstances be used to eat ice cream. In the myth *Tree Cannon* Adam and Jamie made their own from wood and metal, before Jamie got his shirt off to give it a try by drilling a barrel for their cannon. Not his easiest day on Mythbusters…

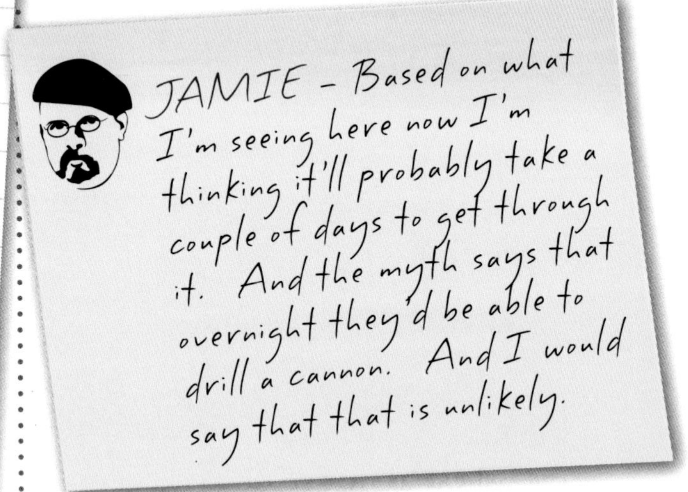

Stack Effect

Modern buildings are pretty complicated beasts, and if you're building and maintaining them you have to be conscious of every little thing, right down to the amount of air going in and out of the place. Too much air coming in and you'll end up with the stack effect where pressure builds up within the building that can compromise some of its structures ... things like windows. This was one of the factors involved in the myth of the *Leaping Lawyer*.

***See also:* Pat Quinn**

***Myth:* Leaping Lawyer**

Stanley Benjamin MD

Gastroenterologist Dr Stan Benjamin has got guts – and he's not afraid to tell people about them. The Mythbusters were not the first, but learned much of value for their attempt to bust open the myth *Pop Rocks and Soda*. Never fear – your stomach can cope with a little candy...

STANLEY – You've got two built in vents, one at either side of the stomach that should be the places that this air goes if you reach those kinds of pressures.

***Myths:* Pop Rocks and Soda**

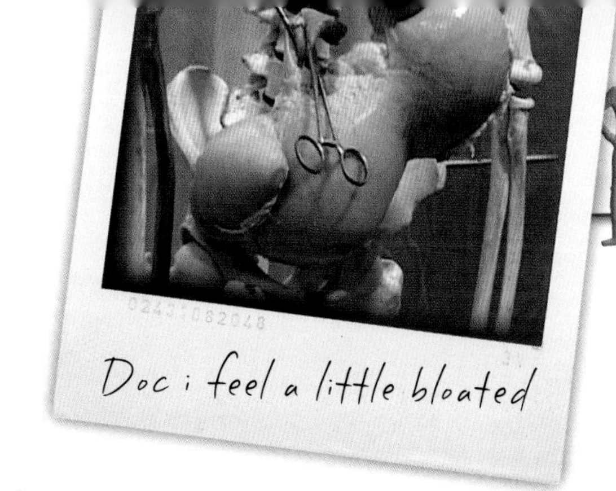

Doc: feel a little bloated

Starboard

Back in ye olde times way, way, way before Ole Evinrude popped an internal combustion engine on the transom of his rowing boat, boats were not steered by a wooden paddle thingy that was dead centre at the stern. They were steered by a bloke standing at the stern who stuck an oar into the water to one side of the boat - more like how dragon boats are steered (if ever you've seen a dragon boat, which is not something we can guarantee – but should you ever see 20 or 30 people paddling like they've gone completely bananas, look out for the much smarter person standing at the stern steering with a paddle stuck in the water on one side). In ancient Norse this was the 'stýri' or rudder and it was stuck in the water on the 'borð' or side of the boat. We're getting close to an answer to the question 'what is starboard' now, and after 161 words we should not be too surprised, because with so many more ancient Norse boaties being right handed, they preferred to pop their 'stýri' on the right hand 'borð' of the boat. Stýri borð ... stýri borð ... stýri borð ...do we get the picture? Cool.

***See also:* port, transom**

Static

Literally, static means 'not moving', and has been applied to electricity that has built up on an object (or person) simply through contact with another object, a phenomenon called the Triboelectric Effect. As the objects touched, electrons from one flowed across to the other, and then cling to that object until they can find something with an opposite charge to hop across to, perhaps the earth, or a close friend's earlobe. The spark that indicated the static charge has jumped from your finger to your friend's earlobe is actually air that is ionised by the charge, and the voltage of the spark could be anything from 1500 (for a 0.5 mm spark) to 10,000 volts (a 3 mm spark). Killer! Well, no – because of the very, very low current, only a few 10 millionths of an amp, you'll only end up angering your friend, or blowing up a gas station. You will not be electrocuted.

***See also:* electrons, Triboelectric Effect, amps**

Steam

When water gets hot enough it changes state, also called a phase transition, and becomes water vapour, which some people recognise as steam, although they could not be more wrong.

***See also:* water vapour**

***Myths:* Steam Cannon, Steam Machine Gun**

Steam Box

Using steam to straighten wood is an ancient art, and for the revisit to the myth of *Splitting an Arrow* Kari had the task of straightening cedar rods to make into authentic arrows. However, the origins of Kari's steam box was not weaponry.

KARI – I've brought a few things from home. I've brought this, which is for facials, and it makes steam. And this is a home hair curling kit which is also to make steam, which, if you're a girl I'm sure you know exactly what these are, and if you're a man you just think I'm crazy.

***See also:* wood, arrows, cedar**

***Myths:* Splitting an Arrow (revisit)**

Steam Cannon

When Adam and Jamie took the opportunity to look at another giant, build-heavy Archimedes inspired myth, did they run and hide under a rock? No they did not! With a minimum of complaint and a maximum of expanding gases, the Mythbusters built, revised, rebuilt, re-revised and finally, re-rebuilt and actually fired a steam cannon. It was not to absolute Archimedean specification by any means, which meant the myth was in the strict sense busted, but they did turn the explosive potential of hot water into a very dangerous weapon. This myth and associated builds was one of the longest and most fraught with difficulties the team has ever dealt with.

JAMIE – The worst case scenario on this is that the whole thing blows up and is so aggressive that we're all thrown back a couple of hundred feet from the explosion and we die.

Steam Machine Gun

Is it possible that a machine gun, powered by nothing but steam, was alive and well and killing people nearly 150 years ago? It was an exciting and deadly rig, but after testing it for range of fire, rate of fire and lethality, the eventual result was busted.

See also: ***US Civil War, Alameda Airstrip, clockwork, hum, John Lamb***

Steel

The material that is synonymous with strength and modernity is an alloy of steel and carbon, with different recipes also calling for a hint of manganese, tungsten, vanadium and thyme. Steel is everywhere and for good reason; it's strong, malleable and cheap. The Mythbusters employ steel whenever string and used cereal packets will simply not suffice.

See also: ***alloy, carbon***

Stephen Cassidy

Having written about the building of the Golden Gate Bridge, Stephen was the ideal candidate to describe how the myth of *Bridge Drop* might have originated.

STEPHEN ... I would think it would be very reassuring to believe that if you're working high steel you miss step, it would be nice if your tool belt went first, broke the fall and you survived.

See also: ***Cooper Cranes***
Myths: ***Bridge Drop***

Sternum

The plate-like bone that covers the centre of your chest. The Mythbusters are frequently tapping away at the sternum chasing one myth or another – can a bullet of ice enter the chest in *Ice Bullet*?

***Myths:* Ice Bullet**

Stevan Thomas

An electrician by trade, the Mythbusters needed him to wire up their *Phone in a Thunderstorm* house rig. But did he think a zap would really get you through the phone?

***See also:* building code**

STEVAN – I can see the telephone or electric devices, because if there is a strike in the house and you get a big surge, that would not be good for anything that's connected with wire in the house, be that a computer. I've certainly heard about people's computers pretty much melting and frying down. I've heard about problems with telephones, but I've never actually seen the melted pieces and held them in my hand.

Steve Harrington

For the myth *Confederate Rocket* Adam and Jamie needed to not only know how to make a rocket, but make a rocket 150 years ago. It was going to take a special kind of expertise …

JAMIE – So you're like a rocket scientist, right?

STEVE – Yeah, exactly. I teach the rocket propulsion class at San Diego State, and I launch my own rockets.

JAMIE – Does being a rocket scientist help you pick up chicks?

STEVE – Unfortunately in the rocket science world, there's not that many women, and they're hunted to extinction.

Steve 'The Pet Shop Guy' Murata

Steve's shop 'Nippon Goldfish Company' is a family business several generations

old, started by Tadayasu Murata. Steve got lucky one day when Adam and Jamie dropped by to pick up a bunch of fish, food and equipment to test the myth of *Goldfish Memory*.

STEVE – Their brains are pretty small. It's about 2 per cent of their body weight, so you can figure out they're not going to have too much of a memory.

Stinky Car

So, you see an advert in the paper for a hot late model sports coupe. The price is unbelievable, but you roll along to take a look just in case. As you hop into the car a problem presents itself; the car stinks worse than a locker full of old socks. Something must have died in it. Indeed, a dead body (especially one that is trapped in an airtight environment) will get extraordinarily smelly; there is a word for the phenomenon – putrescent. BUT can the Mythbusters replicate this putrid myth? Can they make a car stink so bad? Will that car retain its stink through the world's most rigorous cleaning? Will any fool buy it? Yes, yes, yes and yes are the answers to this myth that mixed pig with corvette to end up with a sweet US$2000 – even after two dead pigs were given a little over two months to settle into every nook and cranny of that car. Indeed, they started with such high hopes after an induction to extreme cleaning with a local expert:

ADAM ... talking to Neal and seeing how well this stuff works I think we might be able to clean this car out and it might not smell at all.

JAMIE – Either it is cleanable with the enzyme or it gets ripped out. And we will get that car clean.

But after a few whiffs and with the terrifying sight of the actual car, this was the change:

ADAM – Oh my God. That is horrible.

JAMIE – I think you know, having to get in there and close the car with these two remnants of creatures was probably one of the more horrible things I've ever had to do.

So, for pity's sake; never die in your car.

See also: ***Neal Smither, shipping container, pigs, Chevrolet Corvette, putrefaction***

St Luke's Medical Centre

The good people at St Luke's have given good and timely advice to the Mythbusters on several occasions – firstly it came from Dr Miller in *Buried Alive* (he helped Adam and Jamie work out what dead meant) and secondly in *Jeans Death Shrinkage* where Grant spent many hours in a warm bath under the observation of St Luke's staff.

See also: ***dead, jeans***

Myths: ***Buried Alive, Jeans Death Shrinkage***

Stomach

An acidity of 2 pH, a temperature of 98.6°F (37.0°C), salinity up the wazoo – who would think that was the environment of your stomach? A stomach can generally hold one or two pints (0.45 to 0.9 litres) … but what does it look like? By its nature the human stomach is a capacitance organ. That means it's designed to stretch. Receptive relaxation is the concept in human physiology so it will relax and stretch and stretch up to some limit. But what does it look like when taken out of context?

ADAM … Like a swimming cap. A very, very meaty swimming cap.

Myths: ***Octopus Pregnancy, Pop Rocks and Soda***

Strainometer

Also called a strainmeter, this is a device that can either be used to measure the thickness of an Australian accent, or more normally (as in *Border Slingshot*) to measure the breaking strain of a material.

This requires measuring tape, scales, the material and a head for danger.

ADAM – We're at a hundred pounds.

JAMIE – OK now, you're in the danger zone.

[Help us out here by imagining the sound 'ZAPPOWW-clangnnnnggg'].

JAMIE – Did you see what it was?

ADAM – Looks like on this one we got to about 150 pounds.

Stroke

It's not that the Mythbusters are ignorant of blood clots and their effect on the brain (which is not good) but rather that the internals workings of a different kind of engine have made for better television. A piston engine works on the principle that each full movement – or stroke – of the piston will drive a wheel that can then perform work, as well as recharge whatever fuel the piston is using to create its movement in the first place. The essence of the principle is demonstrated in *Ancient Prototypes* where the build team recreate three 18th and 19th century engines that were supposed to be powered by gunpowder. They didn't work, but the principle is interesting and a fine example of the development of those engineering principles that led to the internal combustion engine.

See also: ***piston, two stroke, four stroke***

Stud Finder

As used by tradespeople and home handy folk, a stud finder (not to be confused with a stuff finder, which, sadly, is sadly yet to be invented) locates wooden support studs, metal beams and even wiring that is hidden behind a wall. Stud finders use a mix of magnets, radar and capacitors to spot all these items, which the sensible worker then marks on the wall with a pencil, and either drills right into them (in the case of a stud) or avoids drilling into them for fear of electrocution (in the case of electrical wiring). The less than sensible paranoid looney uses a stud finder to detect the presence of *Mind Control Chips* that might have been inserted into his body during his trip to the local hospital or blood bank.

See also: ***magnets, radar, capacitors, drills, electrocution, dogs***

Myths: ***Mind Control Chips***

Stupid

There's really nothing we can say about stupid that this exchange between Adam and Jamie in the *Chicken Gun* myth doesn't say in spades.

ADAM – I didn't mean to call you stupid this morning.

JAMIE – Did you call me stupid?

ADAM – I didn't. I said stupid and I was talking to you but I wasn't calling you stupid.

JAMIE – Nobody ever calls me stupid.

ADAM – I've called you stupid but not to your face.

JAMIE – Not and lived.

Sublimation

If you've got a solid lump of something and its fast turning into a gassy burp of the same stuff WITHOUT being a drippy cupful of anything first, then you are watching sublimation in action.

See also: ***phase transition, carbon dioxide***

Subsonic

If supersonic is faster than sound, then subsonic is beneath sound – right? Not quite, although volcanos and earthquakes are known to generate such frequencies, subsonic sound is just sound that you and I can hear (assuming you're not a dog, elephant or axolotl). Strapping young humans like you and I can hear between the frequencies of 20Hz and 20,000Hz, and the older we get the more we lose a bit off each end. Speaking of ends, the myth where subsonics really came to the party was in *Brown Note* but fortunately the lads

demonstrated that no such trouser-filling frequency seems to exist. In *Shattering Subwoofer* there was more action, as their giant subwoofer blasted out decibels sufficient to destroy the roof of car it was built into.

***See also:* hertz, frequency, decibels, the hum**

***Myths:* Brown Note, Shattering Subwoofer**

Suction

Suction creates a vacuum, or near vacuum, and with the right materials and mechanisms you can get something to adhere to a sufficiently smooth surface without glue. This is a cool and useful thing, especially if you want to scale the outside of a building, but Adam wasn't quite up to a 23-storey climb in the *Crimes and MythDemeanours* special.

***Myths:* Crimes and MythDemeanours**

JAMIE – Good thing our motto is always 'failure is always an option'.

ADAM – Well you know, any result's a result, that's for sure … ~%$#&*!

Sulphur

Also known as brimstone to the biblically inclined, this bright yellow element is found on volcanos and inside chemistry laboratories. However it can also be a by product of biological activity – bacteria in sewer pipes can create hydrogen sulphide gas which goes by the name 'rotten egg gas' for a very good reason. Oh, and let's not forget that it's key ingredient to gunpowder AND flatulence…

***See also:* element, gunpowder**

Superglue

The publication of this volume marks more than 50 years of the commercial availability of super glue and NASA (not that we're entirely obsessed by the subject of adhesives and spaceflight or anything). There is a nice little serendipitous tale behind super glue – the inventor was actually trying to develop a plastic gunsight lens, but instead discovered a substance with the crazy name Cyanoacrylate that stuck to anything he tried to handle it with. Useless as a gunsite, but very tenacious as an adhesive – whether you're building a model aeroplane, temporarily sealing a sucking chest wound (seriously – but don't try it at home) or coaxing fingerprints into existence on a CD

case. The Mythbusters keep super glue in their Emergency Bust kit at all times – you'll never know when you'll need something to remain stuck fast to something else in less than a minute.

***See also:* adhesive**

Supersonic

Anyone who has walked into a large room and heard the echo of their footsteps will realise that sound travels, and typically at about 300 metres per second (through air at sea level). This is really amazingly fast, yet certain things can outrun sound. Bullets, very fast aeroplanes and light are three of them.

***See also:* sound, echo**

Surface Tension

The reason that liquids of many kinds break up into droplets (think rain, waterfalls, urine) and allow insects and even cards or razor blades to float on top of it (not so much urine here, think of a bowl of water) all has to do with surface tension. Surface tension is literally that – tension at the surface of the liquid that is greater than the tensions within the liquid. This is a result of the forces at play between the molecules of the liquid; these molecules are all attracted to one another, and so the happy molecules inside your bowl are all tugging together in all directions. However, at the surface the molecules can only tug downwards, and the liquid is this squeezed just a little bit until the surface area is as small as it can get (depending on the kind of liquid you're talking about and its ability to be compressed). Surface tension was the key factor in *The Third Rail* myth, where a stream of urine turned into droplets before it reached the electrified rail – making it impossible to conduct a current. In *Bridge Drop* the lads tried to overcome the surface tension by dropping a hammer into the water before Buster hit it himself, and in *Walking on Water* Adam and Jamie investigated what a Ninja might do to increase surface tension sufficient to walk across a pool (or …more of a puddle really).

***See also:* molecules, hammer, water**

***Myths:* The Third Rail, Walking on Water, Bridge Drop**

hmm almost looks good enough to drink

Surgical Rubber

Used by doctors for all kinds of goopy but life-saving tasks, but after a bunch of tests, the Mythbusters picked up a bunch of surgical rubber tubing to make their *Border Slingshot*. The 1-inch diameter (2.54 cm) surgical rubber tube had a safe pull of five to one.

Myths:* *Border Slingshot

Swimming

The human or animal ability to move though water or other liquid has not yet got its head over the parapet as the focus of a myth, but swimming does feature in several episodes and one or two specials (as so swimming animals like fish and sharks). Quirky Adam trivia – he was featured as the 'drowning lad' in a Billy Joel video clip.

Myths:* *Scuba Diver, Sinking Titanic, Bulletproof Water

Sydney

The home of the Mythbusters (except for San Francisco)

Sydney Harbour Bridge

Those brave soils who built this mighty span … haven't we been here before? Yadda yadda, they thought a hammer would break the surface tension of the water if they fell in. In *Bridge Drop* Adam and Jamie demonstrated that it this wasn't going to save you – as it didn't for the two who died falling from the Sydney Harbour Bridge during its construction. It's the widest long-span bridge in the world you know – 48.8 metres (151 feet), and this probably also makes it the longest wide-span bridge at 1150 metres (3772 feet).

See also:* *Golden Gate Bridge, hammer

Myths:* *Bridge Drop

Syracuse

Home to Archimedes and the supposed location of the city-saving *Steam Cannon*.

T&P Valve

In a device such as a hot water heater, you have two dangers to consider. The first is temperature, the second is pressure. If the thermostat inside the water heater fails, heat will continue to pour into the water heater leading to an increase in pressure as the liquid water becomes water vapour – with a much greater volume (like 1600 times greater!). A temperature and pressure relief valve (feel free to call it a T&P valve if you're in an emergency situation) is a spring-powered device that sits on top of a water heater (among other pressure systems) and will either operate automatically when the pressure reaches a point where it can lift the weight of the spring, or is manually operated by a lever. This action allows enough liquid to escape to prevent the water heater exploding spectacularly and catastrophically.

See also:* *thermostat, water heater, water vapour, steam, water

Myths:* *Water Heater Rocket, Steam Machine Gun

Tadpoles

The infant form of frogs breathes through gills and is known in some quarters as a polliwog. Gradually, a lucky tadpole (the ones not ending up on the wrong side of a fish, a bird, or Adam and Jamie's *Octopus Pregnancy* experiments) will metamorphose into a frog, developing legs, losing its tail and growing a nice pair of lungs. They hop out of the water and go, 'Crikey, was this worth all the effort?' Of course it IS worth it – frogs are delightful creatures (amphibians don't you know) that love nothing more than a meal of mosquitos, and even if they weren't an essential part of the ecosystem we would love them for that fact alone.

See also:* *frogs

Myths:* *Octopus Pregnancy

Tailgate Up or Down? & revisit

Although the sum total of the action in this myth consisted of Adam and Jamie driving identical pick-up trucks into the desert and back with the tailgate up (on Jamie's truck) and down (on Adam's), and then building a scale replica in a water tank of what the air actually does when you drive in a pick-up truck with the tailgate up or down, this was a deeply fascinating myth which annoyed a lot of people. Hooray for that – but the entire result can be brought down to the existence of a curious pick-up truck phenomenon called the locked vortex flow. This is a slow moving bubble of air that flows around in a big circle in the back of your truck – as long as the tailgate is up. This trapped air stops most of the fast moving air flowing over the truck from getting into the truck and adding to the total drag. When you let your tailgate down, the effect of the locked vortex flow is greatly dissipated. Yet the fact that Jamie was able to drive 30 more miles than Adam under identical conditions except for the fact that his tailgate was up was not enough for some, and a revisit was called for. A flowmeter measured the consumption of fuel and re-confirmed the result … but in an interesting twist, changing the solid tailgate for one made of mesh seemed to give you the best of both worlds – a 5 per cent improvement in fuel consumption over the 'tailgate up' option, or driving with a cover on the tray. And that's the final word!

ADAM – Yeah. I really, really hope, and I'm asking YOU, sitting at your computer, not to email me about this. I don't want to do any more fuel efficiency myths.

JAMIE – Yeah. If you don't believe us, go right ahead and drive the way you want.

***See also:* pick-up truck, vortex**

Talking to Plants

Just plain crazy, or uncommon good sense? There are all sorts of legends about gardeners who talk their plants to giant proportions, and even reports of scientists playing music to their leafy subjects to test their responses. The Mythbusters were going to put all these theories on trial once and for all – and where better than the capacious space on the roof of M5? In no time seven

mini-greenhouses have sprung up – enough to make Jamie nervous about low-flying DEA helicopters. However, they were only populated with baby pea plants, plus the latest in drip irrigation technology and a boom box apiece. Kari and Scottie lay down two sets of vocal tracks to play on heavy rotation – the first gently encouraging, the second downright nasty. They fill another two greenhouses with light classical music, and the latest in kidney-chilling death metal. The final greenhouse lives in peace and quiet. Returning a couple of months later the team discover that the sprinkler timer has died – but they can nevertheless measure the following results; there seems to be little difference between speaking sweet nothings and sour somethings, the classical music-listening plants are doing very nicely, but the death metal plants are doing best of all for size, strength and flavour!

***See also:* Byram Abbot, death metal**

KARI – My god – metal is huge! These plants are enormous compared to everything else.

TORY – I think heavy metal rules! ... Totally rules!

Tanning

The process of tanning has nothing to do with lying around in the sun for hours on end. It's called tanning because the main ingredient in the process was tannin. Turning skin into leather was touched upon in the myth of the *Eel Skin Wallet* where the lads wanted to know if an electric eel's 'charge' could linger in a wallet made of his (or her) tanned skin. In the old days it was a phenomenally stinky process, not only because it involved the putrefying skins of dead animals, but because not only urine and poo but brains were used in the process, which would take months. So ... putrescent flesh and brains, urine and poo – hard to imagine something more stinky really, unless it is two dead pigs sealed in a corvette for a few months.

***See also:* skin, putrid, smell**

***Myths:* Eel Skin Wallet, Stinky Car**

Tapeworm

This critter is a parasite that might be found in your stomach. It probably got there after a meal of badly cooked meat (under-prepared pork or beef is a classic suspect) although it you lived in the late 19th or early 20th century you might have purchased (or even been prescribed) a tapeworm so you

could keep your weight down. No, REALLY. Tapeworms consist almost entirely of a reproductive system, with a small head at the top that latches onto the side of your gut. A whale's tapeworm can reach 120 feet (36 metres) but don't be ashamed – human tapeworms can get half as long. Adam and Jamie saw a real (dead) tapeworm in the offices of Jim McKerrow, a parasitologist, when sniping around the edges of the *Octopus Pregnancy* myth.

See also:* *parasite, Jim McKerrow

Myths:* *Octopus Pregnancy

Tarantula

If it's a spider it's scary, doubly so with these hand-sized hairy legs – so Adam might argue at least, and although some of his phobia was rubbed off during the myth of the *Daddy Long Legs* there were still a few shivers to be had when this cheeky chappie was produced for the *Ultimate Mythbuster Special*.

The good news is that a fair dinkum tarantula bite will only be as bad as a wasp sting: some comfort there …

See also;* *fear test, Giant Tanzanian Millipede, African Emperor Scorpion, Corn Snake, John Emberton

Myths:* *Ultimate Mythbuster

Tattoo

The largest organ in a human being is your skin, but despite this, some human beings like nothing better then to pull out lightning-fast needle guns and poke ink into it. While relatively harmless under an MRI as the Mythbusters discovered in *Exploding Tattoo*, a tattoo does hurt when you get one, because there's nerves aplenty all over the place, and the tattoo gun which pushes up to 15 tiny needles simultaneously 80 times a second (or faster) doesn't spare them in the least.

See also:* *skin, Matty the Tattooist

Myths:* *Exploding Tattoo

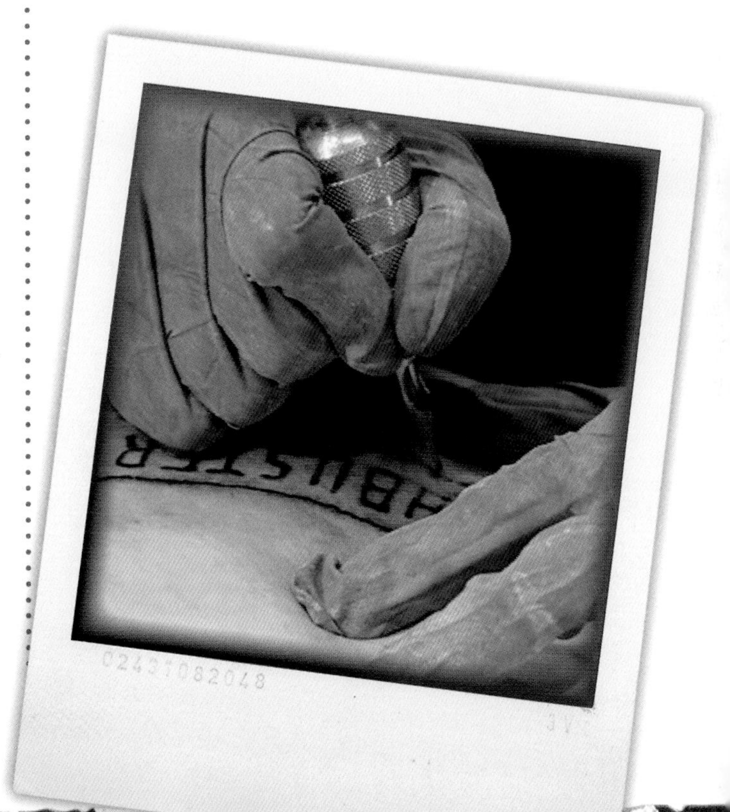

Tchaikovsky

Some described his music as 'plangent' and for good reason; the greatest Russian composer wrote for cannon. The turbulent life of Pyotr Ilyich Tchaikovsky burst through in his music, the most famous piece being the 1812 Overture. The Mythbusters have plundered its stirring sounds on several occasions, but most definitively in the myth of the *Trombone Explosion* where it was suggested that a trombone player stuck a firecracker in his mute and planned to fire it over the crowd.

***See also:* mute, trombone, plangent**
***Myths:* Trombone Explosion, Steam Cannon**

Tectonic Plates

Sliding around in ultra slow motion are the continents of the planet Earth, like a table setting on a boat in a storm. New land is born miles beneath the oceans and slides all the way around the world on a bed of molten rock until eventually it slides back into the inner Earth again. Yet somehow this idea of plate tectonics was treated like the babblings of a madman, and in the end its originator died of shame and embarrassment.

***See also:* the Hum, seawater**

Teflon

Polytetrafluoroethylene to its friends, teflon is a slippery material invented by accident in 1938. Aside from coating pans, it can come in spray-on form, and even as a tape used to create a seal between plumbing parts – and this is where it finds use in the M5 workshop. There is a nice little urban myth that bullets coated with teflon have the ability to pierce body armour … something Adam and Jamie are yet to tackle!

Teflon Tape

Used as a sealant, 'plumber's' or 'thread seal tape' is made of teflon (surprise) and is applied around the exposed threads of a pipe before it is screwed into place. The tape deforms to behave as a sealant between the threads. The Mythbusters turn to Teflon tape for quick seals between pipes without having to mess around with pipe dope.

***See also:* sealant, pipe dope**

Temperature

Temperature has a big impact on everything you do: those couple of degrees that influence your morning jeans versus shorts decision would kill you if they were an increase in your body temperature. And

that's temperature ... just how hot or cold something is, yes? In fact temperature is so much more integral to everything everywhere, and is much harder to pin down. A strong wind will make the temperature feel lower, humidity will make it feel warmer, and to properly understand temperature you need to get down to the molecular level (again?!) and talk about the energy of a single particle. This energy is a function of its motion, and so temperature is fundamentally about how zippy teeny tiny bits of stuff are feeling. They can be feeling very zippy indeed – temperatures of billions of degrees Celsius have even been created by human scientists and that's not even going into the temperature of the Big Bang, the hottest event ever. When temperatures get very low, a particle gets pretty sluggish, until they reach absolute zero (-273.15°C or 0°K or Kelvin) when they just stop – theoretically at least. There's no way of knowing because everything you might have used to measure that particle would have stopped too. Adam and Jamie are frequently dealing with temperatures both relatively high and low – liquid nitrogen is always good for cooling things down fast, and any kind of explosion good for heating things up. Of course, high temperatures can also be useful for sticking things together, as they are in welding. However, not much gets hotter than lightning, which is an explosion (of sorts) that can stick things together.

***See also:* molecules, humidity, body temperature, Big Bang, welding, lightning, Zeroth Law of Thermodynamics, absolute zero, thermal equilibrium**

Tension

Tension comes in many forms and they all happen frequently in Mythbusters. Dramatic tension is a very useful narrative device that keeps an audience on the edge of their seats, eager to know the outcome of a story. Nervous tension is caused by anything from an argument about a plan of action or the fear of an experiment going badly wrong. High tension wires deliver much-needed electricity to homes and special effects workshops all over the San Francisco Bay area (and, yes, elsewhere in the world). Tension also refers to the stretching of a material, and is measured as a force. The

Mythbusters apply tension of all kinds as frequently as possible – a prime example being in *Border Slingshot.* With the episode drawing to a close, a successful test of the giant slingshot had yet to be staged (an example of dramatic tension). Adam and Jamie began arguing about the placement of Rescue Randy in the sling (nervous tension) as well as the actual tension on the many guy ropes that held the giant slingshot together. If only there was some high voltage … oh, and some water droplets to demonstrate surface tension.

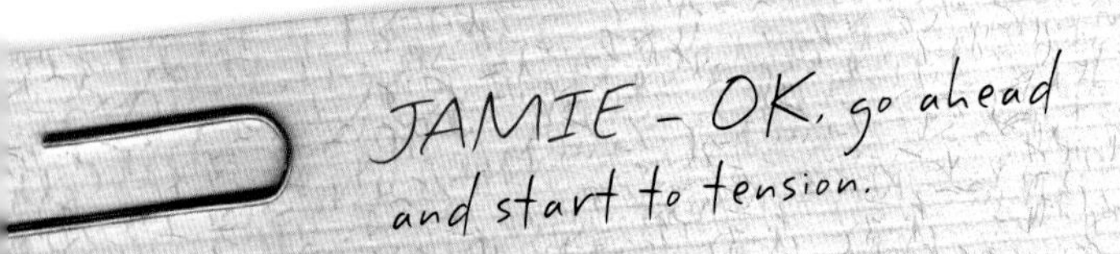

Terminal Velocity

When you're going so fast that you just can't go any faster, then you've reached your terminal velocity and you better hope like hell that you've remembered to strap on your parachute. Other things like pennies or bullets also have a terminal velocity, but not a parachute. In fact everything has a terminal velocity that is dependent on its shape, material and the medium through which it is falling.

Theory

A concept, idea or plan that would require a test before being established as accurate … or otherwise.

See also: ***proof of concept, science***

There's Your Problem

If you've heard this phrase, then you can be rest assured of two things; the tradesman you've just hired to fix your car/pumbing/ heart condition (come on, surgeons are just tradespeople in smocks) has just found the problem, AND they've worked out what they can charge you for fixing it.

Thermal Equilibrium

In the ordinary run of things we tend to describe thermal equilibrium as temperature, despite this being less than accurate. But when your local doctor is taking your temperature because you've caught a nasty virus and you feel like death, you don't want him describing the actions of thermal systems and the stunning simplicity that is the Zeroth Law of Thermodynamics. It's that kind of thing that gets doctors a bad name along with a punch in the nose. Going for accurately then, thermal equilibrium is reached when a system (be that a person,

river or planet) has sufficiently stabilised so that things like its temperature and pressure and so on can be measured.
***See also:* Zeroth Law of Thermodynamics, temperature, thermal system**

Thermal Lance

If ever you're trying to poke a hole in three inches of steel, then you want to borrow a thermal lance. This device can create temperatures of 4000°C (well over 7000°F) by burning rods of iron in an environment super-rich in oxygen. A thermal lance will literally melt anything and everything in its path – nothing on earth can withstand 4000°C, not even underwater. Adam got hold of a thermal lance to make a hole in a steel safe for *Crimes and MythDemeanours 2* and found that not only did it take WAY longer than did the same activity in the movie *The Score* but the heat fried everything in the safe.
***See also:* melting point, oxygen**
***Myths:* Crime and MythDemeanours 2**

Thermal Sensor

Triggered by the infrared energy that human beings release 24/7, a thermal sensor can spot you when you're hot and bothered,

Try doing that with your mobile phone!

or even when you're cool.
Your only chance is to be dead, or wear a fire suit to keep you insulated. You can also try to block the infrared waves with a thick piece of glass, but an icy blast from a fire extinguisher, or a Predator-style mudbath were next to useless.
***See also:* fire extinguisher**
***Myths:* Crime and MythDemeanours 2**

Thermal System

You'd use the term thermal (or, for the scientists, 'thermodynamic') system to describe pretty much any 'something' that you're playing with at the time. Now sure, it might be something as big as a planet or a galaxy (depending on the size of your rumpus room/imagination) or as small as a drop of water, which makes the term a bit suspiciously all-consuming, but … it really is one for theorizing around, not for stocking up on supplies of at the local hardware emporium.
***See also:* Zeroth Law**

Thermistor

A resistor whose resistance changes depending on its temperature. Neat portmanteau too.

***See also:* resistor, temperature, portmanteau**

Thermoelectric Effect

If you see something brazenly turning heat into electricity OR electricity into heat then you are observing the thermoelectric effect in action. There is nothing illegal or immoral in this action, as it takes place inside toasters, hair dryers and hot water heaters all over the world. Adam and Jamie fully endorse the thermoelectric effect, as the San Francisco winter inside M5 can get jolly cold.

***See also:* water heaters**

Thermostat

If you do not wish your living room to become a sauna, your hair dryer a weapon or your water heater a rocket, then you might consider the installation of a thermostat (or three). This device cunningly manipulates the temperature that an appliance can achieve by using a sensor to switch the appliance off when it gets too hot, or on when it gets too cool, hence keeping the appliance and its environment in the butter zone. These sensors can be as excitingly simple as a piece of bi-metal wire or as tediously complex as a digital thermistor.

***See also:* bi-metal, thermistor, water heater, sensors, butter zone**

Third Rail, The

Can urinating on a high-voltage conductor lead to death? The myth suggests that late one evening a passenger – some call him Joseph Patrick O'Malley - is waiting for a train but finds himself caught short. He urinates on the electrified third rail and is immediately electrocuted via a huge zap up the stream of urine. But … really? Could it happen? Adam involves himself in some intimate experimentation:

ADAM – Here on Mythbusters we're prepared to put our pants on the floor for you … I think I've got a hundred mils. Are you ready?

… and the lads build a urination device into a ballistics gel body and set up the rig at the nearest electrified railway track. While urine conducts electricity just fine, it turns out that

by the time the stream of urine has reached the rail, surface tension has changed a unified stream into a bunch of disconnected droplets. Adam and Jamie had to create a pachydermian stream of wee to electrocute their ballistics gel dummy. Although the myth was busted, the lads won't be taking any chances themselves. On the bright side, the guys even had the time to bust another railway myth – can a penny on the track derail a train? The hot, flattened penny that results makes for the quickest myth ever busted on the show.

***See also:* urine, electrocution, surface tension**

ADAM – Wow. Oh yeah. Look at this. Oh my God, they're really hot.

Thomas Hannan

A mechanic skilled in the crafty art of airbags, Thomas knew exactly why none of the build team's attempts at shooting a lock pick into their dummy from the sudden deployment of the side airbag worked.

***Myths:* Airbag Annihilation**

THOMAS – The airbag's actually inside the car, not inside the door.

KARI – So you knew this all along, and this is what you were expecting and you watched us bumble around with this?

THOMAS – Yeah

Thomas Holzer

Geologist, engineer and earthquake expert, Thomas Holzer is also very, very interested in quicksand. Adam and Jamie brought him in to consult on the myth of the very same name …

THOMAS – It more easily forms in a situation where you have really fine sand. In fact geologists call it sugar sand. So most of your quicksand is in real fine grain sand.

ADAM – So Tom the 20,000 pounds of sand we've got here, is it great for quicksand?

THOMAS – Oh this is probably as good as it gets because it's very fine grain, and there's so much surface area here that when the water flows through it, it means that the water can grab onto that and that'll create the quick condition.

***Myths:* Quicksand**

Thomas Paine

As well as being the Father of the American Revolution, Thomas Paine had a knack for invention that saw him prototype a smokeless candle and design a single span iron bridge. If the latter was a successful as his gunpowder engine, however, he might not be held in such high esteem.

***Myths:* Ancient Prototypes**

Thread

Sometimes a thread is a single strand of fibre, but if it's a screw or a nut and bolt you're talking about then a thread turns a rotating force into a linear force, and vice versa. Linear? Rotating? Think about it – when you're working a screw into a wall, or a nut free from a bolt, your rotating arm or wrist action is being translated into 'in' or 'out' motion. Clever? Simple? You bet … and it's Archimedes again…

***See also:* Archimedes**

360 Degree Swing Set

When you were a kid you must have had the experience of going up so high on a swing that you really thought you could just keep on going all the way round. In your imagination you'd swoop down the

other side like a jet coming in to land on an aircraft carrier. However, if you ever tried it with the help of some burly playmates the re-entry would be more like a spent satellite plunging into the Pacific Ocean. And you and your fevered imagination are not alone, for the Mythbusters wanted to take this myth just as far as it was humanly possible to go – even if that meant incurring personal injury, consorting with circus freaks and bikies or ... adding rockets (you knew they were going there). The build team set up a playground swing in the M5 parking lot, and are just placing a few crash mats underneath when Tory makes a discovery ...

TORY – 'Warning. This swing was designed for use by children only. Not for adult use.'

... and 30 seconds later Tory has hit the deck. But in the interest of science they reinforce the swing and continue, and discover the key problem with rotating a swing 360° isn't the weakness of the links, it's the chains themselves. Oh, and gravity. AND centrifugal force. Let's take a step back; once a swing passes the horizontal the chains on a swing set only remain straight when the centrifugal force is as great or greater then the force of gravity. Any less and you fall rather sickeningly towards the ground. It's a different story when you replace those chains with some kind of rigid pole; so Tory, Grant and Kari took a trip with Eric the trapeze instructor, on what the circus folk call a Russian Swing. If only they could have held on to their stomachs they too could have swung a 360° just like Eric ... but it was down to Simulaid Suzi, who first completed the trick with the aid of a couple of bikies, then with the aid of a couple of rockets.

See also: horizontal, centrifugal, gravity, Eric Braun, resonance

Thrift Town

Selling all kinds of hand-me-down items, this chain operates more than a dozen stores in the Western USA. Adam and Jamie are always ducking in to pick up this or that, but when they needed some electricals to test the myth of *Appliances in the Bathtub*, they had to contend with a rigid safety policy.

SALESWOMAN – Thrift Town CANNOT sell hairdryers without GFI switches for safety purposes, which means you know if these are dropped into a bathtub they would turn off.

ADAM – Immediately.

SALESWOMAN – Immediately. Yes.

***See also:* Ground Fault Interruptors**
***Myths:* Appliances in the Bathtub**

Thrust

Most specifically, this is a force of reaction, and occurs when an engine or propeller pushes something in the opposite direction. In a propeller or jet engine, this 'something' is air, pushed back over the wings of the plane by the propeller or back against air itself by a jet. In a rocket engine thrust comes from gases produced by the rocket's propellant, which is expelled from the bottom of the rocket and moves the rocket (and whatever *Jet Car* is attached to it) in the opposite direction, according to the laws of motion (particularly the 2nd and 3rd).

***See also:* force, the laws of motion, rocket**
***Myths:* Jet Car, Ming Dynasty Astronaut, Confederate Rocket and any other rocket related myth...**

Thrust Curve

The curve on a graph that is given by the amount of thrust generated by a rocket engine over time. The area given by this curve measures the overall impulse presented by that engine.

***Myths:* Jet Car**

Tie Clip Mike

A standard piece of sound recordist kit usually attached to a person's clothing (ideally a tie) to catch the glorious wisdoms falling from their mouth and relay them

wirelessly via a pocket-sized transmitter to a master recording unit. In the hands of the Mythbusters of course, it could end up anywhere – even attached to a duck to catch the *Duck Quack Echo*. But … how to attach it?

JAMIE – Duck tape.

***Myths:* Duck Quack Echo**

Tim Sonnenberg

Sonnenberg knows what to do with a foot and a football, and although his kicker's master class left Adam and Jamie fumbling on the 10-yard line in the myth *Helium Football* he wasn't able to pick which ball was filled with regulation air, and which with everyone's favourite noble gas.

TIM – This ball feels a little light. Is it filled with helium?

JAMIE – Well, we couldn't tell you that, could we, or we'd skew the results.

Tissue Box

Who would have thought that a box of snot rags could impart 50 foot-pounds of force at 70 mph? Sheesh. Not only that, the tissue box in *Killer Tissue Box* survived the final test completely intact – not so much as a tissue was torn.

***Myths:* Killer Tissue Box**

Titanic

The Titanic was the largest ship ever when it launched in May 1911, and was the second of three monster Atlantic express luxury liners built for White Star Lines. The first was called Olympic, the third, Britannic (originally to be called 'Gigantic') and all were similarly designed. Yet only Olympic survived more than a few years of service and in fact came to earn the nickname 'Old Reliable' although it did run into a British Navy ship in 1911. One person survived this incident, as well as, FREAKISHLY, the sinkings of BOTH the Titanic AND the Britannic. Her name was Violet Jessup. The Mythbusters have dealt with one Titanic myth, *Sinking Titanic*, which pondered whether a sinking ship would drag you down with it.

***Myths:* Sinking Titanic**

TNT

TNT was used as a yellow dye for many years before it took off as an explosive. To give it its proper name, trinitrotoluene is a proper chemical compound, whereas dynamite is simply a mixture. TNT has become the yardstick for explosive force – all explosions (and other things besides, like meteorite impacts or earthquakes) find themselves describe in terms of the amount of TNT it would take to make the same bang. There's a good reason – TNT is a very, very user-friendly explosive. It is resistant to shock and friction, can be melted and poured into anything, mixed up with other bits and pieces, and is easily identifiable after use by the appearance of carbon soot in the crater it left. In this way, even if the Mythbusters don't let on what they're using to make the big bang, you should be able to tell afterwards. Only eight ounces of TNT were plenty to make a mess of the glass relocker safe in *Crimes and MythDemeanours 2.*

***See also:* compound, mixture, explosions, dynamite**

***Myths:* Crimes and MythDemeanours 2**

Toilet

Going by many names, the toilet is a humble functional object at the best of times, and at the worst of times not worth mentioning. Adam and Jamie have scraped toilets for bacteria, examined their vacuum and aerosol qualities and, naturally, blown them up. Thousands of years back the flush toilet was developed in Western India and only reinvented by European civilization a few hundred years ago. The key to their function is the hygienic disposal of faeces thanks to a siphon (also called the S-bend) – although as was demonstrated in *Toothbrush Surprise* flushing with the lid up can create an aerosol effect, distributing bacteria on micro-droplets of water. Toilets are hard to blow up, but you'll have to flick on to uncover the dangers of the *Vacuum Toilet*

***See also:* aerosol, bacteria, siphon**

***Myths:* Toothbrush Surprise, Exploding Toilet, Vacuum Toilet**

Tom Stein

When Adam and Jamie forget both their shopping list and their truck when they're preparing the big one-day build for the myth *Painting With Explosives* it seems the only one with his head screwed on right is hardware store sales associate Tom Stein.

ADAM – We're building a 10 by 10 foot room, eight feet high. We're going to build it …

TOM – You're making a box.

Ton

Measuring any kind of a ship is a challenge and the larger the ship, the larger the challenge. Is it for this reason that ships are weighed in really silly, old fashioned ways? Tons, deadweight, lightweight, displacement; all are crazy. The 'tons' referred to when measuring out the weight of a supercarrier like the Nimitz (more than 101,000 tons when fully loaded with ammunition and ice cream) are long tons, also called Gross Tons or Imperial Tons. Each one clocks in at 2240 pounds (1016 kg) which makes you wonder why for the sake of 240 pounds or 16 kilos they don't just go for the short ton (former) or the metric tonne (latter). Don't get us started about imperial versus metrics again…

See also: ***pounds, short tons, deadweight, lightweight, displacement, tonne, SI***

Tongue

The human tongue (and occasionally a pig substitute) comes in for some special Mythbusters attention in a range of myths, being piercings, and tongues zapped, frozen and dosed with chilli. But this collection of muscles and taste buds has a key role not only in speech, but also digestion, so treat yours with more care…

Myths: ***Lightning Strikes Tongue Piercing, Frozen Tongue***

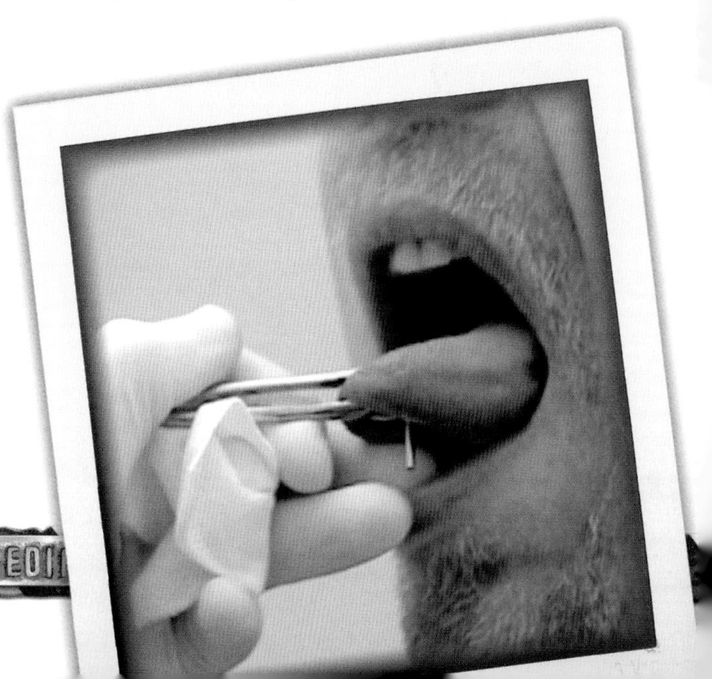

Tonne

A sensible measure of mass. The 1000 kilogram tonne is spelled in the French style, and is too-infrequently referred to by its equally accurate (in fact, more accurate) name the Megagram. However, the tonne it is, and comes via the French from the Latin, where *tunna* meant 'cask', and a metre-tall cask could easily weigh in at around a tonne (or megagram – let's see if it can catch on). A megagram of water would measure one cubic metre – consider that next time you go to the beach.

See also: ***water, SI, kilogram***

Tony Tarantino

Poultry is a family game for Tarantino & Sons, and so where else would Adam and Jamie go for eight four-pound (1.8 kg) frozen chickens for the myth *Chicken Gun*? Did Tony believe that there would be any difference between a frozen or room-temperature chicken at a few hundred miles an hour?

TONY – I would imagine the frozen would be harder ... I think the fresh just might kind of splat.

Tools

You will never ever see Jamie blame his tools – he loves each and every one of them with a passion bordering on the suspicious. Adam on the other hand –

ADAM – I hate this frame. It's ripping my fingers to shreds. A little more comfort in your design. That's all I want.

JAMIE – Go toughen your fingers up, it's good for you.

ADAM – %$#♥^ you! My fingers don't need toughening!

Tools maketh the man, or the woman, and M5 has plenty.

See also: ***vacuform, plasma cutter, hammer, lathe, bench grinder, thermal lance, belt sander***

Torque

The twist isn't just a classic dance, it's a mechanical phenomenon that arises when something suffers a turn. Archimedes was one of the first to recognise that a lever develops force about its fulcrum, and the force is given by the length of that lever. If you imagine this length of lever is in fact the spoke of a wheel (the radius) with the fulcrum point being where an axle might live then the amount of force applied around that point is the torque. It's that simple! OK, back to the levers then. Say you have a see saw that is two metres long from its fulcrum (the point where the see saw sees – or saws) and you're sitting on it pushing it down with a force of about 80 N (we're probably flattering you). This would result in a torque of 160 Nm (80 Newtons by 2 metres). When Adam and Jamie see spin they talk torque – the classic example is the myth of the *90° Turn* from the *Superhero Special.* That's all torque baby! It also turns up in a washing machine in *Killer Washing Machine*, a *Shattering Sub Woofer* attached to a car transmission or a *Levitation Machine* with an engine that's not quite powerful enough to make it levitate.

ADAM – No, no. That sounds bad. It's just too much torque for this motor. Please don't be too much torque for this motor.

Myths: **Killer Washing Machine, Shattering Sub Woofer, Levitation Machine, 90º Turn**

Tortilla

A round, unleavened bread product from central America, best enjoyed with salsa verde, barbacoa or mole poblano. The Mythbusters love a good tortilla, but the challenge to throw one the farthest in *Ultimate Mythbusters* saw them re-rig old machines for greatest distance.

Tortilla Cannon

Created by Jamie for the *Ultimate Mythbuster* building challenge, this was essentially the *Chicken Gun* reborn. But it did shoot a tortilla 73 feet (22 metres).

***See also:* tortilla throw, fear test, guess your weight, egg drop, pain test, memory test, sabot**

***Myths:* Ultimate Mythbuster**

Tortilla Throw

The first of the six *Ultimate Mythbuster* challenges was to build a machine that would throw a tortilla the farthest. Jamie developed a modification on the *Chicken Gun* and Adam on his *Killer Deck* card tossing machine. Although Adam threw the tortilla a respectable 60 feet (18 metres), Jamie bested that on his first try, 73 feet (22 metres).

***See also:* tortilla throw, fear test, guess your weight, egg drop, pain test, memory test, sabot**

***Myths:* Ultimate Mythbuster, Killer Deck, Chicken Gun**

Tory Belleci

With a bite force of 117 Newtons, and a tendency to hurt himself on camera, Tory Belleci was a natural choice to join the Mythbusters build team. The injuries Tory has sustained since then have lead to minor bruises only – from falling off a swing, from licking a frozen pole and from working for Jamie Hyneman since 1994. The classic was when Kari and Scottie let Tory talk himself into an impossible jump over a little red wagon in *Drive Shaft Pole Vault*…

SCOTTIE – Why do I always laugh when you get hurt? That looks so bad.

KARI – I can't believe you did that.

TORY – I thought I was going to make it.

TORY – a Buster wannabe

Toy Car Race-off

You really want to believe that a toy car can beat a real car when both are left to coast down a gentle slope – but we're going to tell you right up front that it didn't happen.

How many toy cars have spent months in development and design, research and modelling, testing and construction? None. Those things count, even with the engine switched off. But the myth started well, by testing a toy car on the wheels of a real car to a speed of 85 mph (136 km/h), and then in the Mythbusters patented wind tunnel to 74.9 mph (120.5 km/h). But after laying down thousands of pieces of plastic track on a real road, the toy car refused to play and kept jumping off onto the road. Talk about aggressive driving! OK, it was the sun making the track warp, so in the end a shorter track was put together, the toy car made the early running but the Dodge took the line … just.

***See also:* Dodge Viper**

Trajectory

Lots of things can have a trajectory: a bullet, a rock, a satellite, the career of a Big Brother contestant. Trajectory is the path followed by an object through space. Try it out yourself by tossing a pair of socks in the air – they trace a path that you could call a *parabola* if only it wasn't for tricky things like air resistance, fluctuations on gravity (apparently) and the aerodynamic qualities of the socks themselves.

***See also:* parabola, bullet**

Transformer

There is more than meets the eye in the everyday, common or garden transformer. Inside that boxy exterior current is being swapped for voltage and vice versa.

***See also:* volts, amps**

The image here is a power adaptor, or more properly rectifier – but it's certainly boxy and … you get the idea.

Transom

You might be comfortable with the word 'stern' meaning the backside of a boat, but the real boatie will pick you up on it every time. The rear surface of the boat is actually called the transom. As you can tell, Jamie is right on top of his naval lingo …

JAMIE – What I'm going to do is take this pipe and kind of bolt it on a swivel thing on the transom of the boat. And I also have to build a kind of a wooden paddle thingy to actually go in the water and guide it.

***See also:* port, starboard**

***Myths:* Air Cylinder Rocket**

TRAVIS FLETCHER

Travis Fletcher is master of an archery guild and no wonder, with a name that means 'the maker of arrows'.

TRAVIS – The splitting of the arrow was actually more likely an archery game that was used in order to train the archers. It was called slisting the wand … an arrow would have been set as a vertical target, either in the ground or against the tree, and then the archers would have attempted to split the arrow or slist the arrow with theirs.

***See also:* fletching**
***Myth:* Splitting Arrow**

TREBUCHET

This is one chunky piece of medieval hardware, designed for one purpose – chucking stuff. Having said medieval, we must now concede that – along with paper and black powder – we have the Chinese to thank for the trebuchet, which dates back nearly 2500 years. Much more accurate than a catapult, a trebuchet works on a similar principle to a sling – with a counterweight which creates leverage on the projectile. When the Mythbusters messed around with the *Boom Lift Catapult* they weren't a million miles away from a trebuchet, but the measly 30 feet (not even ten metres) that Buster flew was well below par for even a modest trebuchet, which were capable of tossing 250 pounds (113 kgs) out to 200 feet (60 metres). This distance was, however, outdone, by the *Border Slingshot*.

***See also:* paper, black powder, slingshot, sling**
***Myths:* Boom Lift Catapult, Border Slingshot**

TREE CANNON

What happens when a log gets lethal? Tree cannons were at the top of the arms race in 14th century England and in eastern Europe even into the 19th. The myth suggested that one night a Hungarian tribe called the Pachish got sick of a local tribe bugging them, so they set about making a cannon. They worked all night and the next morning their pride and joy was ready. They filled it with gunpowder, some kind of projectile, aimed it at the villains, lit the fuse … only to be decimated (as well as disappointed)

when the thing exploded in their faces. 'Where was their lexan™ shield?' we hear you call. Nice point – but … could you really make a tree cannon in one night with medieval tools? In order to recreate the myth and commune a little with the past, Adam and Jamie (mostly Jamie) use old fashioned tools (some of them made in the shop) to prepare a big hardwood log of medieval proportions. Then, would a tree cannon really explode with enough force to kill you? Oh yes – a thousand times yes. Go back and have a look at the footage.

See also: **replica, medieval, Pachish, cannon, projectile**

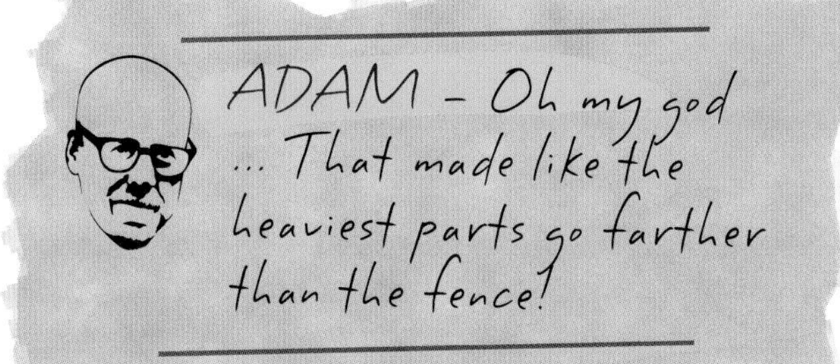

Triboelectric Effect

Materials will tend to either give up or attract electrons when put in contact with other materials. Sometimes the transferred charge will be negligible, but at other times it'll be very apparent. This is called the Triboelectric Effect (named after 'tribos', the Greek word for 'rubbing' – those crazy Greeks). In the myth *Cell Phone Gas Station* Adam based his 'panty static generator' on this principle, and you can easily do something similar at home. If you've got a woollen jumper on a plastic hanger, give the hanger a rub on the jumper and check out the electricity you've generated by holding the hanger next to a slim stream of water from a tap. You should see the water move towards the plastic hanger! If you don't, be scared – you might have slipped into an alternative universe.

See also: **static**

Traction

When friction is turned into motion, we call it traction. What do YOU call it?

See also: **friction ridges**

Myths: **Driving on Ice**

Trireme

Taking its name from the three rows of oars on each of its sides, the Roman trireme was a light human-powered warship that ruled the Mediterranean waves on behalf of the various empires of Greece, Rome and Phoenicia. The Mythbusters had to build a chunk of a replica trireme with close-to original materials for their attempts to bust the myth of the *Ancient Death Ray.*

Myths:* *Ancient Death Ray, Mailbag Special

Trombone Explosion

Also called '1812 Overture' in some fan circles (the ones who don't pay attention) this myth is based on a tale that a trombone player tried to spice up a rendition of the favourite Tchaikovsky toe-tapping cannon-blaster with a firecracker in his mute. Although the idea is to send the mute flying over the audience, the thing instead knocks the conductor off the stage while the player himself is left with a busted horn and significant burns to his lips. Who would have thought? But it is an excellent excuse for grinding up a few rocket engines, and even though the police were called, it was a fun day had by all. Oh, and the myth? Busted.

ADAM – Feel like doing it again?

JAMIE – Sure, why not.

ADAM – You know, it's when you get really excited that I get really nervous. So if you could calm down just a little bit.

See also:* *trombone, mute, Tchaikovsky, Jack Morocco

Two Stroke

This is not a reference to the minimum number of pats you can give your cat to stop her biting you on the ankle when you arrive home, but rather describes a type of engine which manages to complete all the function of a four-stroke motor in half the strokes – which significantly increases the power used to do work. If none of that made sense, then just think of this – each up-and-down movement of the piston in a two-stroke engine is achieved by a small explosion, which creates exhaust that must be removed from the combustion chamber before the next combustion, which is created by fuel which must be drawn into that chamber AND compressed to the point where another explosion will result in another movement of the piston. Accomplishing all these actions in a single up-and-down stroke of the engine means that power is created every time the piston moves down, rather than every second time as in the four-stroke engine. A pity they waste so much energy in heat…

***See also:* piston, four-stroke**

Two-Way Mirror

The mirror that is probably more accurately known as a one-way mirror (think about it) is a classic piece of law-enforcement kit. The smooth and hence light-reflective nature of glass almost does the job for you – try looking into a dark car from a brightly-lit street. However, to up the ante a very thin layer of something nice and smooth and reflective like aluminium is added to the glass to give it extra reflectivity, but which is still transparent from the one side. The key, as with the dark car and bright street, is to have your mirrored room very bright, and your sneaky room very dark. And put a delay on the light switch in there …

***Myths:* Nothing But the Truth**

Ultrasonic Motion Detector

Looking like the toughest security technology to break of all in the special *Crimes and MythDemeanours 2* episode, in the end all it took was Kari holding a regular pulled-off-your-bed cotton sheet above her head, OR walking very, very slowly. What? That's right, although she looked very fetching in both yellow fluffy material and fibreglass matting, the ultrasonic frequencies given off by the sensor were fooled by very modest movement, or by the sonic absorbency of the sheet.

***Myths:* Crimes and MythDemeanours 2**

Ultimate Mythbuster Special

With a whole bunch of myths stunned, hog-tied and bagged out the back of M5, the producers of the show set Adam and Jamie a challenge – each other. They would compete for the title of 'Ultimate Mythbuster' across a series of six challenges that would test their building skills, their ability to cope with fear, their ability to 'guess your weight', their problem solving, their pain threshold and their memory – all wrapped up with packages of classic episodes from the near and distant past. The winner by four tests to one was the Ultimate Mythbuster himself, Jamie Hyneman.

***See also:* tortilla throw, fear test, guess your weight, egg drop, pain test, memory test**

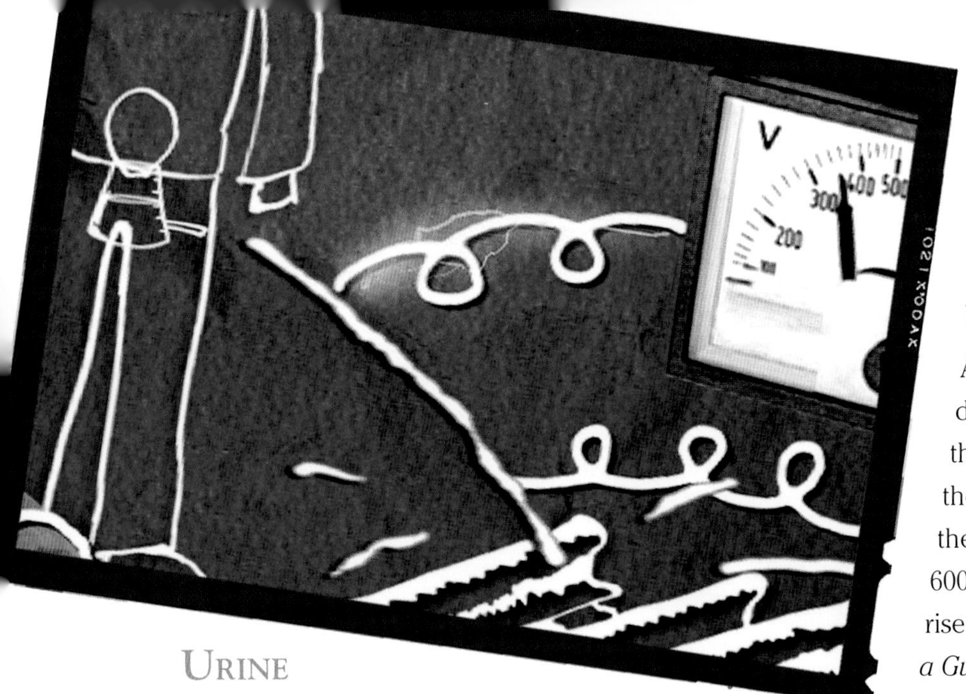

US Civil War

Although this was a bloody, drawn out conflict between the Confederate South and the Unionist North that saw the deaths of more than 600,000 people, it did see the rise of myths including *Son of a Gun*, *Steam Machine Gun* and *Confederate Rocket*.

Urine

When your kidneys are hard at work scrubbing impurities from your blood, do you ever stop to thank them? Do you marvel at the wonder that is urine? No? You should. Adam and Jamie like urine – but chiefly for its ability to conduct electricity (under some circumstances).

Myths:* *Third Rail, Appliances in the Bath

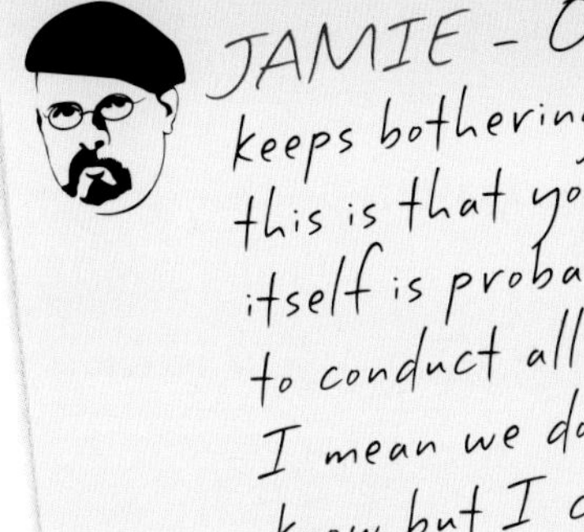

JAMIE – One thing that keeps bothering me about this is that you know, urine itself is probably not going to conduct all that much. I mean we don't really know but I can't imagine that you're gonna be able to conduct current like you would with a wire.

Utility

If it is useful by serving several functions well then what you have is something with utility. Thereafter you may find your self utilising it and would stand accused of being utilitarian when you do so.

See also:* *beret

Vacuum

You may have come to this reference straight from air-tight, and in which case we applaud you. That is a lot of pages to turn to simply follow a thirst for knowledge. You will soon be rewarded in an unexpected way when next you meet a friend whose name begins with J. But let's move away from these predictions (a sideline interest of ours) and onto the complex and fascinating world of vacuums. Whoever coined the phrase 'nature abhors a vacuum' obviously never travelled in outer space or used a pump. A vacuum is what is left when you take all the matter away, and although a perfect vacuum is impossible to achieve (so suggest the quantum mechanics) any kind of ordinary vacuum will be found in a thermos flask, a thermometer and an aeroplane toilet.

Vacuum Toilet

Everyone knows how an aeroplane toilet works? The bowl is cleared of anything you've put in there by means of vacuum suction. You yourself don't want to be sitting there at the time, and that goes double if you're actually in the air (when the pressure differential between the bowl and the bathroom is even greater). But this is exactly the basis of the myth of the *Vacuum Toilet* – that an oversized butt was sitting on the toilet and flushed it while sitting, and the plane had to land so the sittee could be removed. Getting hold of just such a toilet is not easy, and Adam and Jamie borrow one on the promise not to bust the toilet itself (just the myth). Then there's the butt – Kari had her first proper Mythbusters screen time when she was 'volunteered' to have her own shapely butt scanned in, then rebuilt scaled up to 300 pounds (136 kg).

ADAM – There's a science to making butts. Think of all the Twinkies that go in to the actual production of something like this. We're doing in one night what most people spend a lifetime avoiding.

There's endless problems getting the butt onto the seat, and even when they do they discover that safety-conscious designers got there before them; the toilet seat is built not to seal. When they do make a seal and get some suction on the butt, it doesn't take much to break the seal. With the myth busted, Adam hops on for kicks.

ADAM – All right. Expose butt cheeks. Here we go. Oh, ho, ho, ho. All right, that's significant. Oh, ho, ho. Oh my gosh. Oh wow, that was really significant. ... I'm not sure what we proved ... but at least it's good television.

See also:* *vacuum, Mark Pondelick, Wayne Dyer, Interface Aviation

Shrink wrapped Adam

VACUFORM

Mixing heat and plastic can be tricky, but to make plastic packaging for toys, or a plastic mould of Adam's head to fill with ballistics gel, sometimes you just have to do it. A vacuform machine heats evenly over a wide area to get a sheet of plastic all nice and squishy and ready to form, which you then do by sucking it over the mould with a ... you guessed it, vacuum. The Mythbusters have frequent need for the M5 vacuform to make moulds and other bits and pieces, but like all tools the poor vacuform has also been put to more unusual tasks – like heating up 500 disposable lighters in a car until they explode.

ADAM – Yeah. What's going to happen here is we're going to melt this plastic right above my head. We're going to heat it up until it's really flippy, floppy like a piece of cloth. Then we are going to lower it down over these forms, turn on the vacuum under this table. It's called vacuum forming ... And the plastic will cool down and take the shape of these forms, which will then become our moulds. Look at that!

JAMIE – We use the vacuform for all sorts of things. We use it all the time here in the shop ... We use it for toy prototypes, when we're, you know, inventing something.

See also: ***tools***
Myths: ***Exploding Lighters***

VALVE

There are valves of all kinds almost everywhere you look; in your bathroom, in your car, in your stomach. In fact the valves in a stomach are so well made they work fine even when the stomach is removed.

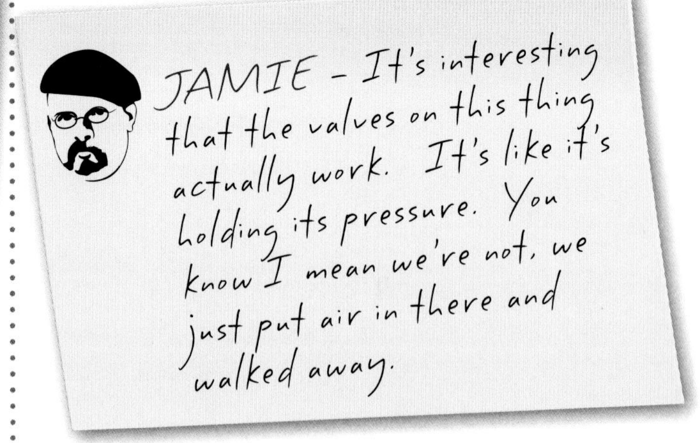

Valves are there to control the flow of fluids – be they liquids or gases – through a system, and the Mythbusters are always messing around with valves big or small in their endless pursuit of the butter zone.
See also: ***pigs, one-way valve, butterfly valve***

VAPORISE

To vaporise something is to turn it into a gas, or the next best thing, an aerosol.
See also: ***aerosol***

Velocity

Is velocity just a scientist's way of saying 'speed' – or is there is a method to their verbosity? Look at something that's still, like a wall or a tree. For those few seconds you looked at it, it didn't move. However, when you see something in motion – whether that's a toy car going down a hill, Buster falling down an elevator shaft or a beam of light (if you've particularly sharp eyes) – you're looking at something that alters its position over time. Velocity is the measurement of that change. If Buster's position in the elevator shaft changes from the top of the shaft to 10 metres down the shaft in one second, then his velocity is stated as being 10 m/s (or 10 metres per second). And how is that different from speed, exactly? Look it up, and do *acceleration* while you're about it.

***See also:* speed, acceleration**

Vertebrae

(a giraffe's one is pretty large)

Vertical

If you've come straight from our definition of horizontal then … apologies: there is actually a little more to it than 'oh, just look at the horizon'. See, we've got it easy here on Earth with all this gravity floating about the place. We can drop a plumb bob at the end of a string, get it to line up with the gravitational plane and 'zockoo' you've got yourself a vertical line. Pop on to a spaceship several light years from the nearest massive body and it's a completely different matter – there is no way to reference vertical (or horizontal). There are other problems as well, to do with any moons that might float by when your plumb bob is hanging and sway it this way or that, and plenty of weird stuff involving material density that a volume such as this cannot cover. Just let it be said that things are not as simple as they seem. Are vertical lines parallel if they're in Beirut and Beijing? We'll leave you to ponder that …

***See also:* horizontal, gravity, mass**

Vertigo

The sensation of whirling that you can get by climbing a crane called The Whirley, hence its name. It is likely to lead to a loss of balance, verticality, and in extreme cases (such as you might experience falling off

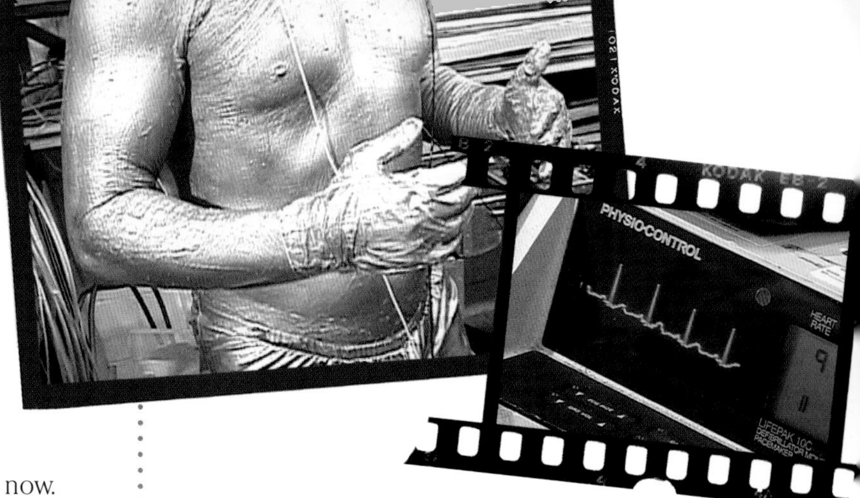

something high enough to give you the experience) of death. But vertigo need not be confined to heights – you can get it any old how. As a matter of fact we've got it now.
***See also:* Whirley**
***Myths:* Bridge Drop**

Vestibular Apparatus

Inside your ears exists a very cunning arrangement of tiny liquid-filled canals that tell your brain exactly how the body within which they exist is balanced. These canals are a lot like a classic spirit level, and do sterling service by keeping you from falling down at regular intervals. Valuable as this is, it is not beyond the occasional mistake – seasickness being the classic example. By wobbling your vestibular apparatus (and the rest of the body attached to it) in just the right way you can turn the breakfast you enjoyed only moments ago into an unpleasant floor covering.
***See also:* seasick chair, falling,**
***Myths:* Seasickness – Kill or Cure?**

Vital Signs

From the Latin *vitalis* meaning 'life' these are the signifiers that it is still lurking around a human being even though it may not be apparent through conversation or spending habits. Breathing is at the top of the list (respiration if you want to be all doctor-y) closely followed by pulse, blood pressure and temperature. Some people like to add pain or the dilation of pupils in response to light, but others think they're just clutching at straws and they should just admit the facts and begin the grieving process. Whenever Adam and Jamie do a test on human beings they always keep an eye out for those vital signs, usually with a crew of paramedics on hand to test them with cunning sensors. The kinds of tests we're talking about usually involve Jamie, as in *Buried Alive* where he got into a coffin and had a few tons of dirt heaped on him, and *Goldfinger* where he was reduced to his knickers and painted in gold latex paint.
***See also:* death, latex**
***Myths:* Buried Alive, Goldfinger**

Volts

Named in honour of a man called Volta, this SI-friendly unit of electrical potential has a

complex definition, but if you think about the pressure of water in a hose then you can't go wrong.
See also: ***watts, amps, electricity***

Vortex

Vortices is a cool pluralisation of a very, very awesome phenomenon known by other names like whirlpools, maelstroms, burbles, dust devils, willy willys, tornadoes, eddies and possibly even wormholes (if you like your astrophysics experimental). A vortex will turn up from time to time in any fluid medium, which probably rules out wormholes to be honest, given that a fluid is either a gas like the air we breathe, or liquid like the water we drink, and not the cold vacuum of space defined by the matter that it isn't. This means that on Earth there's plenty of opportunity for them to turn up and indeed they do, doing lots of damage when they get out of hand. When the lads investigated the myth *Whirlpool of Death* they found that you could certainly expect a decent-sized whirlpool to pull down a swimmer, but any decent-sized ship would be safe unless that whirlpool happened to be spinning at 100 knots – which simply doesn't occur. In the myth *Tailgate up or Down?* (and the subsequent revisit) the lads discovered the existence of a very strange phenomenon called a locked vortex flow – and strangest of all happens in the back of a pick-up truck! This slow moving vortex of air spins lazily around discouraging the fast-moving air around the truck from zooming into the tray and slowing you down. Nice work, and a good reason to travel with your tailgate up (or buy a sedan).
See also: ***whirlpool, burble, pick-up truck***
Myths: ***Tailgate up or Down?, Whirlpool of Death, Penny Drop***

Vulcanisation

Named for the Roman god of fire (Vulcan) this is the process by which the uncured natural rubber is turned into the more hardwearing stuff that your tyres and wellies are made of. It's all about heating up the natural rubber and adding sulphur, which sounds simple enough, but the fuss industry made about it once it arrived on the scene in the 19th century! You'd have thought all their Christmases has come at once (which they sort of had). Suddenly rubber was able to withstand high and low temperature, could be shaped into anything, and lost is typical stickiness. Nice one Vulcan.
See also: ***sulphur***

Walt Arfons

In the myth *Jet Car,* Adam and Jamie attached three hobby rockets to the roof of a Chevy Impala with the hope they could replicate a JATO rocket and blast their Chevy across the dry lakebed at 300+mph (482 km/h). They went fast, but not that fast. However, others have had more luck – with access to more rockets. Walt Arfons attached 25 JATO rocket engines to his land speed vehicle Wingfoot Express II and achieved a speed of 650 mph (1046 km/h).

See also: JATO

Myths: Jet Car

Wan Hu

Not much is known about Wan Hu other than that he was a government official during the Ming Dynasty who was exited by fireworks and interested in astronomy. One day he brought these two interests together in a startling way – attaching 47 fireworks to a chair and launching himself into outer space. Except as the tests in *Ming Dynasty Astronaut* demonstrated quite terrifyingly, he didn't do anything of the kind. He did however impress history sufficiently to get a moon crater named for him, so that's nice.

Myths: Ming Dynasty Astronaut

Washing Machine

The washing (or laundering) of clothes is as ancient an art as clothes themselves (or at least as ancient as having more than one set of clothes – nudity for the sake of laundry only being invented for television advertisements). When the hand-washing of clothes with rocks or washboards gave over to the mechanical washing machine a generation of homemakers muttered 'thank goodness' yet the hanging, retrieving and folding of clothes went on. Today, washing machines are still expert in only a small percentage of the clothing cycle. Adam and Jamie are naturally very interested in laundry arts (Jamie particularly) and took special

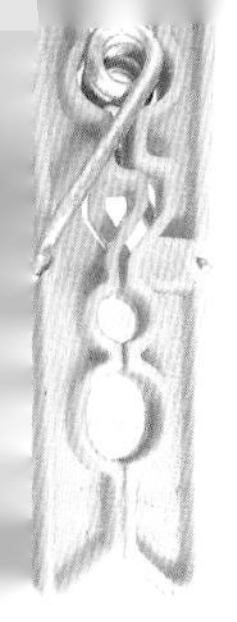
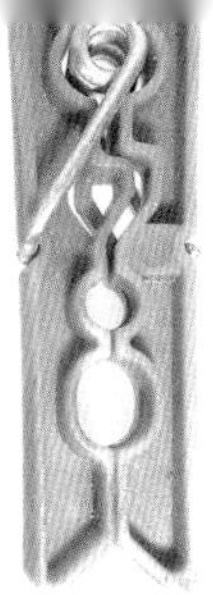

care to include the myth *Killer Washing Machine* in the first season of Mythbusters, despite it being quite silly.
***See also:* white shirts**
***Myths:* Killer Washing Machine, Exploding Lighter**

Wasteland

Jeans store in San Francisco where Kari took Grant to shop for a pair of fitted shrinkable jeans.

Water

Incompressible but expandable, tense but transparent, the clever things about water are almost too numerous to list, but we'll give it a shot. When water freezes into ice it expands slightly and lowers its density, allowing it to float ON ITSELF. When water is heated to a vapour it expands massively, allowing it to become the driving force behind the industrial revolution. Water is life, quite literally, as Adam and Jamie are well aware. They've tackled water in all its phases and all sorts of places – skiied on it, fired bullets into it, tortured each other with it, started fires with it, sunk boats into it, raised boats out of it ... we're calling right now for a water special; who's with us?
***See also:* surface tension, steam, water vapour**
***Myths:* Chinese Water Torture, Hammer Drop, Water Heater Rocket, Steam Cannon, Firestarter, Bullets Underwater ...**

Water Heater

A water heater is an appliance so dull it rates a 'D' on the Mythbusters scale of interesting appliances ... that is, until you misbehave with one. The regular water heater that takes the chill off your bath,

shower and washing-up water is a big pressure vessel that could be quite dangerous except for its thermostat and emergency cut-off switch. If these weren't working, the element inside the heater that does the heating would just keep on pouring energy into that water, which would – under pressure – heat up way above the regular sea-level boiling point of 100°C (212°F). In fact, at 350 psi (the equivalent of being about 230 metres, or 750 feet, underwater) water will only boil at 225°C (438°F). Of course, once 'something happened' to that pressure vessel that exposed its contents to the air around it, the water inside would instantly turn to steam – and steam is a much, much, much, much less space-saving way to store water. Adam and Jamie got to mess around (carefully and from a safe distance) with water heaters in *Water Heater Rocket*, but under no circumstances should you, lest what happened in one house in Minnesota where a water heater tore through a multi-storey house and 150 feet (45 metres) into the air. A dog was killed – no kidding. Myth confirmed.

***See also:* element, thermostat, emergency cut-off switch, steam, psi, sea-level, pressure**

***Myths:* Water Heater Rocket, Steam Cannon, Steam Machine Gun**

Water Heater Rocket

It this kind of plumbing myth that makes the Adam and Jamie's jobs worthwhile. Say you've just bought an old dump for a bargain – before you move in, would you check the rusting water heater for faults with its safety devices because you think it could explode through the ceiling like a rocket? Adam and Jamie recommend you do, despite their preliminary 6 gallon (22 litre) tank doing more 'pfftt' than 'zoom', pressure spells danger. With hundreds of psi (pounds per square inch) in mind, the Mythbusters take their experiment to the Alameda runway. Here, a suitably doctored 30 gallon (113 litre) water heater is brought to the boil at 350 psi, when it launches 500 feet (152 metres) into the air. And if that wasn't enough, Adam and Jamie proceed to build a house (to code!) around a 52 gallon (196 litre) water heater to see if it will actually rocket through the roof. Do you know, it zoomed through that roof like it was made of papier-maché and continued on, up, up and away at great high-speed …

JAMIE – This was a really serious explosion. I mean, even though this is just a water heater, you would be in danger of shrapnel hitting you, you could get severe burns from the steam, and not only that, the shock wave was really significant. I mean, the whole area was reverberating.

Water Vapour

Water that exists as a gas is called water vapour. Water vapour is distinct from steam, which looks impressive yet is simply water vapour forming droplets when the previously hot compressed state escapes into the relative cool of the regular atmosphere. Humidity is the meteorological measure of water vapour in a sample of air, which becomes saturated at only a few per cent – depending on the temperature. Water vapour has increased its volume at least 1600 times from the time when it was a puddle of water, and this makes it perfect for firing cannonballs poorly in a *Steam Cannon*, bullets poorly in a *Steam Machine Gun* or starting an Industrial Revolution.

See also: ***steam***

Watts

It's all about power, and if you're spending it (or making it) at the rate of one joule a second, you're on the money.

See also: ***joule, volts, amps, electricity***

Wayne Dyer

Adam and Jamie consulted Wayne for the myth *Vacuum Toilet*, which suggested that a large woman found herself stuck to the seat of a toilet when flushing it from the seated position.

Myth: ***Vacuum Toilet***

Wayne Harris

If it's loud and inside a car, Wayne Harris is interested. See, he's president of the dB Drag Racing Association, and he took the time to check out the Mythwoofer the lads built to bust the myth of *Shattering Subwoofer.* It is fair to say that he was impressed by the world's first diesel-powered speaker.

WAYNE – I was thinking, you know, you're going to hook it up to the engine. I didn't realise you were going to use the transmission. So you got some serious torque. I don't even know how to convert that into equivalent power.

Weights and Measures

At some stage the rest of the world (that is the United States of America) is going to have to make the switch to decimal. It's absurd. There are a thousand grams in a kilogram, and if you didn't know that, the word suggests as much. The fact that 16 ounces (or something) exist within the common pound is not something you could guess even if you knew the root word for ounce was *uncia* – the Latin for twelve. Adam and Jamie will often revert to their old school, dyed in the wool, zimmer-frame past and speak in pounds and ounces (and only occasionally cubits, spans and shaftments) and then sometimes are bright, sparkling internationalists who revel in grams and kilograms. It's the French revolutionaries who are responsible, and there's a chunk of platinum/iridium alloy sitting inside three bell jars at the Bureau International des Poids et Mesures to prove it. This is the prototype kilogram, so let's not pretend that standard measures – while necessary – aren't just silly. The prototype even gets scrubbed down annually by virginal French maidens to stop it disintegrating. Really (we might be kidding about the 'virginal' bit). Having said that, attempts are being made to reform the kilo and reduce it to something extremely sciency by growing giant spherical silicon crystals in the gentle leafy Sydney suburb of Lindfield.

***See also:* pounds, ounces, kilograms, tonne and all the rest**

Welding

If there was one thing the Mythbusters could not do without it's probably welding. Welding and wood. And adhesives. Oh, and black powder (of course!). In fact, there's LOTS of things the Mythbusters could not do without, and one of them is welding. Welding is a fabrication process in which one piece of metal is adhered to another piece of metal with a third piece of metal, called a weld. Most welding you see the Mythbusters performing is arc welding, where an electric current creates an arc which melts an electrode which becomes the weld. However, many other kinds of welding exist, and we encourage you to find out more about them somewhere else. Arc welding is dangerous and required all kinds of safety equipment because the temperatures and light intensities created are huge, as are the gobs of jumping metal that hop around while you're doing it. Welding has not only been of material support to dozens of myths, but also became the subject of the myth of the *Exploding Lighter.*

What is Bulletproof?

All sorts of stories exist surrounding the supposed bulletproof properties of different objects and materials, and Adam and Jamie were going to set the record straight once and for all. It turns out that 'bullet-proof' is a little bit loose a term to be throwing around. After all, there's all sorts of bullets moving at all sorts of speeds. You could reasonably expect then that a deck of playing, cards, a Zippo lighter, even a Bible might not stand up to a .44 Magnum or a .22 rifle, but surely the Mythbusters own season one polycarbonate blast chamber stands a chance?

***See also:* bullet-proof, lexan™, polycarbonate, firearms**

Whirley

With a reach of 150 feet (45 metres) and a 360° spin (not temperature, we're talking a full circle) this was the mighty crane that Jamie had to scale and man for to test the myth of *Bridge Drop*. Jamie's not great for heights – how did he feel about that?

JAMIE – I want to get the hell off this crane.

Whirlpool of Death

First-time sea-goers have plenty of worries, and not the least of them is the giant whirlpool created in terrifying but unspecified circumstance that sucks down their entire cabin cruiser/luxury yacht/Queen Elizabeth 2. Adam and Jamie want to know what it would take to actually send a giant ship to the bottom of the sea, or a lone swimmer for that matter. After inspecting a few local eddies at the bottom of the Golden Gate Bridge they return to M5 to begin a rather competitive scale test design-off. Adam's concept takes the floor, and before long a 16 foot (4.8 metre) high tank is being filled with 9000 gallons (34,000 litres) of water, scuba supplies are purchased and a new myththern, Jess Nelson, is inculcated to help build two scale vessels of a fishing trawler and a container ship. But scaling their giant whirlpool to the ships presents a problem which revolves around the fact that it would need a whirlpool a half-mile (804 metres) across moving at a suggested speed of mach 3 (or 1020 metres per second) to suck down the container ship.

***See also:* vortex, Old Sow**

White Shirt

Jamie is always in a white shirt – that, along with the moustache, red high-tops and a beret and you have the definition. People think the white shirts stay white because they're made of some exotic NASA-inspired compound. Really it's just about being exact and deliberate and totally conscious of what you're doing at every moment of the day. Right Jamie? Simple discipline and awareness.
***See also:* utility**

ADAM – I thought the shirts had some kind of resistant thing, some kind of new technology, military maybe. But they're just normal shirts. It's like, you know, my world is crashing down around me.

Who Gets Wetter?

In this myth Adam and Jamie tried to uncover the truth behind a riddle as ancient as walking home in the rain; will I get wetter running or walking? Whether you're heading for the tribal cave or the mall, the results were unexpected. After setting up rigorous controls on a set course through a perfect rainstorm, the Mythbusters discovered that in fact, walking would see you getting less wet than running. This myth was in the first broadcast episode of Mythbusters, but the results were later retested and found to be unsound – why exactly? Was it the artificial rain? The neck-entry gimp suits? Who can say? But Grant and Tory's results were the opposite of Adam and Jamie's, and with a more rigorous test and larger sample size and all. Confused? Hmmm … this test we can wholeheartedly suggest you try at home.

Will Abbot

Will was beavering away in the M5 workshop when he got a tap on the shoulder – would he like to join Adam and Jamie on a death-defying replica in *Alcatraz Escape*? The answer was almost certainly 'no', but after promises of a buoyant wetsuit and bragging rights, history now records that Will donned the retro-prisoner garb without complaint (much).

WILL – It's going to be a whole other world. Not to mention the shock of the cold, cold water.

William Miller MD

Dr William Miller was Medical Director at St Luke's Medical Centre. The lads went to him in *Buried Alive* to help them sort out exactly what dead was (no, really, it's important).

See also: dead
Myths: Buried Alive

WILLIAM – So if a patient is not breathing and there's no pulse and there's evidence that the brain is not functioning, then that's the determination of death.

Windows Down v Air-Con

One of the most contested myths ever aired, alongside *Tailgate Up or Down?* and *Ancient Death Ray*. Do you save fuel by closing your car windows and turning up the air conditioning? After 15 laps of the Altamont race track in a behemoth SUV, a computer fuel efficiency estimator seems to put AC in front of windows. However, does that line up with reality? Well, to test that you'd need to set up two cars with equivalent cargo weights and drive them in AC v windows mode until they ran out of gas … and the lads are all set up to do it until a safety call is made on the quality of the tyres. They won't make it at 55 mph (88.5 km/h) for what might be seven hours or more. So … unpack the cars, empty the tanks (MUCH harder than just saying it makes it sound), and pop in just the five gallons (19 litres) each. What do you know? The computer model was wrong; at a safer 45 mph (72.4 km/h) Adam's naturally-cooled, windows-down vehicle picks up 30 laps on Jamie's AC-cooled windows downer. But as with all fuel efficiency myths there just HAD to be a revisit, and indeed it turns out that there was

a blip – the speed. As you go faster the drag of the windows down has more of an impact, and the crossover point is … yes … 50 mph (80.4 km/h). And spare a thought for race-car drivers confined to circular tracks…

ADAM – Oh man! I feel like I'm leaning like this…

Wok

You might choose to describe it as a segmental spherical section or a saucer dome, but the traditionalists will always call it a wok. Born in the helter skelter kitchens of the Orient, the wok is everywhere today. Adam and Jamie bought a dozen or so to test the *Lightning Strikes Tongue Stud* myth – Jamie even had time for art.

JAMIE – I don't know what it is but it's pretty. It's like a big steel tulip.

***Myths:* Lightning Strikes Tongue Stud**

Wood

You can carve it, you can saw it, you can pulp it, you can burn it, you can grow it, and then you can write a cheque on it to buy some more and start all over again. If you were an elephant you could even eat it, but for human civilisation wood has underpinned the development of technology, economy and art for millennia. It also turns up in unexpected places like in cellulose, gunpowder and artificial muscles for robots. Adam and Jamie try and get as much wood into myths as possible just because it's so darn utilitarian and cheap and sexy and fun.

Wooden Paddle Thingy

For a man who knows exactly what and where a transom is, the fact that Jamie was left groping for the word 'rudder' is simple a testament to the fact that his size 42 brain has better things to do.

***Myths:* Air Cylinder Rocket**

Wool

Anyone who happened to grow up on the sheep's back will know that wool is one of the softest, oiliest and altogether most extraordinary textiles around. For a start it is a magnificent insulator – all the tiny gaps in

a woollen knit jumper will keep you warm because they're full of air, and that stops cold air getting through. It works for heat as well of course, which is why Adam and Jamie dressed Buster in a nice woollen sweater and slacks for his trip in the *Racoon Rocket*. Woollen pants were all the go (even in summer!) during the Civil War as well, as was discovered when they shot through them in *Son of a Gun* and along with beaver felt, wool was the material the hats were made of that they shot in *Hat Shooting*.

***See also:* beaver, cotton**

***Myths:* Racoon Rocket, Son of a Gun, Western Myths**

Woos

A person of nervous or cowardly character, for example, anyone without the guts to sit on an exploding toilet, or catch a penny travelling at 64.4 mph (103.6 km/h).

***Myths:* Penny Drop, Empire State Building, Exploding Toilet**

Wrangler

Not just a brand of jeans, a wrangler is an expert in the handling and training ('wrangling') of animals for film or television work. They're usually named for the animal they will be handling on that particular set on that particular day: horse wrangler, dog wrangler, crocodile wrangler (in advertising you also end up with cereal wrangler, ice-cream wrangler, juice wrangler and the Mythbusters themselves added 'biohazard wrangler' in *Exploding Latrine*). Of course, the question Adam and Jamie had to find out in *Goldfish Memory* was, who was the greater fish wrangler – and busting the myth about a goldfish having a memory that peters out every three seconds.

***See also:* octopus, dogs, goldfish**

***Myths:* Goldfish Memory, Birds in a Truck, Skunk Cleaning**

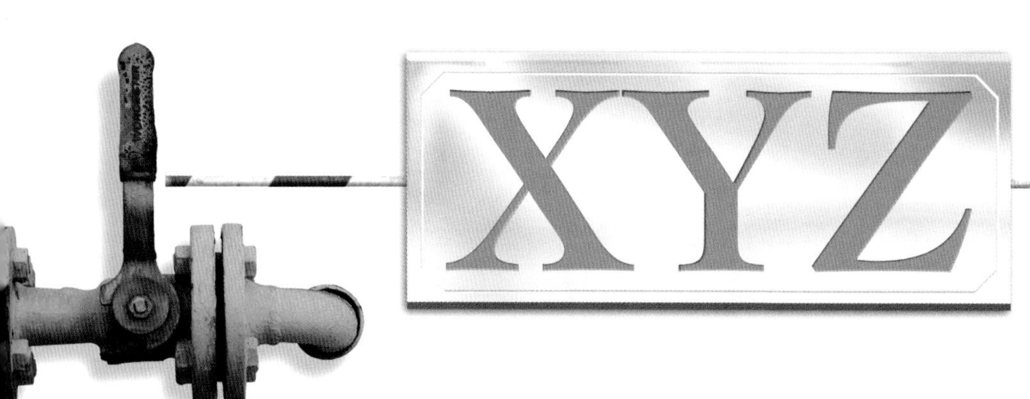

X-Pando™

Far and away this is Adam and Jamie's favourite pipe dope. It comes as a powder, you add a little water to mash it up into a paste, spread it on the pipes you want to seal together … the stuff expands *as it dries!* Brilliant. The company even uses a quote from Jamie as a reference on its website.

***See also:* pipe dope, sealant**

X-Rays

This is a little slice of the electromagnetic spectrum that comes in very handy for looking inside people for *Bullets Fired Up* and other penetrating traumas. However, the fact is that an x-ray can actually do your atoms a bunch of no good by pulling their electrons away.

***See also:* penetrating trauma, electromagnetic radiation**

Yawning

A whole field of research is growing up around the ancient biological practice of the yawn. Who would have thought cracking open your jaw and letting loose a tonsil tickler would be such a burgeoning field of study? There's no point defining the yawn to you – if you've not yawned then you're a zombie, and alien or a super-intelligent artificial intelligence reading this via the internet (in which case – butt out buddy! Pay your money like everyone else!). However, at the core of research into yawning is the idea that inside our brains are things called mirror neurons. These brain cells might – just might – be the seat of language, empathy and consciousness itself. Yawn … hey, wake up – this is key! If you yawn when someone else yawns, it might indicate that these mirror neurons of yours are encouraging you to act in a similar manner: to empathise, and we're understating things just a tad to say that empathy is a fairly important element of the human condition. So don't yawn – just

thank us. By the way, if you do yawn when reading this entry, or the entry below about the associated myth, then there is further proof of the contagion of yawning. Zowee! Call your local neurophysiologist and tell her the good news!

Yawning is Contagious

Yawning and its contagious quality is one of the human species' more curious phenomena, and equally curious in other yawning animals as well (we've just not yet had the opportunity to put baboons or siamese fighting fish or emperor penguins in a waiting room and watch them do it). The Mythbusters have done it with people however, and the results were at the very least interesting. However, why do we care about yawns? Isn't it a little bit yawn-worthy? Not at all! The simple fact is that we've put men on the moon, looked into the heart of the Big Bang and put peanut butter in a squeezie tube but we DON'T KNOW WHY WE YAWN. We also don't know why, or if, it is contagious – that is, if you see someone yawn, you have pretty good chance of laying down a yawn yourself. The initial study was of a control and a test group coerced into reading volumes of tax law. Although the sample was small the test suggested contagious yawning was possible. So dozens more Mythbusters fans were drafted in from the local flea market and left in a specially designed Yawn Lab and seeded with a yawn stimulant known otherwise as Kari. The results?

ADAM – Alright. Well, after testing 50 people in the field, our largest sample we've ever used on Mythbusters, the results are in, and when the people we tested got no seed yawn, no stimulus, they yawned 25 per cent of the time. When they got stimulus, they yawned 29 per cent of the time.

JAMIE – Well it's not dramatic, but it seems like it's pretty good to me. What do you guys think? Busted, plausible or confirmed?

ADAM – Given how large our sample was, I'd say it's confirmed.

Yew

Used ('yew'sed – geddit?) for making traditional longbows, the yew tree is an ancient, venerable slow-growing plant. Its wood displays both elastic and compressive properties, thus when you turn a piece of yew into a longbow, you put the younger more elastic wood on the outside of the bow and the inner more compressive heart wood on the inside. And 'tziiing … duggaduggadugga' you've got yourself an olde worlde weapone of deathe.

***See also:* cedar**

***Myth:* Splitting Arrow**

Zeroth Law of Thermodynamics

The Zeroth Law is real, and defines the understanding of a thermodynamic property that was, in the face of the stirring wisdom of the First, Second and Third Laws of Thermodynamics, thought far too obvious to be recorded. This decision was reversed in order to tidy up the laws early in the 20th century, by which time the first three laws were already very popular and well-remembered. Owing to its 'fundamental' nature, the new law was slipped in before the first (although some in the scientific community question the judgement of this action). Oh … in case you were wondering, the Zeroth Law of Thermodynamics describes how two thermal systems that are in thermal equilibrium with a third thermal system are also in thermal equilibrium with each other.

Zhob

The capital of the Zhob district, the city of Zhob is located on the Zhob river in the Zhob Valley. However, the Mythbusters have never been to Pakistan and the purpose of this entry is simply to make the Zeroth Law feel less lonely (although Zhob does appear in another entry in this volume – can you find it?)

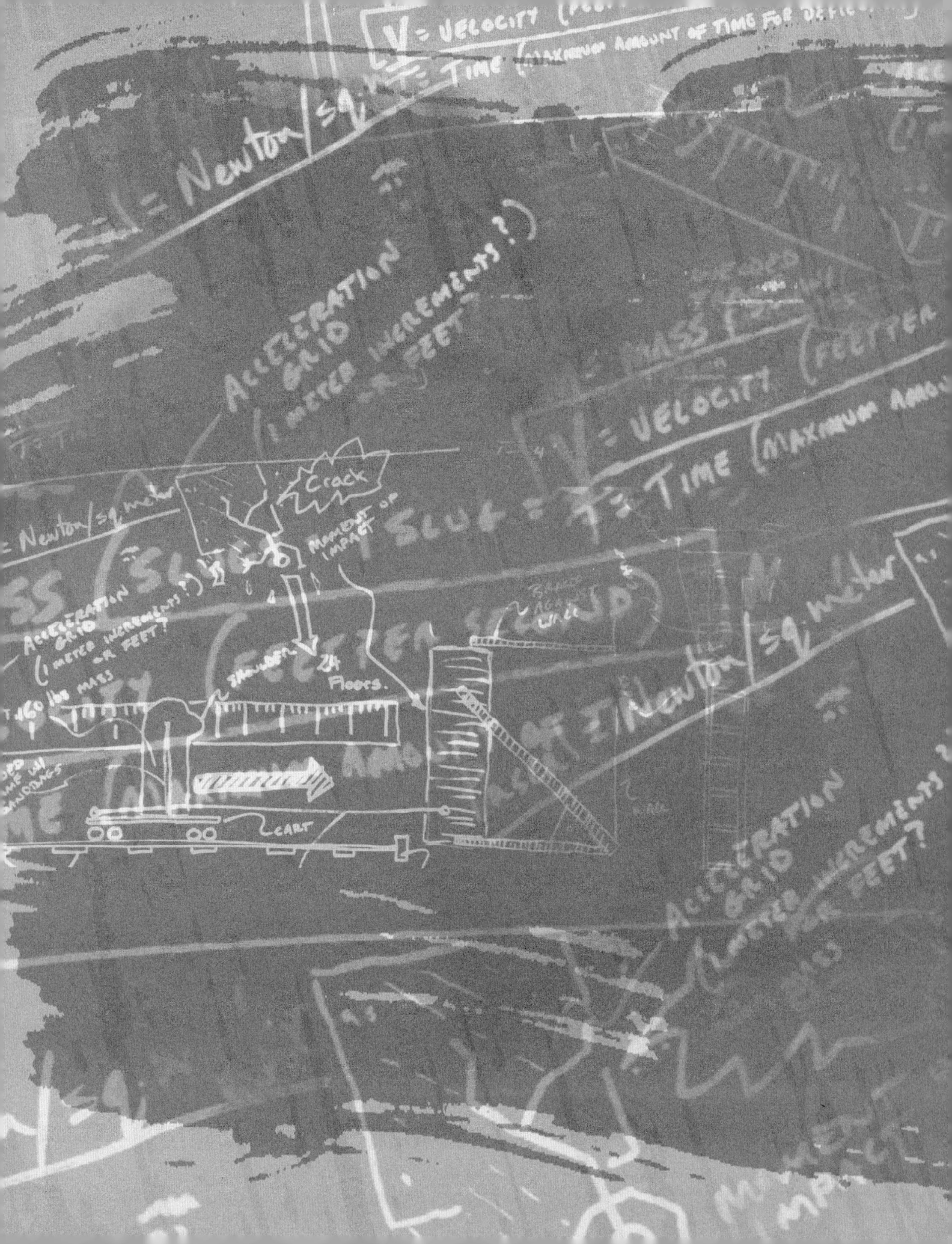

V = VELOCITY
T = TIME (MAXIMUM AMOUNT OF TIME FOR DEFLECTION
= Newton/sq. meter
ACCELERATION GRID
(1 METER INCREMENTS?)
OR FEET?
MASS
VELOCITY (FEET PER SECOND)
TIME (MAXIMUM AMOUNT
1 SLUG
Crack
MOMENT OF IMPACT
BRACED AGAINST WALL
SHOULDER
24 Floors.
160 lbs MASS
LOADED ... SANDBAGS
CART